Burning to Serve

Electricity did not seriously compete with gas lighting and cooking in the home for half a century;
complacency was an insidious threat; this cartoon appeared in the "Gas World" in 1932.

Burning to Serve

Selling Gas in Competitive Markets

by Francis Goodall

The gas-pipes appear to be not only 'the perfection of
civilisation' but the conduits of mighty forces – light, heat and
power – the elements of which were created, gathered and
stored by our heavenly Father through long past ages to
refine, elevate and bless mankind.

From an address by W J Warner at the first exhibition to
promote the uses of gas for purposes other than lighting at
South Shields, April 1877.

Published by
Landmark Publishing
Waterloo House, 12 Compton, Ashbourne,
Derbyshire DE6 1DA England
Tel: 01335 347349 Fax: 01335 347303
e-mail: landmark@clara.net

1st edition
ISBN 1-901522-65-2

© Francis Goodall, 1999

British Library Cataloguing in Publication Data: a catalogue record for this
book is available from the British Library.

Printed by: MPG Ltd, Bodmin, Cornwall

Produced by Landmark Publishing

Price £20 including packing and postage.
To order, send a cheque for £20 payable to
'Burning to Serve' with your mailing details to:–
BtS, 33a Belle Vue Road, Ashbourne, Derbyshire DE6 1AT, UK

for Liz,
Robert, Stephen and Helen

For half a century from the 1880s
most cookers looked like this

Contents

Abbreviations

AGA	American Gas Association
BCGA	British Commercial Gas Association
BoT	Board of Trade
Btu	British thermal unit
CO	Carbon monoxide
CPECG	Compagnie Parisienne de l'Éclairage et du Chauffage par le Gaz (Paris Gas Co)
cu ft	Cubic foot
cv	Calorific Value
CWG	Carburetted Water Gas made by passing steam through incandescent coke and enriching the resultant gas with oil.
EAW	Electrical Association for Women
GLCC	Gas Light and Coke Co
IGE	Institution of Gas Engineers. Successor to the British Association of Gas Managers (est 1863), renamed the Gas Institute in 1881. The IGE dates from 1903.
LCC	London County Council
NGC	National Gas Council
NTGB	North Thames Gas Board
P&C	Parkinson & Cowan
PEP	Political and Economic Planning
PP	Parliamentary Papers
SBGI	Society of British Gas Industries (est 1906)
SMGC	South Metropolitan Gas Co

Definitions

CANDLEPOWER

A measure of gas quality based on its luminosity.

'A comparison of the light from a gas flame of 5 cubic feet per hour in a standard Argand burner with the light from a best quality spermaceti candle of six to the pound weight and burning at the rate of 120 grains per hour.'

CALORIFIC VALUE

A measure of gas quality based on the heat content of gas.

A British thermal unit will raise one pound of water by 1 degree Fahrenheit.

1 Therm = 100,000 Btu

1 Therm = 29.3 KWh

Coal gas typically had a cv of 450-500 Btu per cubic foot

Natural gas has a cv of around 1000 Btu per cublic foot; this is equivalent to 39 MJ per cubic metre.

1 MJ = 11.13 KWh

PRICES

These are expressed in pre-decimalisation form,
ie 12d = 1 shilling; 20s = £1

METERING

Meters measured the quantity of gas used, not its quality.

Meters are either ordinary (ie credit meters) or prepayment. Prepayment meters are also referred to as automatic, coin or penny-in-the-slot meters.

Undertakings had to specify the quality of their gas either by candlepower or, from around 1910, they could elect to supply to a declared calorific value. Declared values were subject to verification by the Board of Trade.

Introduction

Today gas is taken for granted, that is to say, natural gas. However natural gas was a late arrival in Britain. Before it came on the scene there was the British coal gas industry which was the largest in the world, substantially bigger than its US or German counterparts between the wars. Its success was by no means assured. Three times over the last hundred years its demise was quite reasonably expected. When the first electric light bulb was invented in the late 1870s, virtually all gas was used for lighting. With the potential advantages of electricity, no-one foresaw that gas could withstand the challenge. After the 1914-18 war when the use of electricity for lighting and power had grown enormously, who would have expected gas to continue to be the major household fuel for cooking and lighting, particularly as the government favoured electricity? After 1945 with the advent of atomic power and consumer electronics, gas went through a bad patch but re-invented itself as 'High Speed Gas' and came to dominate the fire and central heating markets; 'Mr Therm' who for 25 years had 'burned to serve you' in numerous advertisements was retired.

Various factors contributed to the survival of the industry; technology, marketing, entrepreneurship and the competitive spirit engendered by often being cast as the underdog. There was creative tension between old-style engineers and those who saw the future in aggressive marketing. There was also tension between the gas engineers who considered themselves professional men and the appliance makers whom they described as tradesmen. This book, based on a doctoral thesis, describes for the non-specialist a century in the life of a vital and fascinating industry, a few of its towering personalities, the major successes (and failures) of its marketing and much more.

The story of the gas industry is not only one of marketing endeavour; it also concerns an industry questioning its core function at various times. In the early nineteenth century the Bodmin Gas Company's terms and conditions specified that:

> The Company will convey the Gas to the fronts of the Houses, in those Streets through which the mains are carried; all connections to which are to be at the expense of the customer.

This apparent determination to leave the customer to his own devices was however qualified by a second condition:

No burner or Fittings of any kind to be used but those approved by the Company.

Even then some managers felt that some control was to be exercised over how customers utilised gas. Of course gas was both inflammable and poisonous and so some precautions may have seemed necessary. Nevertheless there is an underlying tension between the functions of providing a commodity and providing a service. At some stages the service element predominated while at other times engineers preferred to confine their efforts to making and distributing the gas.

By the end of the nineteenth century the problem was still as acute as ever. Serious competition had appeared for the first time and might have been expected to have made an impact on attitudes in the gas industry. This did not happen; undertakings (gas suppliers, whether private company or municipally owned) were still more concerned with providing a commodity than satisfying their customers and, incidentally, countering the opposition. According to a correspondent to the *Gas World* in 1893,

It is somewhat remarkable, more especially in these days when the use of the electric light is extending so greatly into private houses, that the gas companies have hitherto failed to take any part in the development of a better system of burning gas for lighting, for heating and for cooking purposes...

It would greatly contribute to the benefit of the consumer if the companies would issue a list giving reliable information, derived from absolute and exhaustive tests, as to the best and most economical burners...

The companies have not thought it worth their while to devote attention to the improvement of the combustion of gas...

It is time that the directors of gas companies should recognise that their true function is that of tradesmen seeking to sell their goods to the best advantage, to supply the best articles and to do the largest trade possible. Hitherto the theory has been, "Here is the gas, burn it; we are graciously pleased to supply it, to make the consumer pay for measuring it, to charge for it and collect the money; for the rest the public can go to the gasfitter, or the stove maker, and do the best they can for themselves".

> The railway directors taught by the stern law of
> competition... have condescended to cater for the public and
> offer such advantages that they attract even those who have
> not hitherto cared to travel... It is for the gas companies to
> learn the same lesson.

During much of the 20th century the service ethos has been
predominant, particularly during the years of nationalisation. This
emphasis has now been reversed with a vengeance throughout the utility
sector. In 1999, parts of the gas industry are planning to supply their
customers with electricity while the electric companies are planning to
supply gas. Other utility companies are proposing to combine the supply
of water and telephone services as well as gas and electricity. This
however is a new development following privatisation of the utility
markets. With most marketing directed to offering the cheapest
commodity package, far less emphasis now seems to be placed on
customer service. It is too early to say what the outcome will be.

Can a financial value be placed on good service? Does it contribute
towards a total marketing package? Certainly as described later, it was an
essential element in countering competition. It must also have
contributed to British world supremacy in the coal gas business.

As there has been some ambiguity and change over time in its leaders'
perception of the core business of the gas industry, it is desirable to look
at it from the outside, as it were. A different starting point has been
selected, looking at the industry not from the viewpoint of the supply
undertakings but from that of the appliance manufacturers. A surprising
volume of archival matter was found. Another perspective came from the
gas press. There were two magazines competing for the attention of gas
managers. The *Gas Journal*, which began life as the *Journal of Gas
Lighting and Water Supply*, tended to regard itself as the voice of the
'establishment' and as a journal of record; it was very wordy. The *Gas
World*, formerly *Gas and Water*, set up in opposition to appeal to the
younger engineers unhappy with the complacency of many of the senior
men in the industry. Because of its critical stance, it was a much more
useful source in the attempt to understand the workings of the industry.
(Both journals abandoned their interest in water when electricity came on
the scene; gas then merited exclusive coverage.)

Because of the different perspective, the emphasis has necessarily been
on markets for gas and how they were won, rather than technical change.
Surprisingly the marketing of gas in competition with other fuels has
attracted vitually no attention. There are books on the history, technology

and organisation of the industry, but these look at gas supply in isolation. There are in fact very few historical studies in any field of business which focus primarily on the building of markets.

Returning to the main starting point of this study, in the face of electrical competition in the 1880s what was the gas industry to do?

- Would it do as the Americans did, and start to supply electricity? This option was considered but not adopted, except by a few municipal authorities.
- Should the gas industry try harder to do what it had done before? This was what most gas managers did.
- Another option was to look for new uses for gas, and more efficient ways of using gas.

This, the most promising route for future success, was almost entirely explored not by gas engineers but by the makers of cookers, fires and water heaters. In fact, as shown here, many of the initiatives which allowed the gas industry to flourish came from outside the ranks of British gas engineers. Crucial technical developments were pioneered abroad. For example the gas mantle which revolutionised gas lighting in the 1890s, the oven thermostat and the Ascot instantaneous water heater all kept gas one step ahead of the competition.

A hundred years ago the word **stove** was used to describe anything using gas other than for lighting purposes, ie. cookers, gas engines etc. Even today there is some overlap in common parlance where stoves may be for cooking or heating. To avoid any confusion the word **appliance** has been used here instead of stove to describe domestic apparatus, cookers, fires, water heaters and so on.

The regulation of the industry in the early years is touched on. It is still too early to judge the effectiveness of the regulatory authorities set up in the 1990s following privatisation, especially in the context of utilities diversifying to confuse the boundaries between their regulated and unregulated activities. This must await a future study.

This book is based on the author's PhD thesis, *The British Gas Appliance Industry 1875-1939* (London, 1992) but with much additional material covering the years up to the 1990s. To avoid distracting the reader from the narrative, there are no footnotes but in addition to the following short list of books recommended for further reading, more detailed sources of information for each chapter are given at the end of the book.

Chantler, Philip; *The British Gas Industry; an economic study*
(Manchester University Press, 1938)
Chantler gives a valuable factual study of the industry and its statutory framework. Chantler was largely responsible for the PEP *Report on the Gas Industry in Great Britain* (PEP, 1939). He sets out sensible ideas for the re-organisation of the industry.

Chandler, Dean and **Lacey**, Stephen; *The Rise of the Gas Industry in Britain*
(Gas Council, 1949)
A useful description of the early days of the industry.

Wilson, John F; *Lighting the Town; a study of management in the North West gas industry 1805-1880*
(Paul Chapman Publishing for British Gas plc North Western, 1991)
This provides a detailed academic study of how the earliest gas companies were set up, financed and managed.

Williams, Trevor I; *A History of the British Gas Industry*
(Oxford University Press, 1981)
This is an excellent study giving particular weight to changes in the technology of the industry, including conversion.

Ashworth, William; *The State in Business: 1945 to the mid 1980s*
(Macmillan 1991)
Covering all the nationalised industries, this gives a valuable overview and critique of their performance.

Falkus, Malcolm; *Always Under Pressure; a history of North Thames Gas since 1949* (Macmillan 1988)
Falkus describes very readably one of the boards at the forefront of the modern industry, its struggles and its management. This brings up to the time of privatisation the story whose years before nationalisation were told by **Everard**, Stirling in *The History of the Gas Light and Coke Company 1812-1949* (Benn 1949).

Hutchison, Sir Kenneth; *High Speed Gas; an autobiography* (Duckworth1987)
Hutchison was at the centre of the industry and was a powerful influence on its management, technology, marketing and conversion; he tells a fascinating story.

Apart from Everard's, there are many other histories of individual gas undertakings. There is a wealth of historical and technical books in the library of the **Institution of Gas Engineers**, Portland Place, London.

The **National Gas Archive** is at Partington, Greater Manchester

I am most grateful to the appliance makers who gave me permission to examine their archives, sometimes even supplying a boiler suit to protect my clothes while I was hunting through their storerooms. These included:-

Thorn-EMI	R & A Main (1897-1949)
	Parkinson and W & B Cowan (1900-1949)
	William Sugg (1881-1894)
Cannon Iron Foundries	Cannon (1895-1949)
Glynwed	Sidney Flavel
Potterton	Thomas Potterton
TI Domestic Appliances-	Richmond (1890-1934)
Radiation	Fletcher, Russell (1892-1900)
	Radiation Ltd (1932-1938)
Gas Spares	Ascot Gas Water Heaters (1930-1949)

The Institution of Gas Engineers kindly allowed me unlimited access to their library and photocopying facilities, which was of enormous assistance. The records of the Society of British Gas Industries are at the Modern Record Centre of the University of Warwick. Mr W C Carter very generously allowed me to inspect and borrow from his personal collection of gas industry artefacts and records including the minute books of John Wright & Eagle Range (1890-1949), which he rescued from a rubbish skip.

I am most grateful to the *Petroleum Economist* who permitted me to use copyright material from the *Gas World* which ceased publication in 1996. Cannon and Leisure Consumer Products lent illustrations for the book.

I was honoured to be able to interview many senior figures in the industry, including notably George Behr, the first sales manager of Ascot, then well on in his 80s and P Crawford Sugg, a seventh generation gas expert. Any errors of fact or interpretation are mine alone.

None of this work would have been contemplated without the support of colleagues at the Business History Unit of the London School of Economics. I mention in particular the warm welcome I had from Dr David Jeremy (now Professor, Centre for Business History, at Manchester Metropolitan University); he generously introduced me to historical research and business history. Without him I would never have contemplated academic research nor historical writing, nor the prospect of a PhD. He made many useful comments on an earlier draft of this book. I value his continued friendship and the opportunity of working with him. I benefited greatly from the steady encouragement of Professor Theo Barker and my supervisor Dr E H Hunt, and stimulating collaboration with Dr Terry Gourvish, current director of the Business History Unit. I am most grateful to them all.

Origins of the gas industry: 1792 to the 1870s

Today it is taken for granted that lighting comes from electricity. In 1870 the only lighting available on tap was by gas for those who could afford it. This was manufactured gas, made from coal in a gasworks; natural gas superseded coal gas in Britain only in the 1960s and 1970s. There simply was no public electricity supply. Virtually all the gas made was used for lighting homes, streets, shops and factories. Because of its cost, only better-off householders could use it, but gas lighting was widespread in shops, commercial premises and factories. Such non-domestic business probably accounted for around half of all gas sold. For those who could not afford gas, the alternatives were oil lamps and candles.

Change was on the way. By 1880 electric arc lamps could be used for lighting streets and large open spaces such as railway stations. The first floodlit football match took place in Sheffield in 1878; four carbon arc lights powered by steam generators were used. Arc lamps however competed head-on with gas in only a relatively small part of the total lighting market. Most gas lighting was indoors where arc lamps were unsuitable. As soon as some means of interior electric lighting could be devised, the whole of the gas market would be at risk. This was the threat posed by the light bulbs of Swan and Edison, invented in the late 1870s. There was no doubt that the challenge was very serious indeed. As soon as the technology could be scaled up from the laboratory to the market place and the price brought down to something comparable to gas prices, electricity would offer advantages of convenience and cleanliness that gas lighting could never match.

Some commentators forecast that gas would quickly move into terminal decline. Others took the view that there would be a market for gas for the foreseeable future. After all, the gas supply industry was well established; in Britain there were almost 2 million customers, that is, homes and businesses using gas. Dr Siemens of the well-known engineering firm said at the time that it was 'simply absurd to talk about gas lighting being superseded'. What no-one could have counted on was the forceful response of the gas industry to competition. It managed both to protect its lighting business and to develop new markets for gas. This did not happen overnight and the individual gas companies had allies in their struggle. The appliance makers, who produced the cookers, water heaters and so on were crucial in helping traditional gas engineers to change their ideas when for the first time they found themselves in a highly competitive market. As well as shifting from almost total reliance on lighting for their business, the industry also created a new mass market for gas in the millions of poorer homes where it was previously unknown. It was so successful that the British manufactured gas industry, as well as being the first in the world, remained the largest. Between the wars it was substantially bigger than the American gas industry and around three times larger than that in Germany; these are both countries whose industrialised economies are not so greatly different from the British. This book will look at the developing market for gas, looking for clues to account for this exceptional performance.

For the first three quarters of the nineteenth century, the British gas industry was almost exclusively concerned with providing a lighting service on tap in streets, factories, offices and the home. Gas had considerable advantages over the alternatives, candles or oil lamps. It was there whenever it was turned on and, without attention, it would continue to provide light for as long as required. Gas lights were fixed rigidly, could not be knocked over or spilled and so there was less risk of accident or fire than with oil lamps or candles. In fact in the earliest years of the industry, it was the safety aspect rather than its convenience which commended it to investors. The first large installations of gas lighting, from 1805/6, were in the textile factories and warehouses of Lancashire and Yorkshire, where fire was a serious hazard. Large scale public supply dates from 1812.

'The Gasman's Arms', from a lamplighter's Christmas broadsheet, c.1815. The Latin motto reads 'Light from smoke'.

In the early 1870s the industry saw little need to question its traditional way of doing business. It had no competitors who could provide a lighting service for commercial premises and better-off homes, which accounted for virtually all the gas produced. It is true that the possibility of using gas for other purposes had been recognised and demonstrated from the earliest years of the industry. Gas was not only suitable for lighting; its inherent heat content meant that it could be applied to other tasks. By the 1870s it could be used to fuel engines, to heat water, to cook and to warm rooms. Only for lighting however did it enjoy a major competitive advantage. For cooking and heating of all kinds, coal reigned supreme and, for most purposes, steam and muscle were still the only sources of motive power. Gas engineers therefore gave little thought to potential non-lighting markets for their product.

The near monopoly in providing a lighting service was not without its disadvantages. The industry had become complacent. Although it was subject to statutory regulation, this was not onerous. Gas shares were well-regarded, those of the leading companies being highly rated by investors as a steady source of dividends, almost as highly as railway shares. The satisfaction of shareholders was not matched by that of customers, many of whom thought very badly of the service they received. Indeed the performance of many companies was so poor that they were bought out and operated as municipal concerns to general satisfaction. In the early 1870s the industry's revenue from its sales of gas (and coke) amounted to £14 million each year. There was no reason to doubt that the industry's progress would continue steady and untroubled in the future as it had in the past.

This complacency was soon to be comprehensively shattered. The new electric light promised a better, cleaner and more convenient service than gas. It was hardly surprising that many at the time thought the days of the gas industry were numbered. However the industry showed a resilience and capacity to innovate that its detractors did not anticipate. In Britain particularly it continued to expand and prosper.

The achievements of the industry in creating new markets are all the greater when it is remembered that in the 1870s when the challenge came, virtually all gas sales were for lighting; by 1939 lighting only accounted for around ten percent split between interior and street lighting. Over this period numbers of customers had increased from under two million to over 11 million, and the volume of gas sales increased sevenfold. Where were these new markets found? How did the industry withstand electrical competition in the face of an apparently

superior lighting technology? Did it succeed because of better
organisation, technology or entrepreneurial vigour? These are the
questions to be answered. Before examining the reasons in more detail,
and the state of the coal gas industry in the 1870s, it is helpful to trace its
growth from its earliest years.

The development of gas supply in Britain is customarily dated from 1792,
the year in which William Murdock (1754-1839) lighted his cottage in
Redruth by gas. At the time Murdock was employed by Boulton & Watt of
steam engine fame to erect their engines to pump water from Cornish tin
and copper mines. Murdock though self-taught had great mechanical
aptitude; indeed he has been described as the greatest mechanically
inventive genius that Scotland has produced. In his spare time he amused
himself by experimenting with new technology of all kinds. From around
1784 he was exploring the possibility of producing small, fast-running
steam engines which could have been useful as winding engines for the
mines. These were very unlike the ponderous mine engines he was
installing for Boulton and Watt; Watt however was not convinced of their
commercial importance. Similarly Murdock made a couple of working
model steam carriages, but in the face of discouragement from Watt, never
patented his ideas or developed them into a working prototype. In this he
differed greatly from his near contemporary, Richard Trevithick, who also
worked on improving the performance of steam engines and steam-driven
vehicles. Murdock lacked Trevithick's confidence and commercial drive
and seemed content to work within the constraints set by his employers.
    In another field, Murdock began to interest himself in improved forms
of lighting in the mid 1780s. It seems likely that this may have been
triggered by hearing that his employers had taken up a British agency for
the newly-invented Argand oil lamps. These used a circular wick and a
glass chimney to provide a stronger current of air to the flame. These
simple steps increased light output by 50%. The same principle was later
applied to gas lamps. Boulton & Watt seem to have done nothing to
promote these; they even failed to secure a patent. Their attention was
focussed on the engine business. Murdock, rather than experimenting to
improve the lamps themselves conceived the idea of lighting his whole
house from a single gas generator. The possibility of heating fuel in a
closed vessel (retort) to produce an inflammable gas had been known for
around a century, and experimental demonstrations had attracted some
interest. Bladders could be filled with gas to provide storage and a

portable means of lighting. Murdock's idea was to connect his retort by pipes to various rooms in his house to provide the very first permanent lighting installation. There is nothing to suggest that Murdock's interest in gas was anything other than pragmatic and utilitarian. He was inventive but had no interest in becoming an entrepreneurial visionary. There is no evidence, for example, that he ever considered the potential of gas for any purposes other than lighting. As with his earlier experiments on steam engines and steam carriages, he was discouraged by Watt from devoting his time to anything but the engine business. However, owing to a fortunate chance, a few years later he was actively encouraged by his employers to develop his ideas on gas lighting.

While Murdock, the self-taught mechanic, was busy lighting his home in Redruth, experiments into gas lighting were also being undertaken by his contemporary Philippe Le Bon (or Lebon, 1767-1804) in France. Le Bon came from a different background. He was a graduate engineer trained at the École des Ponts et Chaussées. His vision for the future of gas was much more wide-ranging than Murdock's. Le Bon himself wrote; 'Gas will cook your food, it will keep it warm at the table, will dry your washing and provide the heat for your washing, baths, laundry and your stove.' Le Bon even envisaged the possibility of some form of internal combustion engine powered by gas. He was granted a French patent for the manufacture of gas in 1799 and over the next couple of years gave demonstrations of his 'Thermolampe', a self-contained gas-making plant providing both light and heat; this used wood rather than coal as fuel. Sadly he did not live to see his ideas brought into practical use; he was set upon, robbed and killed in a Paris street in 1804. It was however from his vision and the practical demonstrations he gave that the British gas industry may be said, at second hand, to originate.

By chance, one visitor to Le Bon's demonstrations in Paris was Gregory Watt, James Watt's younger son. Gregory was very familiar with Murdock's work on gas lighting as he had been sent by his father to stay with Murdock to learn the practical side of the engine business. Gregory wrote home to suggest that, if the firm was planning to do anything with Murdock's light, they should lose no time as he had heard that Le Bon was planning to use gas for similar purposes. By this time Murdock had been recalled to Boulton & Watt's Soho, Birmingham, factory, where he had been continuing his experiments intermittently, and making a gas plant to light part of the premises. After fitting up the Soho works with gas lighting, Boulton & Watt sent Murdock to install lighting for other factory owners, notably Phillips & Lee of Salford in 1805-7.

Gas lighting had particular appeal for factory owners. It was not only cheaper than candles or oil lamps but was more convenient and, in particular, much safer as it reduced the dangers from fire. This was a serious hazard in wool and cotton mills and warehouses; indeed, some insurers refused absolutely to cover such risks. To protect themselves, many Lancashire industrialists combined to set up a mutual insurance business. Because of their special knowledge of the risks involved and their expertise, they were able to quote much cheaper rates than the large London insurers.

In consequence of this special interest in gas to reduce risks of fire, many of the early gas companies in the Lancashire textile towns were set up by local businessmen to light their mills; providing gas for street lighting, shops or homes was a secondary consideration. Without knowledge of gasmaking technology themselves, they turned for practical help to Boulton & Watt or to Samuel Clegg (1781-1861). Clegg, who had been Murdock's assistant, left Boulton & Watt in 1805 to set up his own gas lighting business. He quickly became a more important figure in the early history of gas supply than Murdock himself, and has been described as the gas industry's first great technologist. For the next few years, Clegg and Boulton & Watt continued to provide gasmaking plant for individual customers. Around 1812, Boulton & Watt pulled out of the gas business to concentrate on their core steam engine business; Murdock turned his attention to other interests. Shortly afterwards, Clegg moved to London to take advantage of the opportunities opening up there.

The early promoters of gasworks had strictly limited objectives. They wanted a gas supply for their own premises and, if it was convenient, were happy to light a few street lamps and other premises along the route from the gasworks. There was as yet no idea of initiating a universal system of gas supply. This had to wait for a German entrepreneur, Friedrich Winzer (1763-1830) who had also been present at Le Bon's demonstrations.

Winsor's first experiments.

Far more than Gregory Watt or Murdock himself, Winsor, as he became, immediately grasped the immense potential of Le Bon's ideas if applied to supplying the general public. When Le Bon refused to sell him a Thermolampe, he constructed his own replica and demonstrated it in his home town of Brunswick. After failing to stimulate any great interest in gas there, it being after all during the Napoleonic wars, he came to London with its greater business opportunities.

Winsor was an inspired propagandist in his attempts to develop a public gas supply. He hired the Lyceum Theatre in London to give spectacular demonstrations (including the use of gas for cooking). He did not restrict himself to promoting a new technology; he also promised enormous profits for investors. According to him, a £50 share in his proposed National Heat and Light Company would give an annual return of £6,000! Winsor attempted to patent the process of gas manufacture and he and his backers tried in 1809 to obtain an Act of Parliament which would have given them exclusive rights throughout Britain to provide a public gas supply. This was fiercely opposed by Boulton & Watt who presented conclusive evidence from Murdock of his early experiments and his installations, especially that for Phillips and Lee, which predated anything Winsor had done. This was set out in a paper given before the Royal Society, for which Murdock was awarded a gold medal; the citation commemorates his work on 'gas for the purpose of furnishing a new and economical light.' Winsor's backers finally gained their Royal Charter in 1812 and the Gas Light & Coke Company (hereafter GLCC), the first gas company in the world, was established. Its powers extended over the Cities of London and Westminster and the Borough of Southwark only; other parts of the country were free to set up their own companies.

Winsor soon parted company from the GLCC; they awarded him a small pension for his efforts. His extravagent claims and lack of technical or managerial experience were an embarrassment to the new company; his flamboyance was anathema. Disappointed, Winsor went to Paris as soon as Le Bon's patent expired, in the hopes of repeating his London venture. He set up a company and started street lighting in Paris in 1817, but his company failed a couple of years later. He died there, impoverished, in 1830. The GLCC's centenary history was magisterially disapproving of the man who provided the impetus for its establishment.

If only the salt of prudence had commingled with his leaping blood, a practical issue might doubtless have been reached much earlier.' He was 'the impresario... fitly to his occupation, a foreigner... evidently vagabond by temperament.

Early investors were concerned about risk of gasholders exploding; here Clegg demonstrates that if damaged, holders would leak but not explode. This picture shows the size of early gasholders.

The new company appointed Samuel Clegg as their engineer in 1813, taking advantage of his reputation and proven experience installing gasmaking plant and lighting in the north of England. He gave the floundering efforts of the GLCC a sense of direction. He actually made gas in the new works to supply the GLCC's customers. By the end of 1815, 26 miles of mains had been laid. In 1817 Clegg left after a dispute over pay. He had made an enormous contribution to the industry in designing viable gasworks and supply systems, contracting, purification, inventing the meter, and so on. He later moved to other spheres of invention, including marine steam engines and the (unsuccessful) atmospheric railway system which was taken up for a time by Brunel.

The example Clegg set in London to develop the technology of gas supply became the pattern for the small group of men like himself prepared to tackle the practical and managerial challenges involved in the setting up of many early gas companies. These included men such as Grafton, Hargreaves, the Barlow and Malam brothers and Samuel Peckston. Peckston, a naval purser, lost his job at the end of the war in 1815 but was introduced by a shareholder friend to the newly-formed GLCC. He clearly had enormous aptitude for practical experimentation. In 1819 he wrote the first textbook on the industry, establishing principles that were to govern gas manufacture for the next 75 years. A year or two later he became a contractor on his own account.

By 1823 all the twelve towns in the UK with a population of over 50,000 had a statutory gas undertaking, one granted powers (and obligations) by Private Act of Parliament. Three years later almost every town with over

10,000 had an undertaking. In 1829, around 200 undertakings had been established in the UK and by 1847 the number had risen to 488. Of these 110 were incorporated by Act of Parliament, the remainder being privately owned or incorporated under trust deed. Gas was also becoming established in other countries. Winsor's failed Paris gas company has already been mentioned; by 1830 many French provincial cities had gasworks. The first works in Belgium was set up in 1819 and Holland in 1826. The first American demonstration of gas was in Baltimore in 1802. David Melville of Newport, RI lit his own house in 1807 and like Murdock went on to light several cotton mills between 1813 and 1817. The first public gas supply was in Baltimore in 1817, in New York in 1823 and in Boston in 1828.

This rapid spread of gas lighting was due to its convenience, its role in reducing fire risks and its relative cheapness. Murdock himself suggested that his installation at Phillips & Lee reduced costs by two-thirds by comparison with tallow candles or oil lamps, although this was probably an overestimate. Gas was attractive to shopkeepers as it could provide high levels of illumination. It was also useful as a means of providing street lighting. In fact in Manchester the first gas works was set up by a public body, the Police and Improvement Commissioners, to provide a lamp over the police station door; encouraged by its success they sought general powers to light the streets and supply gas to the public.

In all of these cases the early pressure of demand came from non-domestic premises. Even in 1847 over half of all gas sales were to shops. Gas lighting took much longer to establish itself in the home. The reason was simple. The coal used for gasmaking contained sulphur and other impurities. Unless gas was purified effectively at the works, there would be an offensive smell when it was burned. This was presumably deemed unimportant in factories and was immaterial for street lighting. However, in the home it was a serious disadvantage. This problem was recognised from the earliest years of the industry. The first gasmaking plant to incorporate a purifier was installed by Clegg at Stoneyhurst College in 1811 even before the establishment of the GLCC. One possible solution was tried in the early years, using whale oil rather than coal as the raw material for gasmaking. This was several times more expensive than coal gas. Although it gave a 'better light with less offensive fumes and less unwanted heat and was better suited to interior lighting... where its cost was less of a disincentive', it had disappeared from the market by 1836, driven out by competition from coal gas. Purification and the disposal of by-products and waste remained a persistent and intractable problem throughout the nineteenth century. This was a matter entirely in the gas engineers' court.

There was another potential source of trouble. If burners were faulty or incorrectly adjusted, they would still smell, however well the gas was purified. As late as 1890 the *Gas World* commented that 'too often still does the presence in the house of a gas cooking stove make itself known through the olfactory organs of a caller on the doorstep'! The problem could be caused by faulty design of apparatus, inadequate air for combustion or the lack of an adequate flue. Carbon monoxide (CO), a natural component of coal gas, is odourless and highly toxic; if gas is not burnt completely (ie. if the flame is starved of oxygen), CO is given off. Incomplete combustion of gas is not only very unpleasant; it is a serious health hazard, causing headaches or even death.

This problem of inefficient or faulty apparatus was one which the supply industry neglected for virtually the whole of the nineteenth century. Most gas engineers took the view that their responsibility stopped at the customer's meter. A few gas companies were so afraid of the risks of doing anything other than making gas that they would not fit or even hire out meters. Customers had to buy their own meter and get it fixed privately if they wished to use gas. In the words of the *Gas Journal* in 1880;

> What possible excuse can be offered for the practice of compelling a consumer to fix his own meter 'because the Company are afraid of the responsibility for explosion?' ...This and other impediments would vanish at once if the line now drawn at the entrance to a consumer's premises were abolished, and the Gas Company undertook to enable their customers to get the full benefit from that which they buy... Considerations such as these open up a most promising field for the enterprise of gas makers, by whom the great advantages it offers should be speedily enjoyed.

There was no standardisation of apparatus and no technical yardsticks by which gas service could be judged. Customers bought what they liked, and gas engineers accepted no responsibility, formal or informal, for fitness for purpose or efficiency. This was an understandable position as long as business was increasing and there was no competition. However the corollary was that gas though useful was not necessarily desirable or popular. Its uncertain status is captured in the Cruikshanks' illustrations of London life in 1821 showing candles in the drawing room, gas in a smart gin palace and oil lamps in a drinking den. Although these were drawn only a few years after the establishment of the GLCC, the situation they portrayed remained unchanged for the next half-century. Those who could afford them used wax candles in the home, at least in the main family rooms. These had long been a status symbol, evidence of conspicuous consumption. Jane Austen in *Emma* (1816) has the snobbish Mrs Elton describe one of her acquaintance thus; '...she moves in the first circle. Wax candles in the schoolroom! You may imagine how desirable!' Even if gas were installed, it might replace simple oil lamps or tallow (animal fat) candles but only slowly made its way above stairs. A generation later, describing the 1850s another novelist, Anthony Trollope, a keen observer of social nuances, had Mrs Proudie, reforming wife of the new bishop of Barchester, remark; 'There is no gas through the house, none whatever, but in the kitchen and passages. Surely the palace should have been fitted through with pipes for gas, and hot water too.'

Despite its convenience and steadily falling prices throughout the 19th century, by the 1870s gas had signally failed to establish itself in the mass domestic lighting market and was not seriously contemplated for other purposes. This is a little surprising, considering that the possibility of using using gas for cooking and heating as well as lighting had been demonstrated in both Paris and London just after 1800. Three quarters of a century later, when there were almost two million gas customers, gas cookers were still very rare. Until the 1870s, hardly anybody dreamed of buying gas for anything else besides the lighting of his premises. A similar situation existed in other countries such as America. Why was this, when gas had been widely adopted for lighting?

There were two prime reasons. First, gas had not convincingly overcome the considerable practical drawbacks experienced when it was used for lighting; nor did it carry any social cachet or novelty value. According to the Borough engineer of Liverpool, giving evidence to the Parliamentary Inquiry into lighting by electricity in 1878, 'standards of lighting cannot be regarded as satisfactory. Gas burners, ... though convenient, often made rooms stuffy; people who could afford gas lighting sometimes preferred candles.' He himself used wax candles in his reception rooms. The stuffiness of gas lighting was caused by heat as well as fumes, particularly when chandeliers or other elaborate fixtures incorporating many burners were used. Confirmation of the prevalence of this problem is to be found in textbooks and makers' catalogues, which often suggested the installation of special ventilating ducts to carry away the fumes. Indeed the vitiation of air caused by gas was one of the selling points used by electric companies in the 1880s, when they were trying to create a market for their product. This was before the perfection of the gas mantle in the early 1890s, discussed in chapter 7, which improved the efficiency of gas lighting several-fold and greatly ameliorated the problem of excessive heat.

The other prime reason for the failure of gas to break into non-lighting markets must be the relative cost of gas against that of other fuels, especially its chief rival, cheap coal. In the 1880s, despite the price coming down steadily, it was still reckoned that gas for cooking or heating cost four times as much as coal. The better-off had solid fuel kitcheners. The poor had to manage without even a small range, relying on an open grate; 'their only resources are a dirty frying pan during the week; and sage and onions and a baker's oven on Sunday'. Towards the end of the century the author of *Buckmaster's Cookery* could claim that 'science has not yet produced a good economic fireplace suitable for the houses of the working classes.' This suggests that there was a large potential market for domestic cookers if the right appliances were available at an affordable price.

Even then, efficiency and price were not the only criteria to be satisfied; somehow the innate conservatism of the British would have to be overcome. There was the prevalent notion that the only way for meat to be roasted was in front of an open fire. Even as late as 1910 the *Encyclopedia Britannica* was able to claim that 'No kitchen can be complete without an open range, for it is almost impossible to have a properly roasted joint in enclosed kitcheners... A brick or earthenware oven is preferable to iron...' By the time this was written, around $2^1/_2$ million gas cookers had been supplied. Apart from objections from traditionalists, there were also pseudo-scientific objections to overcome. Some medical men of the late nineteenth century believed that food cooked in gas ovens would somehow become impregnated with poisonous fumes and would create a public health hazard!

The British love affair with the open fire was incomprehensible to others. On the continent of Europe the closed stove for cooking and heating was preferred for its efficiency. In America closed stoves had replaced the open fire for cooking and heating in the majority of homes by the end of the Civil War; only traditionalists of British origin disliked them. Edwin Chadwick, the great 19th century social reformer, visited the Paris exhibition of 1867 and saw the efficient coal appliances then available. Afterwards he remarked that it would take at least a generation before the British could be persuaded to give up their open fires; he would have been nearer the mark if he had said at least a century.

Despite the disadvantages of cost and smell, there were a few recorded instances of gas being used for cooking in the first half of the nineteenth century. Apart from the demonstrations given by Le Bon and Winsor, the first was around 1824. Samuel Clegg, many years later, recalled seeing some workmen at the Aetna Ironworks, Liverpool cooking their lunch over a home-made burner which they had fashioned from a piece of gaspipe. Using their employer's gas and being in large open premises, neither cost nor smell would have worried them too much! In the early 1830s John Robison, secretary of the Royal Society of Edinburgh, designed and made a small cooking burner to 'heat water in the butler's pantry using an aerated gas flame.' In a letter of 1831 to the *Mechanics' Magazine* describing his invention, Robison said that several of his friends had similar burners for general cooking purposes. Unusually for the period, the gas and air for combustion were pre-mixed; the flame was prevented from lighting back by a metal gauze, on the same principle

(right) Two advertisements for cooking apparatus from 1852.

(below) Merle's cooker of 1835.

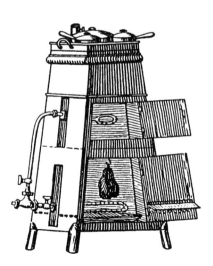

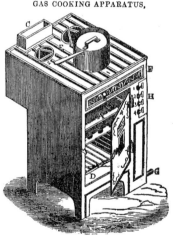

PRIZE MEDAL FOR GAS STOVES.

C. RICKETS,

MANUFACTURER of APPARATUS for advantageously applying GAS HEATS to CHEMICAL, CULINARY, MANUFACTURING, and various DOMESTIC PURPOSES, No. 5, ACAR-STREET, STRAND (opposite Charing-cross Hospital), London.

GAS COOKING APPARATUS,

MADE BY

G. THOMPSON and SONS,

ENGINEERS, ECCLESTON WORKS,
PIMLICO, LONDON,

who also manufacture all descriptions of Valves, Machinery, and Apparatus for Gas and Water Companies.

as Davy's safety lamp. This was probably the first purpose-designed gas cooking apparatus, and there is a replica in the Science Museum, South Kensington. Robison's appliance was for heating a kettle or pan. A few years later, Merle in France produced a cooker with three compartments for roasting, baking and heating liquids. Elsner of Berlin produced his own version of the Robison appliance in 1848. None of these appliances made the slightest impression on the universal popularity of solid fuel for cooking at the time.

Another person who was experimenting with gas cooking apparatus in the 1830s was James Sharp of Northampton. He was a skilled mechanic, who had been apprenticed to a watchmaker. He made instruments, undertook gasfitting installations and assisted in the management of the Northampton gas works. In 1835 one of his 'cookers' was used for a banquet at St Albans, to demonstrate the potentialities of gas for cooking. This was probably little more than a metal cover to direct the heat of numerous gas jets on to the food. Sharp moved to Southampton in 1847, where he again tried to popularise gas cooking and had several domestic cookers made to his designs by a local mechanic; one of these is on show in the Science Museum.

In the same year, a correspondent to the *Gas Gazette* reported that he bought a 'gas cooking apparatus from a London house' after enjoying a meal at a friend's prepared in 'a hot closet fitted up in such a way as rendered it a very tolerable gas cooking apparatus.' This was a burner made by Ricketts, whose advertisements were addressed to 'the proprietors of hotels, managers of club-houses, inns, taverns, coffee and chop-houses or any other establishment where a strong clear economical heat is desirable at a moment's notice, day or night'. Ricketts would supply burners himself for £1/16/- or would licence 'country ironmongers and gasfitters' to manufacture themselves. He advertised that he had made cauldron burners for the Rochford poor house near Southend, and for several industrial establishments. The price quoted suggests that he was producing ring burners for simple cooking equipment such as cauldrons, rather than gas cooking ranges which might have displaced coal ranges.

As well as engineers and ironmongers, a few chefs began to interest themselves in the potential of gas for cooking. Alexis Soyer (1809-58), the noted chef at the Reform Club in London, became increasingly fascinated by the technology of cooking and the nutritional value of food as well as its taste. He took the opportunity of his appointment to redesign the kitchens at the Reform Club in 1841 in accordance with his ideas. As well as installing the usual coal, charcoal and steam-heated cooking apparatus, he introduced a couple of small gas cookers to be used in conjunction with a charcoal stove for made dishes. These gas burners were obviously a novelty; in his description of the Reform Club kitchen which, he said, could serve as a simple guide for fitting up the kitchens of the wealthy, he described them at some length;

> My new gas stoves... afford the greatest comfort ever introduced in any culinary arrangement; each stove is divided into five compartments, each having a separate pipe and gas cock... The fire may be regulated to any height you may think proper by means of the brass cocks, turning the gas either full or only partially on. It possesses also the following advantages: you may obtain the same heat as from charcoal the moment it is lit, it is a fire that never requires making up, is free from carbonic acid which is so pernicious, especially in small kitchens, and creates neither dust or smell (except the gas should neglectfully not be properly turned off), and by my last improvement it is also now quite free from smoke... The gas stoves also tend to greater economy, as they are not lit until the moment wanted, and then only the quantity required, and then may be put out the moment it is done with... no heat whatever being created in the smallest kitchens by the use of gas stoves.

It is clear from Soyer's full description of his kitchen that gas played only a very small part; he was not heralding a completely new departure in cooking methods. Indeed, the impression is gained that he included one or two novelties in his kitchen plans to strengthen his claim to be the foremost kitchen planner of the day. On the strength of his reputation he received many commissions to 'contrive and arrange numerous noblemen's and gentlemen's kitchens... at very moderate expense'. Another novelty was a waste trap he designed to prevent the drains from becoming blocked. The description of this was as lengthy as that of his gas stoves.

It is interesting that Soyer had his stoves made by Ricketts, mentioned above. 'Mr Rikett (sic) constructs them to perfection at a trifling expense according to their merit'. Ricketts however did not mention either Soyer or the Reform Club in his advertisements. Soyer designed other cooking appliances, including a gas cooking range, the 'Phidomageireion', capable of producing dinner for eighty people but inappropriate for normal households.

In 1850 Soyer left the Reform Club to set up as a restaurateur on his own account; his business failed but he remained a public figure. As an example, when he presided at the roasting of an ox for the 'agricultural dinner' at Exeter he made a 'cooker' of bricks and metal sheets sheltering numerous gas jets. His presence attracted attention and his use of gas was widely reported. His interest in gas seems to have been a publicity-seeking search for novelty rather than a prolonged attempt to introduce gas to a wider market.

Chef, inventor, prolific author (Mrs Beeton drew on his work) and social reformer, in 1847 Soyer was commissioned by the government during the Irish famine to set up kitchens in Dublin to provide cheap nutritious soup for the starving; it was said that he provided 26,000 servings daily. Later he travelled to the Crimea at his own expense to advise on catering for the military hospitals. He designed field kitchens for the British army; his designs for these continued in use until the 1930s. For neither of these projects did he use gas.

Despite Soyer's enthusiasm and prestige, gas failed to gain widespread acceptance for cooking. It was not as though simple burners were unknown, as the advertisements of Ricketts have shown. Thomas Webster's *Encyclopedia of Domestic Economy*, first published in 1844, illustrated a gas meat roasting cylinder, which may have been the prototype for Leoni's cookers of the 1870s. Leoni, another chef, gave up catering to set up his own business making lighting fittings as well as appliances. Leoni was a frequent advertiser in the trade press in the 1870s and 1880s. His appliances never became popular, although many small ring burners were sold as an adjunct to a kitchener. As Soyer had shown, these could provide instant heat when required, for example first thing in the morning before the kitchen range was alight, as an alternative to the small charcoal stoves often present in the kitchens of the well-to-do.

One joint, one dish of potatoes roasted, and two pies baked in one hour, at the expense of one pennyworth of gas.

A joint of 6 lbs. roasted in 1 hour—consumption of gas 20 feet—cost one penny (at 4s. per 1000); 10 lbs., 1½ hour; 15 lbs., 2 hours.

Four quartern loaves of bread baked in one hour.
£5 5s. complete, without flue.

Leoni's cooker appears very adaptable.

The main reason for the lack of success of such gas appliances was their running cost. Gas cost several times as much as coal, despite Clegg's (somewhat optimistic) view in 1851 that gas cooking stoves, though not yet perfect, were already economical. Concerns at the cost were aggravated as employers feared that servants through ignorance would treat the gas as they used a coal range, leaving the burners alight long after cooking was completed. This is unsurprising when it is remembered that the only heating in the kitchen would have come from the coal range. Mrs Beeton appreciated the cleanliness and controllability of gas but worried about servants forgetting to turn off the gas.

They are in the habit of leaving the burners of the boiling stove on top of the cookers [presumably an auxiliary gas ring on the coal range] blazing away... in fact it is suspected, from morning to night these burners are kept going, especially in the winter time.

By the middle of the nineteenth century, interest in the possible use of gas for cooking had been shown by scientists, chefs, gas engineers and manufacturing ironmongers, keen to develop a new business. The Great Exhibition of 1851 provided an opportunity for the display of the latest in kitchen technology. It might have been expected that the organisers would have been keen to promote gas cookers as representatives of a new technology. After all, gas had already achieved considerable publicity value from the efforts of Soyer and others. Nevertheless, a gas exhibit would be expensive and potentially hazardous. The organisers, worried about fire risks, would not allow appliances to be demonstrated 'in practical operation through the agency of gas', though some were on display.

Modern kitchen technology was, instead, represented by coal burning iron ranges or kitcheners which had been developed from the early part of the century. These were pre-eminent in the Victorian kitchen. Kitcheners represented a partial break from the long tradition of open-fire roasting, without completely subordinating British roast beef to principles of fuel economy and efficiency. By largely enclosing the fire, it was possible to use the heat more efficiently for several ovens and hotplates; as well as economising on coal, kitcheners meant that working conditions for the cooks were also improved. Some were relatively small, rather like today's Aga ranges; others could be as much as five metres wide. The efficient closed stoves so popular in Europe and America never found favour in Britain, where an open fire for roasting was considered essential. The Patent Kitchener shown at the Great Exhibition by Sidney Flavel of Leamington was awarded one of only seventeen gold medals. Flavel was on old-established firm, dating from 1777, which had specialised in grates and ranges. In 1861 its foundry was described as the largest of its kind in the world, with 100 employees and producing 50 ranges per week. The firm only turned to making complete gas appliances, as distinct from castings for other makers, in 1916.

Despite the ban on live demonstrations, some makers put gas appliances on display at the Great Exhibition, while the Gasfitters' Mutual Association, disappointed at the lack of opportunity for practical demonstrations, organised its own independent display nearby. One maker at least, describing his cooker in the official catalogue, foresaw the potential of a mass market.

> The employment of coal-gas for cooking will soon be universal. The ease and certainty with which the heat from the flame can be regulated, its cleanliness and its economy are advantages of too great importance to be overlooked. At the proper moment for the cooking, the gas fire is lighted and the required degree of heat obtained at once and maintained uniformly; when the cooking is done the fire is turned out instantly. The number of gas fires or flames can also be increased or diminished at pleasure to suit the requirements of the case.

This was William Strode, who also made lighting fittings and gas meters; his advertisements appear from time to time in the gas press. His business continued until around 1900, possibly as a sub-contractor for other makers, after which nothing more is heard of him.

Strode's description of the benefits of gas far outstripped what the technology of the time could produce. The reality was that there was continuing experimentation, some ideas being more practical than others. One patent of 1855 described a cooker made of double sheets of glass between which wallpaper could be hung, an early example of colour co-ordination in the kitchen. Another had a water jacket round the oven so that, in theory, the gas would cook and heat water at the same time; it would have done neither adequately. This was Millington's Little Gem, advertised as suitable for a family of eight. It was made entirely of bright tinned iron with a gas ring at the base; the interior was advertised as a roasting oven and the top for boiling or stewing. Advertisements appeared in the *Gas Journal* and *Gas World* and also in the *Ironmonger*, which was trying to encourage an interest in the gas business among its readers, without much success, it must be said. Despite the flurry of invention, this was not associated with any notable improvement in performance. One 'cooker' could only achieve a temperature of 150° F in the roasting compartment. Another produced a small explosion each time the door was opened; as a contemporary pointed out, this slight explosion, harmless in itself, proved fatal to the reputation of the apparatus.

Hare's cooker of around 1850.

During the 1860s and 1870s there were dozens of small foundries and sheet metal works which would turn their hand to producing gas equipment ordered by customers, rather as Ricketts had done twenty years earlier. The casual way in which gas cookers could be made is implied by an official report on a cooker displayed at the Paris exhibition of 1867. This was one of the smallest cookers on show, made by T Phillips and costing around £3. It was the only gas cooker shown, although many coal ranges were on display. It was described as follows.

This apparatus consists of a cylindrical (sheet iron) case standing on one end, and being about 30 inches high. In one side is a door, which when opened displays a shelf at a distance of about eight inches from the top, dividing the interior into two, the upper part being for baking, the lower for roasting. In the latter the meat hangs by a hook in the centre, and the whole is heated by a ring of burners round the bottom, a tray standing in the middle to receive the gravy. On the top of the apparatus is a concentric ring burner, over which a large vessel can be boiled, and under which meat can be fryed; and at one side of it are two burners for boiling smaller vessels. The apparatus is provided with a main and branches to each of the several parts, and all necessary stop cocks. It was connected with a standard metre [sic] by means of gutta percha tubing.

For roasting, 'the proper temperature was obtained by diminishing the gas jets to about half an inch in length'. The report suggested that the cooker might be made more useful and economical by reversing the position of the baking and roasting places and by having a double casing to conserve heat. As Phillips' name did not survive as a maker, he cannot have had great success with his cooker. The potential of gas for occasional cooking was noted appreciatively by another observer.

We found the workman in charge (at the exhibition) cooking his breakfast over a very small and convenient gas-stand attached to the cuisine, which he would probably accomplish for less than a halfpenny's worth of gas and a saving of half an hour over lighting and getting up a coal fire.

Until the later 1870s gas cookers were still developing along two separate paths, the circular sheet iron type favoured by Leoni and the cast iron variety, notably those advertised by John Wright. Both were being extensively advertised in the trade press and it was by no means certain that the cast iron appliances which later became synonymous with gas

Wright cooker of 1870 (left) and range of 1881 (right).

cooking in Britain would supersede sheet metal appliances. During the course of the 1870s the advertisements placed by Wright show how the appearance of British cookers changed and evolved. In 1869 cookers had what look like separate gas rings on top of the oven; these must have been bolted on in some way as they have rigid gas pipe connections. By 1876 the gas rings are set into the top frame of the cooker. Four years later the burners were set below hotplate bars with the typical arrangement of today's freestanding cookers. According to one technical expert, the first cooker with 'a modern look about it' dated from the early 1870s.

The technical development of gas appliances was greatly helped by the development of the aerated (or atmospheric) burner in the 1840s and 1850s. This is usually associated with the name of Bunsen. Robert Bunsen needed a simple means of producing a hot smokeless flame for his new laboratory at Heidelberg; his burner used the momentum of the gas to entrain and pre-mix air for combustion before the mixture reached the burner orifice, and it was possible to adjust the shape of the flame. The aerated bunsen burner made possible accurately drilled cast iron bar and ring burners, which were essential for the development of cookers, water heaters and fires. Important as this invention was, it did not immediately influence the market for gas. Appliance development proceeded somewhat faster, and most appliances thereafter, cookers, fires and water heaters, used bunsen burners. The growth of the market was hindered less by technical than commercial factors; gas was too expensive relative to its competitors.

The development of other domestic gas appliances was as long-drawn-out as that of cookers. The first patents for using gas for space heating were granted in the 1830s. Early stoves seem to have been flueless, suitable for heating churches and shops. The idea of using gas in domestic hearths may well have been triggered by the appalling problems caused by smoke pollution in London and other major towns. Change would not come quickly. Edwin Chadwick, reporting on the Paris exhibition of 1867, commented on the inefficient way coal was used in Britain by comparison with continental heating stoves, and the consequential severe problems of smoke pollution. Chadwick could foresee no early solution.

> In England this change will only come about by slow
> degrees... It will take more than a generation to do away
> with the cheerful blaze of the fire in every room and to prove

to the multitude the waste of heat and accession of draughts caused by it.

He reckoned that 90% of the heat in coal burned in open fires was allowed to go to waste. The report did not gloss over the problem of the high cost of gas but quoted an expert who suggested that gas might become more economical for heating and cooking purposes when it came down to 4/- per thousand cu. feet (perhaps a third cheaper). This was still grossly optimistic given the prevailing price of coal.

Even where customers could be persuaded to give up their open coal fires, their problems were not over. The first gas fires were made by piling lumps of incombustible material such as pumice on top of a row of gas jets in a grate. Do-it-yourself instructions were published in the gas press so that any entrerprising engineer could make up fires for his customers. One method was as follows:-

> Place some Stourbridge clay in a suitable vessel (say a pail), mix it with water to a pasty consistency, and then keep adding small fibrous asbestos fibre as you mix, until it will take no more, getting at the end as much asbestos to as little clay as will thoroughly combine. Then take out small portions about the size of hens' eggs, squeeze them in the hand into the most jagged and awkward shape you can, and put them in a warm place to dry. They are then ready for use as recommended for pumice but much superior.

The writer goes on:-

> I can say nothing in favour of the economy of the gas fire, but the efficiency of the one I here recommend is beyond dispute... !

Given the general lack of understanding of the principles of gas combustion at the time, it is hardly surprising that practically all these home-made appliances were characterised by the deposition of soot and the production of evil-smelling compounds. Needless to say, these problems were not aired in the gas press of the time! The first distinctively radiant gas fire made by Wilsons of Leeds appeared in 1877; this led to a period of vigorous development. The Wilson fire used a metal mesh as its radiant source; others used platinum wire, asbestos fibres (in the form of long 'bottle brushes') or hollow ball (or 'skull') radiants. The first columnar radiant was introduced in 1908; this quickly became the norm and was not superseded until the late 1930s, when block (Portcullis) radiants were introduced.

Early water heaters were little more than gas rings under tin baths.

THE "MAIN" GAS FIRES.

THE "PRINCESS"
Superior Artistic Design.   Highest-Class Finish.
HAND-PAINTED TILES.

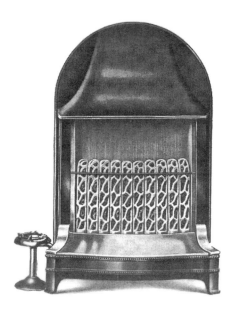

SUGG'S PATENT BATH
(No. 4365).
FOR THE USE OF SALT WATER,
HEATED BY GAS.

THE "SABRINA."

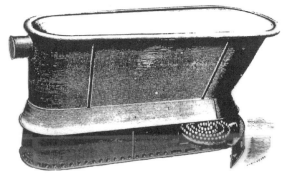

(above left)
An elaborate cast iron fire with 'skull' radiants; the openwork frame had provision for circulating convected heat.

(above right)
Fires between the wars concentrated on maximising radiant heat.

(left)
An early bath heater.

One shown at Paris in 1867 had no arrangement for flueing which, as the testers carefully remarked, was unsatisfactory. The first significant innovation in water heater design came from outside the gas industry. B W Maughan, a decorator and signwriter from Clerkenwell invented the 'geyser' for heating bath water in 1868. Clerkenwell had long been associated with clockmaking, and several gas meter firms set up there, no doubt because the gearing for meter indexes is not dissimilar from clock gearing. It is therefore possible that Maughan had some acquaintance with gas equipment before he made his geyser. This was beautifully decorated, as might have been expected; it is in the Science Museum, South Kensington. In practice it could have been lethal, as there was no provision for a flue, although Maughan himself was well aware of the need for adequate ventilation.

Having invented the concept, he was uninterested in developing it further. He sold the rights to raise money to fund his other inventions; one of these was a flying machine to be powered by an internal combustion engine using gunpowder as fuel! The rights to the water heater were bought by J H Barralet, who later joined Parkinsons, an old-established business which made gas meters. The firm's history stretched back to the earliest years of the gas industry. It was founded in 1816 by Samuel and John Crosley, two tinsmiths who worked for Samuel Clegg, who invented the gas meter. This was the man, mentioned earlier, who was the first great engineer of the Gas Light & Coke Co. William Parkinson, a skilled mechanic, had been engaged in the coaching business, then in decline because of the spread of railways; he took over the meter business in 1845 on the death of the Crosleys, and later diversified into appliances.

Despite this experimentation and innovation, the quality of appliances left much to be desired. In 1870 the *Ironmonger* expressed its concern about the general quality of the appliances being offered to the trade and questioned whether gas cookers were as economical as they were claimed to be. Twenty years later, the situation was virtually unchanged; appearance and performance of appliances still left much to be desired. According to the *Gas World* in 1890,

> Gas fires... are heartless irritating imposters to sit by,
> however satisfactory for keeping damp out of rooms or for
> gently warming bedrooms...

And again,

> ... It is impossible to deny that gas has been gravely
> discredited of late in one of its domestic applications by

several casualties arising out of the heating of baths by the
'geyser' system.. which supplies the want, but at a certain
risk, which unfortunately is only too real.
Fatalities would be a more appropriate word than casualities.

The failure of gas to make progress outside the sphere of lighting was not
unique to Britain. By the time of the 1878 Paris exhibition, the
Ironmonger reported that French companies were exhibiting cooking and
heating stoves, many of which were enamelled, making them much easier
to clean than the black-leaded stoves made in the UK. Despite the high
technical quality of the French goods on display, better than British
manufacturers could achieve, there was still no evidence of a mass market.
Although the USA had its first gas undertaking as early as 1817, before
Vienna, Paris or Berlin, there was until around 1870 no greater interest in
using gas for cooking than in Britain. In that year the *Scientific American*
was engaged in a debate on the relative merits of coal and gas for cooking.
In view of the generally flimsy character of many gas cookers, which were
often 'so feebly or thinly constructed as to lack the power of sufficiently
equalising the distribution of heat to cook with thorough efficiency,' it
suggested the need '..to devise some way of equally distributing and
confining heat in the ovens of gas stoves without the use of thick plates of
iron, soapstone or other material.' As it said, the commercial possibilities
for the successful inventor were attractive.

It was in 1879 that the first modern gas range was advertised by an
American maker. Also in 1879 the American Meter Company sent a
representative 'to select and import for them the best makes of French
and English gas cooking stoves adapted for use in the US.' Sample
cookers from the British makers John Wright and Thomas Fletcher were
imported; there is no mention of French appliances being brought in. In
Australia too, gas cookers were being put together by local makers in the
later 1870s and also being imported from Britain. Fletcher, mentioned
here as an appliance manufacturer, qualified in dentistry (he wrote a book
Dental metallurgy) but became interested in gas burners and small
furnaces. He set up his own burner and furnace business in Warrington in
1872 and became a recognised expert in burner technology. Solid cast
iron British appliances such as those of Wright and Fletcher did not suit
American tastes. 'In the United States... the gas cooking stoves in general
use are of a cheaper and flimsier make than would find favour here [in
the UK].' Despite these attempts to meet local needs by offering British

technology, appliances were no more popular in the United States than in Britain. In 1884 it was doubtful whether as many as a hundred gas stoves were sold in the entire City of New York and 95% of all sales of gas in the US were for lighting purposes. This was at a time when any gas-using apparatus other than an engine or a lighting fitting was referred to as a stove.

In neither America nor Britain did gas appliances yet appeal to a mass domestic market, despite some optimistic claims. *King's Treatise,* (1878; a 3 volume manual for gas engineers) reported that, over the previous 10-15 years, 'the small factories of gas-stove makers have become large ones and new firms have embarked on the business so that gas stoves and all sorts of apparatus are now made by the thousand and at reasonable prices'. This was a serious exaggeration, if major appliances (as distinct from simple ring burners or lighting burners) are concerned. For example, R & A Main, who had the bulk of the cooker business in Scotland in the late 1870s, managed to sell no more than one cooker per month despite energetic publicity. Similarly, a good few years later, in the early 1890s, the GLCC had supplied only 6-7,000 cookers to its 200,000 customers. Despite the efforts of a few forward-looking gas managers to build this new load, it seems doubtful whether there were more than 10,000 major appliances of all sorts in use in Britain in the mid 1870s, or perhaps 20,000 at the outside, when there were almost two million households with a gas supply.

The gas industry had dominated the lighting business for almost three quarters of a century and now it faced a serious challenge. If its lighting business were lost, it needed alternative markets. If in the later 1870s only one in every hundred gas customers had any sort of appliance other than a gas ring, this suggested that finding such markets would be a desperate struggle. This was the reality of the situation; unless a solution were to be found quickly, the industry's long term prospects looked bleak indeed.

The challenges confronting the industry: 1870s and 1880s

During the 1870s the competitive situation for the gas industry, with its dominant position in the lighting market, changed completely. The threat came first from paraffin rather than from electricity. It was in 1859 that "Colonel" Drake first struck oil in Pennsylvania. Processed into kerosene (paraffin) lamp oil, this came just when demands for artificial lighting were growing strongly as America's population grew and industrialisation proceeded apace. Mineral oil, which gave a far more brilliant light in lamps than vegetable oils, quickly replaced tallow candles in the greater part of the American market. The wealthy still enjoyed their wax or whale oil candles, which cost several times as much as tallow candles; gas lighting was largely confined to town centres. A burgeoning demand for kerosene led to an uncontrolled rush to prospect for and produce oil. Very soon production outstripped the needs of the American home market. Under the influence of Rockefeller's Standard Oil, American paraffin was 'dumped' on the European and other markets to bolster prices in America.

While the price of gas was coming down, the reduction was negligible compared to changes in paraffin prices. At the time of the Paris Exhibition of 1867, paraffin cost 15-20% more than gas for lighting. Thereafter, American paraffin came flooding on to world markets. According to national figures compiled by the Board of Trade, the price of paraffin fell dramatically relative to that of gas and coal. Between 1871 and 1881, the price of gas nationally came down by just over 10%; by contrast the price of paraffin fell by over 50%. This explains why, in the 1880s, according to one commentator, 'the most formidable competitor with coal gas is mineral oil, and not the electric light'. The *Morning Post* in 1888 was more measured in its comment.

The threatened invasion of the electric light has in no way damaged the position secured by gas, whatever the effects of cheap mineral oil may be... the convenience and safety of gas will prevent it from being driven out of the field.

This cost advantage for paraffin continued right up to the end of the century. Between 1881 and 1901, gas prices came down 10% but paraffin prices were cut by another 25%.

In Britain as far as poorer domestic gas customers were concerned, the cheapness of paraffin outweighed its relative inconvenience. Even if gas pipes had been installed by builders or landlords, many turned back to oil lamps. Apart from price, oil enjoyed another advantage. It could be paid for by the pennyworth or weekly; householders were not faced with a monthly or quarterly bill as they were with gas. By contrast, for commercial and industrial customers the convenience and safety of fixed gas lighting was paramount, even if it carried a slight cost penalty. Similarly the advantages of gas for street lighting precluded any serious threat from oil. In any event, gas for street lighting was usually sold at a very substantial discount from the regular price; this was a concession the companies were forced to make to win the agreement of local authorities to the breaking up of roads for mainlaying. The relative cheapness of oil for other customers was therefore immaterial.

As if competition from paraffin were not bad enough, the 1870s also saw the beginnings of competition from electric lighting which was potentially even more convenient than gas and could therefore neutralise what had been one of the great selling points of gas. The possibility of some kind of electric lighting had been known since the earliest years of the gas industry. It was in 1808, four years before the establishment of the first gas company, that Sir Humphrey Davy demonstrated an electric arc to the Royal Institution in London. This required a large battery of electric cells to provide an adequate charge to produce the arc. Only with the invention of the Gramme dynamo in 1870, providing a continuous source of power, did electric lighting move into the realm of practicality. Jablochkoff's 'candle', an improved form of arc lamp for street lighting, was used to provide a spectacular display of electric lighting in the Avenue de l'Opéra to coincide with the Paris Exposition of 1878. This was widely reported. To counter the adverse publicity, the Paris gas company arranged a special display of the latest gas lighting in the adjacent Rue du Quatre-Septembre. Lacking the appeal of novelty, this gas display attracted little attention, even though the cost for providing a comparable standard of lighting was only a third of that for electricity. Attempts by the promoters of electric lighting in Paris to light other streets were frustrated as the city authorities refused to pay more than they did for gas.

In Britain, Parliament, which had long taken an interest in gas matters and the exclusive monopoly powers granted to authorised gas companies, began to take an interest in electric lighting. A Select Committee on lighting by electricity was set up to advise on whether the electric light should be adopted and also whether gas companies should be authorised to supply; the committee reported in 1879. It found that

The electric light has not yet made that progress which would enable it in its present condition to enter into general competition with gas for the ordinary purposes of domestic supply....
Electricity... had established itself for lighthouse illumination, and is fitted to illumine large symmetrical spaces, such as squares, public halls, railway stations and workshops... It is used in Paris for lighting shops... and has recently been used in England for the same purpose. Many trials have been made for street illumination with greater or lesser success.

This of course was written with arc lighting in mind, rather than the light bulb which would appear within a few months and which would ultimately transform the situation. The committee took the view that gas companies had no special claims to be considered as future distributors of electric light, and that 'electric light companies committed to their care might have a slow development'. The committee were happy to encourage legislation when the demand arose to 'give all reasonable powers for the full development of electricity as a source of power and light'. This was enacted as the Electric Lighting Act of 1882.

In 1881 there were major displays of electric lighting at Billingsgate and outside the Mansion House in London, where three 20 metre pylons were erected to support Siemens arc lamps. The display was not an unqualified success. As the *Illustrated London News* reported, there was hardly any flickering at first, but later 'some unsteadiness was shown'. Another disadvantage was that the carbon rods for the lamps lasted a maximum of 18 hours before they had to be replaced. Similar trials were undertaken in America. In a number of cities, Cleveland, New York and San José, for example, powerful arc lamps were mounted on pylons to light whole neighbourhoods. In Detroit twenty square miles of the city were lit by arc lamps fixed on 122 towers up to 50 metres high. Apart from the practical problems of servicing these lamps, the contrast between the brilliantly lit area under the lamps and the relative gloom in the areas furthest away was far greater than with the softer gas light from numerous gas street lanterns spaced at shorter intervals. Because of the contrast between bright and dark areas, it proved necessary to provide far more arc lamps to achieve an acceptable coverage than theoretical calculations suggested. Despite the better standard achieved, electric street lighting proved expensive; in New York in 1885, it cost fifteen times more than the existing gas installation. Nevertheless, for shops, the brilliance was a great advantage, attracting custom from less brightly lit premises. As one commentator said, pedestrians could walk by shops of the same character lit by gas without even seeing them, so attractive was the brilliant (electric) illumination further on.

The onset of competition did not escape the notice of investors. In 1877, shares in British gas companies fell by between 10% and 16% in response to news of the invention of the Jablochkoff candle. Even though the gas industry was supplying around one third of a million street lamps, these only accounted for perhaps 2-3% of all sales, almost all the rest being for indoor lighting. Much indoor lighting was in commercial premises, where the risk from electricity was greatest. There are no figures available for London, but in Paris no less than 55% of all customers were industrial or commercial; this gives an indication of the extent of the threat to gas from electric arc lamps.

In the following year Edison's announcement of his electric light bulb represented a threat of altogether a different order. For the first time electrical technology could light small interiors as well as railway stations and shops. There was what the *Economist* described as 'a panic fall in the value of gas shares in the London market'. This was matched by intense short-term speculative interest in electrical shares. As one example, shares in the Paris electric company rose to almost two-and-a-half times above their issue price before falling back below par. Even the *Ironmonger* trade journal felt it necessary to warn its readers that 'the enormous amount of gambling now going on is almost wholly responsible for the fictitious values attached to some of the (electric) companies' shares'.

There are a number of reasons to explain the enthusiasm of customers for electricity as an alternative to gas. There was the novelty value. Electricity had general environmental advantages. Its generation was perceived as an attractive science-based process, clean and labour-saving, producing a modern, convenient and efficient fuel. By contrast, gasmaking was seen as a crude and filthy process producing unpleasant by-products such as tar, ammonia and sulphur compounds; gas was smelly and hazardous. Gasworks were often situated in low-lying areas close to town centres where their polluting impact on the environment was inescapable. The *Illustrated London News* captures the prevailing mood in its picture of half-naked gasworkers stoking flaming retorts at the newly-opened Beckton gasworks in east London (which replaced several inner city works) and compares them with a workman throwing a switch to operate Gramme's Electric Light Apparatus. Of course the boilerhouse to power the dynamo was not shown.

A gasworks retort house.

In the 1880s when the threat from electricity became apparent, there had been only modest developments in gas technology since Murdock's time. It was discovered quite early on that if the gas came through a slit rather than a round hole, it was fanned out; with more surface area it gave more light. Metal burner tips or jets were designed to produce flames of various shapes described as cockscomb, fishtail or batswing. If however the shape of the flame was distorted by damage to the tip, dirt or corrosion on the burner or even draughts of air, the light output was substantially reduced. In the latter half of the 19th century, considerable efforts were made to improve the efficiency of lighting burners. Ceramic burner tips introduced in the 1860s were a considerable advance. These did not corrode like metal tips and the flame retained its shape; they produced two or three times as much light as a simple pinhole burner which gave a candle-shaped flame.

These were simple burners. Efforts were also being made to improve the Argand burner with which Murdock was familiar. Gas Argand lamps were developed in the 1860s in both England and France. At 2/6d to 5/- each, they cost many times more than Bray or Sugg ceramic jets at a penny or two apiece, and so they made little impact on the general lighting market. Their high capital cost could not be justified for most purposes when contrasted with cheap ceramic jets. Over the next twenty years there were further attempts to improve gas lamps, with intensive and recuperative burners; these like the Argand produced only slightly improved performance at considerable cost and so had little long-term significance.

Without the necessity for expensive lamps the quality of lighting could be improved for everyone if the gas could be made more luminous, that is, with whiter rather than yellowish or blue flames. The colour of the flame was dependent on the type of coal used for gasmaking. One particular grade of coal, cannel, from Lancashire, the Lothians and north Wales produced a very much more luminous gas flame than common gas coal. It was often mixed in small quantities with other grades to ensure that gas reached the desired lighting quality. Cannel was however very expensive and in short supply. Other options were to enrich the carbonising coal with a suitable oil additive or to carbonise the coal for a shorter period than the usual 10-12 hours, as the most luminous gas was produced during the early hours of carbonisation; heating coal for the usual time produced more, but less luminous, gas. Carbonising with shorter cycles meant that extra coke was produced for the same quantity of gas; the additional revenue from coke was insufficient to compensate for the lower quantity of gas produced per ton of coal, and so the cost of gasmaking rose. All these options for increasing the luminosity of gas, cannel, enrichment or a shorter cycle, carried a cost penalty. As the objective of engineers was to produce as much gas as cheaply as possible, they were careful not to produce a higher quality of gas than was strictly necessary.

The legal minimum luminosity was specified for every gas undertaking with statutory powers (authorised undertakings). Authorised undertakings had a monopoly within their area and they could break up the streets to lay mains.; however their prices, dividends and gas quality were subject to regulation. The gas they supplied had to reach certain standards of purity; it also had to be of a declared luminosity, defined in **candlepower.** In the absence of an objective scientific method of measurement, the light from gas in a standard burner was compared visually with that provided by best quality spermaceti candles, 6 to the pound weight and each candle burning at the rate of 120 grains per hour; results were only accurate within about plus or minus 5%. In practice undertakings tried, not always successfully, to send out slightly more luminous gas than the legal requirement to keep a margin for error, as they were subject to penalties if they sent out sub-standard gas. Safety margins were usually from 1 or 2 up to 5 candlepower above the prescribed figure.

Not all undertakings supplied gas of the same candlepower. Each agreed a figure with the Board of Trade, determined largely by the quality of the usual sources of coal used. The figures prescribed varied widely between undertakings although most were in the 14-16 candlepower range; others ranged from an exceptionally low 10 at Knottingley in Yorkshire to 25 in Perth. In a couple of towns in Scotland, both of which had a prescribed figure of 14, Kirkintilloch sent out 28 candle gas and Dunbar 30 candle gas. Occasionally undertakings sent out two qualities of gas. For example until the mid 1870s the GLCC sent out common gas of 14 but had a specially supplied enclave where only the more expensive cannel gas at 20 candlepower was available. The separate cannel gas supply was discontinued when the candlepower of common gas was raised to 16, partly in response to complaints about the poor quality of gas.

There was to some extent a trade-off between gas price and quality, although most gas engineers could only draw on a limited range of potential coal sources unless they were to incur substantial additional transport costs. Customers had no such choice; they could only take what was supplied. Whether they were aware of small variations in candlepower is doubtful. Whilst in principle the candlepower of gas could have been increased as a pre-emptive strike against electric competition, this would certainly have made gas lighting more expensive. This was the last thing that the industry wanted at the time.

Although gas lighting was very simple in principle, this did not prevent it from being used to produce most impressive effects. Batteries of jets could be combined into elaborate lighting fittings in both domestic and non-domestic settings. Wall lights, standard lamps and even chandeliers on rise-and-fall fitments were produced in great profusion to match the opulence of mid- and late Victorian interior design. In theatres gas was used for general and stage lighting and sometimes even for special effects, despite the very real risk of fire. For one production in Paris there was on the stage a burning house complete with flames and smoke which collapsed. The effects were so realistic that on the opening night the playgoers quite reasonably thought the whole theatre was on fire and rushed to escape; they were not to know that the theatre's firemen were standing by with hoses behind the stage in case anything went wrong. After the early excitements the play went on to have a long and successful run.

As an extreme example of what could be achieved by gas lighting around 1880, the main chandelier of the Paris Opera House incorporated 550 burners in 112 globes and weighed over six tons. For the stage, elaborate lighting effects to suggest different times of day or night could be produced by a team of 36 men operating gas valves under the direction of their own conductor. One of the most serious problems with this kind of stage lighting was to prevent the dresses of the performers being set on fire by the footlights! Of course major installations such as this generated vast amounts of heat and special ventilation was necessary. In the Covent Garden theatre a flue 2.3 metres in diameter was fitted above the chandelier; this worked so well that patrons complained of the cold draught as soon as any door into the auditorium was opened. Even in Victorian parlours, the cast iron ceiling rose above the central light fitting was often of openwork, partly for decoration but also to accommodate a ventilation duct to carry away the heat and fumes and reduce the risk of damage to decorations.

The existence of such prestige installations should not blind us to the conditions the average member of the public was more likely to experience. For a start, most homes had no gas. Even if there were gas lighting in the home, it was unlikely that customers would get the service they hoped for. Many companies found difficulty in maintaining adequate pressure in their distribution mains at all times, even though, as a matter of policy they kept pressures as low as possible to minimise leakage from the system. Leakage was a serious matter for the supply industry. For most of the nineteenth century in much of the country, it was estimated that 'unaccounted for' gas amounted to twenty per cent of all gas produced. Unaccounted for gas was the difference between what was supplied, as measured by the works meter, and what was registered on customers' meters. By around 1880 the figure was down to fourteen per cent on average, although many engineers managed to achieve much better figures, seven per cent or even less, by careful attention to metering, dealing with leaks and the avoidance of excessive pressures in the mains.

There were various technical arguments which could be advanced by engineers for keeping pressures low but from the customer's point of view low pressure meant poor service. This is exemplified by the case of the Manchester man who bought four gas fires in the late 1880s. He wrote to the gas press to complain that at times his fires had gone out 'for want of gas. This, besides being annoying, is dangerous.' In the circumstances his complaint was very moderately worded!

Even if enough gas were available at adequate pressure, the customer was still not certain of getting good lighting. The first official comment on the efficiency of gas lighting, or indeed any aspect of gas utilisation, came from the Metropolitan Gas Referees, appointed to prescribe methods for gas testing and to report, in 1869. First they bemoaned the lack of any adequate testing gear. They concluded that 'the existing system of photometry as applied to gas is extremely defective'. Coming from an official body, this was no technical quibble. To carry out their study, they tested a whole range of burners against their standard, a Sugg Argand, and uncovered an astonishing variation. 'We found that the kinds of burners in common use are extremely defective, thereby entailing upon the public a heavy pecuniary loss as well as other disdavantages.' Most burners produced only half as much light as the standard burner, and many only a quarter. In the absence of regular standardised testing and sufficient knowledge of utilisation among engineers, it is hardly surprising that most customers getting a poor service might conclude that their problems were intrinsic to the gas rather than their own apparatus.

The fact that companies had to declare the candlepower of the gas they supplied was not necessarily of great benefit to customers. This is clear from a cartoon published in 1877 in *Fun*, just about the time when electric lighting was first in the news.

'Gas is very bad this evening.'
'I'll just get a light and see where the flame is.'
'Where the deuce is the flame?'
'I say, Mr Gas Company, your gas is very bad – just step in and see.'
'Illuminating power of fourteen candles', murmured the Company to itself as it stepped in.
'Why, you've got the candles alight – it says nothing about fourteen lighted candles.'
'Blow 'em out. Now then, the gas beats them hollow!'

This shows the company's inspector, supremely uninterested in the customer's problems or their cause, confident that his gas will meet the regulatory standards of the day. At the time there was no obligation on gas companies to maintain a statutory minimum pressure in all distribution mains. It is possible therefore that the customer was simply not getting enough gas from the street. It was however equally likely that there was something wrong with the pipes in his house or his burners.

For the great majority of the population who had no gas in their homes, their opinions would be based on what they thought of street lamps. If an acerbic comment of 1870 in a trade paper for ironmongers about a new pattern of lamp-post is typical of general experience, the public would not be impressed.

> [Street] lamps though they may be called, lights they are not ... little feeble spots of illumination which exert but a faint influence outside the hideous little oblong glass coffins in which the adulterated gas is satirically sheltered from the wind.

Elsewhere it commented that the street lamps of the day merely emphasised the surrounding darkness without shedding illumination.

Dissatisfaction with the performance of the existing gas companies naturally arose as these gave the appearance of collecting their money without providing an adequate degree of service in return. They seemed oblivious to the reasonable needs of their customers as long as sales and revenue were growing. Customers felt a sense of helplessness, that they were powerless to influence the practices of the undertakings. This was indubitably a factor in the municipalisation movement, especially in the third quarter of the 19th century. It had become clear that the unfettered competition beloved of legislators in the early years of the century was wasteful and inappropriate for 'natural monopolies' such as water or gas supply. The appalling state of water supply and the link between bad water and ill health had been demonstrated in public health enquiries in the 1840s. While gas did not have public health implications, it was widely felt that improved lighting should be spread into poorer areas as well as into the homes of the rich. Associated with the idea that some degree of statutory control was essential came the concept that municipal ownership might be appropriate and should not be opposed, even if it were not actively encouraged. Civic consciousness in the newly formed boroughs gave rise to the view that municipal services might be better than those provided by any private company and redound to the credit of the borough. Indeed, when the supporters of municipal ownership of the Croydon Gas Company were unsuccessful in the 1887 vote to decide the issue, the *Gas World* considered the result

> unfortunate... had the works been managed by the Council for the benefit of the town, a few short years would have seen a material reduction made in the capital account, and meanwhile gas would have been sold at a lower figure than a company can reasonably be expected to sell at.

By 1865, 28 municipal corporations had taken over their own gas supplies. Over the next twenty years a further 82 private undertakings had been purchased by municipalities. (This trend was matched in water supply, 61 undertakings being municipally owned by 1865 and a further 134 by 1885.) If existing undertakings had been economically and efficiently managed, this move to municipal control would never have gained the momentum it did.

Despite their statutory monopoly, it must not be assumed that authorised undertakings had unfettered powers to set prices as they wished. Although the industry was growing steadily during the last quarter of the nineteenth century and bringing its prices down, it was still regulated under legislation introduced under very different economic circumstances. The possibility of gas exploiting its monopoly against the public interest had been recognised by government from the earliest years of the industry. The Gasworks Clauses Act of 1847 restricted dividends to 10%; this was perhaps over-generous to the companies against a background of falling costs. From about the same time, it also became common for companies seeking statutory powers by private Act of parliament to be required to accept a maximum price written into their Act. There was however no mechanism for monitoring the fairness or otherwise of the specified maximum price, set independently for each company, and no procedure for amending it. Companies with a modicum of competence would have experienced few problems keeping within a pre-set maximum and thus being able to pay handsome dividends whist remaining a very safe investment.

In London, rather different arrangements for regulating prices were in force. The Metropolis Gas Act of 1860 determined a uniform maximum price for the whole of London, but this became excessive as coal prices fell and the efficiency of gas manufacture improved; the rigidity and unfairness of this arrangement was plain to see. Customers were not confident that prices were falling fast enough to reflect improved gas-making technology, lower input prices, economies of scale and so on; in the absence of competition, was gas too expensive? Attempts by, among others, the Metropolitan Board of Works to have the price of gas reduced were ineffective. The Board of Trade, responsible for regulation after 1870, had the power to appoint commissioners to rule on prices. Ironically, on the only occasion that prices were officially revised by the commissioners (for the GLCC in 1873), the change was upwards, because in that year, against the long-term trend, the price of gasworks coal doubled for a few months, and the GLCC had mishandled its bulk-buying contracts. During a period of falling costs, a system of regulation such as this gave undertakings little incentive to improve their efficiency or to cut prices. and gave a widespread impression that gas companies were concerned only with their profits and cared little or nothing for their customers.

Earlier it was described how some municipalities were buying their local gasworks to provide a better service for gas customers and to use any profits for the benefit of ratepayers in general. This development clearly worried some leading engineers. George Livesey (1834-1908) used his presidential address to the British Association of Gas Managers in 1874 to suggest that the risk of municipalisation would be greatly reduced if gas companies could accept that their interests and those of their customers were identical. One of the major causes of complaint was the inflexibility of the maximum price system, which appeared to protect company dividends irrespective of customers' interests. Some other way to regulate prices and profits had to be found.

Livesey was the outstanding gas manager of his generation, then chief engineer of the South Metropolitan Gas Company (SMGC) but soon to become its chairman. A couple of years earlier in evidence to a Parliamentary select committee he had floated the concept of a 'sliding scale' whereby the level of dividends which could be paid out was linked with the price of gas; lower gas prices meant higher dividends, and vice versa. There would in effect be a partnership or community of interests between the company and its customers. The idea was at first greeted with dismay by the other London companies. However he came back to this idea in his presidential address. The Commercial Company's Act of 1874 included provision for the sliding scale, a similar clause was adopted by the SMGC the following year and the sliding scale soon became widespread. The usual rate for adjustment was for dividends to vary by 0.25% for each penny increase or decrease in the price per 1,000 cubic feet of gas. There was a consensus that the sliding scale provided a satisfactory compromise between the conflicting interests of customers and suppliers.

Having been introduced in the mid 1870s, by 1900 almost half of all authorised private companies were using the scheme and these supplied two-thirds of the total output of all private companies. The sliding scale gave companies a serious incentive to bring their prices down. This was certainly one of the factors, along with new technology and incipient competition, to improve the awareness and performance of the supply industry. Lacking this incentive, and as described later subject to constraints that did not concern private companies, municipal undertakings without shareholders and dividends to pay were generally much slower to seek alternative markets. The sliding scale, defined as it was in cash terms, was only appropriate for regulation when prices were generally stable. During and after World War I with rising costs and prices, other schemes for regulation of gas prices became necessary to prevent dividends being eliminated completely.

The Board of Trade, although nominally responsible, was ill-equipped to monitor gas prices, even if it had wished to become involved. The fairness of the sliding scale depended crucially on the original datum level, the 'standard price'. It was the good fortune of the supply industry that the sliding scale was introduced during a period of falling prices; reduction of gas prices was undemanding and it was easy to maintain dividends at the maximum permitted. As an indication of how some companies took advantage of their entitlements under the arrangement, a couple of examples, admittedly exceptional, from the 1900 Board of Trade returns may be cited. In Harrogate where gas was selling at between $2/4^3/_4$ and $2/8^1/_2$d, the standard price had been set at 5/6d; in consequence Harrogate was paying a dividend of $16^1/_2$%. In East London the Commercial Company was charging 2/6d, had a standard price of 3/9d and was paying dividends of $13^1/_2$%. Even the Board of Trade recognised that 'a bad bargain may have been made,' but excused its inaction on the grounds that 'a bargain under statute is entitled to be respected'.

As the *Gas World* remarked in the 1890s, 'as a general rule gas companies are prosperous concerns'. It might have added that they were also complacent. The comfortable profitability of most gas companies meant that, without unduly strenuous efforts to improve efficiency, capital was readily available for investment either in plant for gas manufacture or for business expansion. This was to be an important consideration when undertakings began to supply prepayment meter installations from the mid 1890s onward; this development is described in chapter 5.

One consequence of the apparent ease with which good profits could be made was that the industry attracted its share of fraudulent company promoters. These men made a practice of buying up small run-down country gas (and water) works, which could be bought for a few hundred pounds, and selling shares to greedy and gullible investors. The promoters would issue grandiose plans for the development of the business and its glorious prospects, including 'guaranteed' dividends; as an example, investors in the impressive-sounding Kent County Gas Co (in reality the Wadhurst gas works) were promised a dividend of 14% per annum. They would then seek to sell shares for 15 or 20 times what the company had cost them. They were helped in their deception by the high regard in which the best gas company shares were held by investors, almost on a par with gilt-edge securities. The promoters would usually undertake the operation of the works under a lucrative management contract (typically for 5 years) and would buy supplies at inflated prices from other companies they controlled. For a few years investors would be satisfied with promises of jam tomorrow, or dividends paid out of the capital they themselves had subscribed. When the capital had been spirited away and the investors became restive, the business would be liquidated, leaving the investors with a derelict and unimproved works and nothing to show for their investment.

One notorious case widely reported in the gas press was that of the Markyate gasworks. This was sold for £450. A few months later shares for £30,000 in the 'South Luton Gas Co' were offered, of which the vendors of the works would receive £23,250. The promoters on this occasion were Walter Darby and Henry Warwick Gyde, 'more widely known under various aliases than under their real names.' Gyde, who had already served five years' penal servitude for a previous fraud, was sentenced to another five years after unsuccessfully attempting to suborn the jury; Darby absconded.

The gas press did its utmost to warn gullible investors of the activities of known swindlers, giving reports of their activities month after month. These were insufficient to deflect greedy and ignorant investors. There was a steady stream of flotations at 'absurdly inflated prices... which for impudence and audacity would surpass many of the most risky ventures in times of speculative mania.' Promoters clearly welcomed the opportunities to feather their own nests. W T Stears, during his examination for bankruptcy in one gas company fraud case, ingenuously suggested that 'if he had been able to float another company... he might have kept out of the bankruptcy court'! Eaton, an amazing confidence trickster, 'recklessly audacious, impudent and unprincipled,' was linked with upwards of 50 fraudulent companies over twenty years or more. As an example of his methods, in 1912 he issued a circular commending the purchase of certain gas company shares, apparently endorsed by Admiral Lord Fisher, Sir Boverton Redwood and other notables (who naturally had no inkling that their names had been used). As the circular did not bear a printer's imprint, Eaton (and the printer) were each fined £5.

Eaton's activities were cloaked in a deceptive veneer of respectability by his association with Sir C B H Soame Bart. (a bankrupt solicitor, later struck off). Soame's father could not prevent him inheriting the title, but only left him an annuity of £100 per year, which would cease if he became bankrupt. Even during the 1914-18 war Eaton's activities continued; at the outbreak of war he was commissioned as a colonel but was forced to resign after irregularities in mess accounts were discovered. He was finally brought to book in 1928, when he was sentenced to 4 years' penal servitude after an astonishingly successful and lengthy career of deception.

After this diversion into the financial undergrowth, we return to the state of the industry around 1880. With the invention of practical arc lighting and electric bulbs within the course of just a few years, gas had apparently lost its advantages of cost and convenience to other fuels and technologies, and there appeared to be a distinct possibility that gas would in the course of time be driven from its main market. Despite much scaremongering at the time, it was clear that gas was well-established and its demise would be a long-drawn-out process.

This however was not something about which the gas industry could afford to be complacent. It had no new appliances in the pipeline to offer its customers. It seemed unconcerned with appliance efficiency; indeed the impression is gained that some engineers were happy with this state of affairs as, in their minds, efficient apparatus equated with reduced sales, leading to lower profits. The industry had never faced a serious competitor. It enjoyed an easy regulatory regime as the price of its statutory monopoly. It knew nothing of marketing its products and on occasion seemed intent on ignoring the reasonable needs and concerns of its customers. These were left to their own devices, seeking help wherever they could find it, possibly helped by the local plumber, gasfitter or ironmonger. The knowledge of such men on gas utilisation was based purely on trial and error, and was often abysmal. There were no published standards, no regular comparative testing and no courses where fitters (or gas engineers for that matter) could seek to improve their practical and theoretical knowledge.

It is no doubt correct that the gas engineer's first preoccupation must be with gas making and distribution. It is also incontestable that the manager of a gas company, usually a gas engineer, should be aware of his market and should endeavour to meet its demands while making a profit. It is interesting that the *Gas Journal*, which tended to speak for the gas engineering establishment, suggested progress might originate from the enterprise of appliance makers (what it called the 'gas makers') rather than from the supply industry itself.

As their well-understood world was collapsing around them, gas engineers had to come to terms with change, whatever their personal preferences. In 1884 the president of the North British Association of Gas Managers was to concede that the attitudes of his fellow engineers had been seriously at fault in earlier years.

> I think we must honestly confess that it is largely due to the threatened competition of electric lighting that our profession has been thoroughly roused from a condition of 'use and wont' to one of activity and progress.

His claim that there was a general situation of activity and progress in the mid 1880s was something of an exaggeration. Nevertheless there were certainly signs that the supply industry was beginning to come to terms with change.

The onset of competition not only shattered the comfortable stability in the lighting market. It also threw into sharp relief a number of questions which have been of continuing concern in gas industry thinking ever since. What exactly is the function of gas supply companies and how, if at all, do they differ from any other commercial organisation? What responsibility, if any, should they accept for the way in which their gas was used, including the aspect of safety – gas was explosive and highly toxic, after all. In essence, should the supply industry accept the same responsibility for regulating utilisation that the government accepted for regulating gas quality, setting and policing standards?

This raises enormous practical difficulties. Who should set standards, the companies themselves or independent referees such as the Metropolitan Gas Referees, and what part should government play in the process? If individual customers failed to comply with standards, whether of apparatus, installation or standard of repair, should gas undertakings have any authority to enter private property to repair or disconnect the customer's own non-complying apparatus? Should any powers to disconnect equipment be restricted to what was actively dangerous, or might it be extended to anything that did not meet the company's standards for the time being, even if it was not actually lethal? Should undertakings without parliamentary authority have the same responsibility for safety as authorised undertakings? It must be said that the industry never showed the slightest interest in seeking such draconian powers of regulation. The corollary was that it had to change its perception of its role. It was to be not merely the purveyor of a commodity, but the provider of a service to customers. This was to have implications for the type of apparatus to be supplied to customers, which would have to be reasonably fit for its purpose, and hence with relations with the appliance makers.

Should the industry by itself or in partnership with the makers (and perhaps even the government) undertake testing and set standards of efficiency? Should the industry, as a necessary part of its responsibility to customers, set up a trading department to ensure that efficient appliances were available for sale or hire? Should this be in competition or collaboration with the makers themselves and other retailers? Should it be extended to the installation and servicing of equipment?

It might be expected that any extension of role from the simple supply and distribution of gas would have financial implications for the company. This too would have to be considered. Should private companies be obliged to accept any of these wide-ranging responsibilities if the result was to be a heavy financial burden on the shareholders? The dilemma might be particularly intense at a time of severe competitive pressures.

These questions have no clear-cut answers. They are posed with the benefit of hindsight. It is however helpful to bear them in mind when considering not only the position a century ago, but also whether the same questions are equally germane in today's very different world.

The structure of the industry in the 1880s

Despite the shock of competition, the gas industry still enjoyed many advantages. The challenge from electricity and paraffin was directed against an industry that had been in existence for over half a century, well-established throughout the UK. In 1882 there were almost two million customers, that is, premises both domestic and non-domestic with a gas supply. The industry's annual receipts from sales were over £12½ million. All large towns, most small towns and many large villages had their own gasworks, some municipally but the majority privately owned. Many of these undertakings were very small. By 1900, when the number of customers had increased to 3,700,000, four fifths of all undertakings still had less than 5,000 customers, and almost half less than 1,000, as shown in the table below. There were even a dozen undertakings with less than 100 customers, Chew Magna (with 45) being the smallest private and the Invergordon Lighting Commissioners (52) the smallest municipal undertaking. Only 11 undertakings had more than 50,000 customers.

SIZE OF UNDERTAKINGS BY CUSTOMERS; 1900
NUMBER OF UNDERTAKINGS

No. of customers	Private	Municipal	% of Total
< 1,000	225	87	45
1,001-5,000	153	89	35
5,001-10,000	36	33	10
10,001-50,000	29	24	8
> 50,001	4	7	2

The Board of Trade annual returns, from which these figures are taken, show only those undertakings statutorily authorised to provide a gas supply. Some companies never obtained statutory powers, but had to negotiate arrangements to dig up roads with the local authority; as a quid pro quo, gas for street lighting was often supplied at a substantial discount, 50% or more less than the normal price. Unauthorised companies were mainly very small. There were a few larger ones which never sought statutory powers; a couple were operated by railway companies to supply their workshops and incidentally the homes of their workforce. The obligation to supply would obviously have been an unacceptable constraint for gasworks associated with industrial premises. The number of unauthorised undertakings remained around 2-300, some surviving until nationalisation in 1949, when they accounted for only 2-3% of all gas manufactured.

By contrast with these very small undertakings, some were large by any standards. Taking stock market value as a yardstick of size, rather than value of output or numbers employed, in 1904 the Gas Light & Coke Co (GLCC) ranked 16th in Britain, below the Bank of England and J & P Coats but ahead of Imperial Tobacco; the thirteen other larger firms were all railway companies. By this criterion the South Metropolitan Gas Co (SMGC), the other large London company, was ranked 37th. In that year these two had 354,000 and 190,000 customers respectively; other large undertakings were Glasgow (194,000), Manchester (142,000) and Leeds (92,000), all municipally owned.

Interestingly, the two large London gas companies only achieved their dominance during the 1870s as the result of a series of amalgamations. In 1870 the GLCC, serving parts of the Cities of London and Westminster, was in serious trouble. It had difficulty in meeting customer demand from its three small works, which were too cramped to expand and in any event were causing serious nuisance from smell, pollution and the traffic congestion associated with moving coal and coke. The company's prices had been so high that around 1850 the Corporation of London encouraged the formation of a rival company, the Great Central, the effect being to bring the GLCC's prices down from 7/- per thousand cubic feet to 4/- within a couple of years. The GLCC under its chairman Simon Adams Beck decided to concentrate all its production on a riverside site where colliers could unload direct, and settled on a 150 acre site at Barking, Essex. The inauguration of the Beckton works not only solved the GLCC's production problems but enabled it to offer bulk supplies to its neighbours, who had similar difficulties. Over the next few years eight companies amalgamated with the GLCC, which from supplying only one seventh of London's gas in 1869 now supplied two-thirds. Offers of amalgamation were also made to the Commercial Gas Co, supplying part of the East End, which declined and to the three companies on the south bank who instead combined under the leadership of the SMGC and its formidable engineer George Livesey.

The small average size of individual undertakings has been stressed because of its effect on the ability of the industry as a whole to react to external challenge. It would be unreasonable to expect that the man who owned and operated the Chew Magna gasworks should be a marketing expert, ready to adopt the latest commercial and technical ideas for building his business. By contrast, the larger companies certainly had the resources to implement changes in commercial strategy if they chose. From the 1890s new ideas tended to originate with the largest companies such as the GLCC and SMGC. Ideas were disseminated through consultancy work undertaken by prominent engineers, through Institution of Gas Engineers meetings and through the gas press. Engineers of smaller companies followed the example of larger companies when they felt they could afford it, or when pressure for change became irresistible.

Small companies, even if financially weak, were of course the last to face competition. Where an electricity company was planning to provide a public supply, there were advantages in setting up if possible where there was a large potential market rather than in smaller communities. This meant that for most small gas companies there was no serious competition until the development of the national grid between the wars. It is little wonder that change came to the gas industry patchily over many years and that complacency was to be a severe handicap when competition finally arrived.

Before the first World War the larger companies at least had a good record of paying steady dividends and were popular with investors. There was a wide choice of stocks and shares available, not limited just to the largest companies. The *Stock Exchange Official Intelligence* for 1900 gave details of the capital and dividend performance of 88 British gas companies, of which 8 were combined gas and water companies. (There were no combined gas and electricity companies listed, although some local authorites supplied both). For those interested in investing in foreign gas companies, there were 27 in all five continents from which they could choose. By contrast, only 27 British electric companies were listed for 1900. In addition to the 88 listed gas companies, shorter details were give of another 160 British and foreign gas and electric companies whose shares were less readily tradeable. This meant that if companies wished to raise capital beyond what they could afford from retained profits, there were financial markets accustomed to handling issues on their behalf. If the gas industry wished to seek out new business opportunities, the raising of capital was unlikely to have been a problem for any but the smaller companies.

The industry was well established geographically and financially. It could also point to the fact that its prices were falling steadily. The following table gives prices for two major undertakings, one private and one municipal from the earliest days of the industry.

GAS PRICES, 1825-1900
(d. per 1,000 cubic feet)

	Manchester	London (GLCC)
1825	168	180
1830	144	162
1840	84	108
1850	60	48
1860	54	54
1870	38	38
1880	36	36
1890	30	27
1900	23	28

The fact that prices were coming down should not be taken to imply that they could not have fallen more quickly had commercial pressures been more severe. The effect of competition on the GLCC's prices following the establishment of the rival Great Central Gas Co, mentioned above, is notable. The immediate result was that the GLCC brought its prices down in stages from 7/- to 4/- over a couple of years. When an accommodation was reached between the rival companies, prices rose again to 4/6d.

There were various reasons for this general fall in prices. Improved methods of gasmaking played a part, and there were some economies of scale. Large purchasers of coal such as gas undertakings could buy in bulk in the summer months when prices were low and stockpile against peak winter demand. The larger companies employed their own agents to monitor the state of the market and some even operated their own colliers. The GLCC for example, which could order 100,000 tons on a single contract, moved from sailing brigs carrying up to 500 tons of coal to long-term charter of steam screw colliers in 1853. Although the capacity of these was not much greater than that of the larger brigs, they significantly cut transport costs as long as no time was wasted during loading and unloading. Their effectiveness was so apparent that several were chartered by the government from the GLCC and the Imperial, another big London gas company, during the Crimean War to carry out military supplies and hospital equipment for Florence Nightingale.

It was not only in buying that economies could be made. Gas under-takings had the considerable advantage that they produced coke as a by-product (in round terms, one ton of coke for every two tons of coal carbonised). Coke prices tended to follow those of coal fairly closely; this provided a hedge to insulate the industry to a considerable degree against external price shocks.

As prices fell, sales continued to rise steadily. In London sales increased over tenfold between 1837 and 1880 and doubled again by the end of the 19th century;

GAS SALES; LONDON (MILLION CU FT)

1837	1,600
1849	3,200
1869	9,885
1879	17,635
1889	20,649
1899	34,057

No national annual sales figures were collected before 1881, but those thereafter for authorised undertakings published by the Board of Trade show a pattern similar to that in London.

GAS SALES; UK (MILLION CU FT)

1887	56,241
1902	91,956
1912	126,002
1920	295,857
1930	313,046
1937	341,985
1946	446,124

Not only did the number of authorised undertakings increase steadily in the later 19th century. Between 1880 and the inter-war period the nature of the market for gas changed dramatically, illustrating just how successfully the industry (and its suppliers) responded to competition in the lighting market. In 1880 lighting represented well over 90% of sales, but accounted for only around 10% in 1939. Similarly, output figures by themselves give no indication of improvements in efficiency which were dramatic, not only for lighting but also appliances, as is described later. What is clear is that competition from electricity and paraffin may have somewhat impeded but could not prevent the growth of the market for gas.

Although it sometimes seemed that the gas industry would be unable to take advantage of its position as the predominant supplier of convenience lighting on tap, the economic climate was in its favour. National prosperity was growing, and this was gradually translated into improved standards of living for the great bulk of the working population. Customers were demanding and some could afford higher standards of convenience in the home. In the mid 19th century, gas lighting was a symbol of comfortable middle class living standards. Being a gas consumer in those days was described as 'almost as good a mark of respectability as keeping a gig'. Gas was not however spreading quickly into working class homes as quickly as might have been expected, even though people were prepared to invest in leisure. Quite substantial items such as sewing machines, bicycles and pianos were to be found in homes with relatively modest incomes, encouraged by the widespread availability of hire and from the 1860s, hire purchase. To the Victorians a piano, even more than a perambulator, symbolised respectability, achievement and status. The reason for the effective exclusion of gas from most working class homes was simple. These were rented. If the landlord was unwilling to pay to have gas installed, weekly tenants with no security of tenure certainly would not.

There was another factor that might potentially work to the advantage of gas but was largely unrecognised in the 1880s. Because gas was used almost exclusively for lighting, the main demand came at night; in consequence gasworks and, particularly, distribution systems were stretched for only a short time during each twenty-four hour period. To some extent the timing of the carbonisation cycle, typically 10-12 hours, could be geared towards matching periods of high demand. Another way of meeting peak demand was by providing storage in gasholders to smooth out diurnal variations and to give a something of a buffer against changes in the weather which could affect demand. Despite their size, gasholders could meet only a few hours' consumption and they were expensive to build. During the 1890s the cost of storage was brought down as the building of enormous gasholders was pioneered by Livesey of the SMGC; the largest at East Greenwich had a capacity of 340,000m^3, spacious enough to accommodate the Albert Hall. The cyclical nature of demand remained a challenge to the ingenuity of gas engineers as long as the industry relied so heavily on the lighting market for its sales and on the relatively inflexible coal carbonisation process.

In this connection it is surprising that British managers were slow to take advantage of new methods of gas manufacture which had already passed through the experimental stage elsewhere. The carburetted water gas (CWG) process was invented in France in the 1850s and introduced there in 1865 and in America in 1873. The process had various advantages. It could be brought into operation in a few hours, rather than the couple of days necessary to heat up carbonising retorts ready for gasmaking; it therefore provided much greater flexibility. It required relatively little labour, important in that period of troubled labour relations; it also needed little space relative to output. The process used coke, which was sometimes a glut on the market, plus oil for enrichment. It is not clear why CWG should have attracted so little interest in Britain. Possibly the coke market was better developed in Britain while American managers could buy oil very cheaply but could not sell their coke. The first British CWG plant was built for the GLCC in 1889, by which year there were 300 such plants operating in America.

There was however spare capacity in the system, particularly in the morning. If new daytime markets could be identified, the marginal cost of supplying them was far less than meeting an equivalent increase in peak-load lighting demand. This explains the very great interest in building up the appliance market, especially for domestic cookers, as these would be used mainly during the day. Indeed, in the years leading up to the first World War, when lighting was still the major load, undertakings could afford to subsidise the domestic appliance business whilst maintaining their overall profitability. Just how how much scope there was for building up daytime sales without a corresponding increase in overall production capacity is clear from the following graph, which shows send-out in Manchester. In 1903, when most sales were still for lighting, the period of high demand is just one third of each twenty-four hour period. By 1936, when large numbers of cookers and fires were in use, the peak had shifted to midday and demand remained high over two-thirds of each day.

In 1903 when Manchester had 142,000 customers, less than one in ten had a gas cooker. By contrast, in 1936 when there were almost 217,000 customers, four out of five had cookers. Over these 33 years the number of customers increased by 50%. Evening consumption (6pm – midnight) fell slightly but daytime consumption (6am – 6pm) more than doubled; gas sales overall increased by 40 per cent, although average consumption fell slightly because gas was reaching the smallest homes. Despite the higher lunchtime peak demand, fixed plant such as gasworks and mains were operating at a higher load factor and semi-variable revenue costs already being incurred, such as wages and the cost of leakage from mains, would be lower per cubic foot sold as off-peak sales increased.

As early as 1880 there was serious consideraton of ways to improve the load factor; the thinking was set out in a leading article in the *Gas Journal*

MANCHESTER; 1903 AND 1936

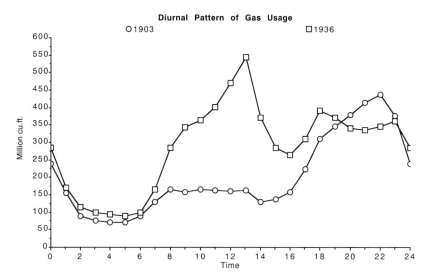

Diurnal Pattern of Gas Usage

in that year. In the words of the article, 'consumption during the day would be of much more value to a Gas Company than an addition of the same value obtained from ordinary lighting sources', ie. involving an increase to the peak load. The question remained, where was this additional daytime business to come from? At the time, no-one foresaw the enormous growth of business, predominantly for cooking (although the lighting load continued to grow until the 1920s) which, as illustrated above, shifted the peak demand from the evening to the middle of the day within relatively few years.

One suggestion was that all gas sold for non-lighting purposes should be separately metered and charged at an off-peak rate. This was perhaps practicable in non-domestic premises, but the cost and inconvenience made the idea unsuitable for ordinary family homes. A few undertakings, both in Britain and elsewhere, tried to put this idea into practice but soon abandoned the experiment. Nevertheless, the concept of positive discrimination in favour of off-peak non-lighting business was at the root of much gas industry thinking for the next quarter century at least. It was against this background that the move into the business of hiring cookers at cheap rates, described in a later chapter, must be viewed. This, together with the invention of the Welsbach mantle, described in chapter 7, contributed to the steady growth of the gas industry, and this contrasted sharply with the disarray of the electricity supply industry before 1914.

Back in the 1880s it must be borne in mind that the technology of electric lighting and supply was not yet sufficiently developed to offer a serious challenge in the main lighting market. An embryo industry was taking on a very-well entrenched competitor. As mentioned earlier, the 1879 Select Committee on Lighting by Electricity found that electricity was not yet competitive with gas for domestic lighting. Although the technology was embryonic in the early 1880s, it was developing fast and offered great prospects of flexibility and convenience. The first domestic electric lighting installations were status symbols for the seriously wealthy, Lord Salisbury, Sir William Armstrong the shipbuilding magnate and Lord Kelvin among others. Prestige installations in the House of Commons, Savoy Theatre, Mansion House, British Museum and British Academy soon followed. There was however at this stage no public electric supply; current had to be generated where a supply was required and this was expensive. Potential customers could not simply apply to a local company for a supply as they could with gas, but had to organise their own generation.

The immediate consequence of the Electric Lighting Act of 1882 facilitating a public supply was a stock market boom in electrical shares. This quickly collapsed, to be followed a period of depression lasting some years. Most of the £1^1/$_2$ million subscribed by the public during the boom was frittered away in legal expenses, promoters' fees and patents for often fraudulent inventions. This false dawn gave gas a breathing space to come to terms with the reality of competition and to prepare a counter-attack.

In retrospect the wisdom of moving the emphasis of the industry from production engineering towards developing new markets is obvious, as was the decision to give greater emphasis to appliances rather than lighting. At the time the balance of advantage was by no means so clear-cut. Previously gas engineers had been satisfied with their role in making and distributing gas, whose advantages for lighting in their view were self-evident. They had been content to leave the development of the market to customers who came to them asking for a supply and to the gas fitters and plumbers who installed the pipes, meter and fittings. There were also the makers of appliances; the cookers, fires and water heaters whose first manifestations were described in chapter 1. As it was the makers who persisted in experimenting to find new uses for gas, and who deserve much of the credit for the later growth of the industry, it is worth spending a little time on them and their antecedants.

The first involvement of outside makers was in the construction of meters for installation in gasworks to measure the output. Meters only became common in customers' homes from the middle of the century when small accurate meters were available, the trend starting in provincial towns and then in London. According to one expert in 1849,

> Gas companies are now... beginning to appreciate the merits of the gas meter... The time is not distant that meters will be universally adopted and with equal benefits to buyer and seller.

Prior to that, customers contracted to pay for a certain number of lights for a fixed number of hours, in effect a rental for a gas lighting service. In Bodmin well before 1850 the company charged an annual fee of £1 to supply a single jet from dusk until 9 o'clock, £1/4/- till 10 o'clock or £1/8/- till 11 o'clock. Larger burners cost more; a batwing or a 16 hole Argand cost £3/10/- up to 9 o'clock or £4/5/- till 11 o'clock. One eighth of this annual charge was to be paid in the Lady-Day and Midsummer quarters and three eighths in the Michaelmas and Christmas quarters. Customers were allowed an extra hour's light on Saturday nights. If they were caught using light for longer than contracted for, they would be charged for a full quarter at the next higher rate and they were reminded that the flame was not to exceed five inches in height! Some gas engineers used to turn off the supply at the works during the day to prevent customers using gas outside the contracted hours. It was traditional to use the term 'gas rental' for gas revenue as late as the 1880s, long after metering had become obligatory (except for street lamps).

Making meters required skills in sheet metal work and brassware for the index mechanism. Many of the first recorded meter makers were tinsmiths or brassfounders. These included the Crosleys who helped Samuel Clegg make the first meter in 1816. Others active in the 1820s included Thomas Glover, William Cowan, James Milne and R Laidlaw, most of whom made decorative lighting fittings and burners as well as meters. Glover and Cowan later joined forces with appliance making firms.

The first specialist makers of appliances came from a different group of trades, general contracting (Sugg; Potterton), sheet metal work (Ewart; Charles Wilson) but predominantly from a foundry background (Cannon; Eagle Range; Flavel; Main; John Wright, etc). For men whose main business interests lay elsewhere, it was obvious that if this new gas appliance business was to grow, it would have to be actively promoted. They recognised and set out to exploit its potential. The early use of gas for cooking was described in chapter 1. Water heating was achieved by means of a large gas ring under a bath until Maughan, a painter and signwriter from Camberwell, produced his purpose-designed 'geyser' water heater in 1868. Charles Wilson made the first radiant gas fire, as distinct from gas convection stoves, in 1877. Despite the optimistic claims of their promoters, gas appliances in the 1870s lacked a mass market. Admittedly appliances were still primitive and costly to buy and run, but most gas engineers were preoccupied with the lighting business. They were also reluctant to accept the makers, who could and would help them, as worthy partners in building new mass markets.

This reluctance to work with the makers was aggravated by two problems. First there was a widespread ignorance among gas engineers of appliances and how they were installed and operated. The second was a much more serious problem. Engineers lacked the basic commercial skills necessary for success in marketing consumer durables, and most had no interest in learning them. They were anxious to distance themselves from what they referred to disparagingly as 'trading' as a means of emphasising their status as professional men rather than 'rude mechanicals'. Professional status had only recently been achieved with the establishment in 1863 of the British Association of Gas Managers, later to become the Institution of Gas Engineers (IGE). This followed the example of the civil engineers (1818), architects (1834), mechanical engineers (1847) and naval architects (1860). In their minds, engineering fell clearly within what might be described as professional duties. Creating new markets, tackling competition, co-operating with appliance makers, ironmongers and fitters was just as clearly trading. As such it was repugnant to the more traditionalist British engineers.

Such deep-seated attitudes were very resistant to change. In 1898, the president of the Institution of Gas Engineers gloried that its members were senior professional men who

> were not in any way connected with trade undertakings or manufacturing concerns... they did not regard trade and commerce with contempt in any way, but as engineers professionally trained for certain responsibilities and duties, they ought not to mix themselves up in trading matters... they should not be connected with business beyond that which the duties and responsibilities of their office compelled... they should be entirely disinterested...to devote themselves and their energies fully to their special work.

Comments such as this should not be taken entirely at face value. Many senior engineers acted as consultants before setting up their own practices, some notable late 19th century examples being John West (1839-1922), W A McIntosh Valon and Corbet Woodall (1841-1916). West set up his own business supplying mechanical stoking machines and continuous vertical retorts for carbonisation. Valon was a consulting gas and water engineer. Woodall set up a consultancy business with a world-wide reputation (he went as far as Japan to advise gas companies there) and later became Governor of the GLCC. Others took advantage of their professional position in rather less savoury fashion; they enhanced their earnings by accepting what was euphemistically called commission on the orders they placed on behalf of their undertaking.

One of the most blatant cases of collecting 'commission' gave rise to what became known as the great Salford gas scandal. Its origins lay in the toleration, if not overt approval, of the practice of paying commission by a majority, probably a large majority, of gas managers. In 1888 it was said that three quarters of the customers of one meter firm accepted commission. The gas press was not entirely unsympathetic towards gas managers, some of whom were so ill-regarded and badly paid by their managements that they would be susceptible to any inducements offered. The *Gas Journal* referred in 1877 to

> ...the vast majority of gas managers [who] are most inadequately rewarded...they often receive less than a banker's or a merchant's clerk who has only to make entries and add up figures from ten to four o'clock.

A few years later it spoke of 'petty concerns whose ill-paid managers are agape for plunder'. Press reports of the period suggest that municipal gas committees in particular appeared to be liable to resent the payment of a reasonable salary to the gas manager on the basis that it was an easy job to run the gasworks - anyone could do it! No doubt they were also aware of the prevalence of offering commission; why should they as ratepayers foot the bill for an appropriate salary if others were prepared to make up the difference through payment of commission? The very normality of the practice on the fringes of proper moral conduct made the acceptance of commission unremarkable. In the words of the *Gas Journal* in 1887, 'the evil that can be called by some euphonious name is already bereft of most of its guilt'.

The man at the centre of the great Salford gas scandal was Samuel Hunter, JP and Wesleyan Methodist local preacher, the engineer and manager of the

Salford Corporation gas undertaking. He was highly regarded by his gas committee and by his fellow gas engineers. With Livesey and Corbet Woodall, he was one of the three gas engineers called to give evidence to the Select Committee on Lighting by Electricity in 1878. Even before the Salford affair, Hunter's career had not been free of controversy and suspicion. He had been engineer at Rochdale when critics of the Corporation gas committee complained that their gas cost more than gas in neighbouring towns. Even the *Gas Journal* commented cautiously in 1874 that the price paid by Rochdale for coal 'looks high considering the geographical position of the town in relation to the coalfields, but we do not suppose the Corporation could do better'. In hindsight this was an over-generous judgement, but Hunter could obviously charm almost all with whom he dealt. The criticism of the management of gas affairs in Rochdale came from political opponents of the ruling group, and so the gas committee closed ranks; after an enquiry behind closed doors they decided to take no further action. Shortly afterwards, Hunter moved to a better-paid appointment in Salford. Rochdale even gave him a year's consultancy work.

> After all the annoyance which a sensitive man must have felt at the persistent attacks of two ill-natured members of the Rochdale Town Council, it must be a great satisfaction to Mr Hunter to be appointed (almost unanimously) consulting engineer to the Rochdale undertaking.

Soon after his arrival at Salford in 1876, Hunter cancelled a long-running contract for the purchase of coal from a well-known and very large coal dealer, Ellis Lever of Bowden. This was a matter of great importance for Lever as Salford purchased around 100,000 tons of coal a year. A couple of years later, Lever began to make allegations of corruption in the allotment of coal contracts and to mention Salford and Hunter by name. He was in an excellent position to know the truth as he had been (and probably still was) a notable payer of commission himself. Hunter sued for libel and Lever, unable to prove his allegations, was forced to make a retraction.

A few years later Lever returned to the attack. Just before the mayor was due to affix the Corporation seal on certain coal contracts, he received a telegram from Lever. 'Bribery, corruption and fraud have prevailed in your Borough to an enormous extent for many years'. The mayor felt he could not proceed until 'they could get at something not quite right that was supposed to be going on'. The allegations pointed directly at the gas engineer. Hunter felt he had to take some action as once again the performance of the gas undertaking under his management was being compared unfavourably with that of neighbouring undertakings, notably Manchester. Salford's gas cost more, and the capital employed was substantially more.

Hunter had taken pains to maintain excellent relations with his gas committee, no doubt helped by generous hospitality. He could afford it. He was a self-made man receiving £800 pa. from the Corporation but he admitted to investments of £50,000. He lived in ostentatious luxury in an £8,000 house with liveried servants. Latterly he had adopted the style of a country gentleman, buying a country house and riding to hounds. Lever's allegations stung the gas committee into starting an action for criminal libel against Lever, associating Hunter in their action. This time, Lever was clearly prepared for the libel action and put up a stout defence. He was able to produce a witness (the gas engineer to Wigan Corporation) whose testimony on commission payments was damning as far as Hunter was concerned. Evidence was given that Hunter typically demanded 1/- per ton (or say ten per cent) as the price for awarding a contract. Lever was acquitted, to great public acclaim. When he went home he was met and accompanied on his way by the local brass band! Despite the setback, Hunter still apparently enjoyed the confidence of his committee.

A short time later, another query arose. Hunter was called to account by his committee for obtaining money by false pretences. A local firm of coal merchants changed hands and the new manager asked for formal confirmation from the Corporation that the payments being made regularly to Hunter in respect of orders placed were with the knowledge and authority of the gas committee. Hunter produced a document purporting to be signed by the chairman of the Salford gas committee stating that the committee did not object to the payment of commission to their gas manager. It was a forgery.

Now the tables were turned with a vengeance. Hunter, who during the earlier case had stated under oath that he had received no commission, was indicted for perjury and forgery, convicted and sentenced to 5 years' penal servitude. According to *The Times* the sums in the indictment represented 'only in a very small degree the amount of plunder which the defendant had received'. Investigations to date had discovered payments to Hunter of £22,000. Surprisingly, Hunter still retained the loyalty of his committee even after his conviction. They decided not to pursue him for full recompense. Indeed Hunter, impudent as ever, was able to persuade them that he would enable them to recover £10,000 overpaid by suppliers in respect of commission if they petitioned the Home Secretary for mitigation of his sentence. (The petition was unsuccessful). Hunter was to inform the committee of the names of those who had given him bribes so that they could take proceedings to recover the money! In fact Hunter used this agreement to screw out more payments for himself from his victims as his price for remaining silent. Lever declined to co-operate and was denounced to the Corporation, who sued. The Corporation managed to recover a few small sums, but nothing like the £10,000 Hunter had persuaded them they might receive. The judge in Lever's case was particularly scathing on the role of the Corporation. 'The agreement between the Corporation and their agent after discovering the bribes was immoral, contrary to public policy and utterly invalid'. The position of the Town Clerk of Salford in the affair was equivocal; he fled when financial irregularities were discovered in his own department (involving a mere £700) and a warrant was issued for his arrest as a fugitive debtor. Although the Salford scandal revolved round coal contracts, there can be no doubt that Hunter and men like him exacted commission on many other categories of goods supplied.

By their very nature, corrupt payments cannot be quantified. To put Hunter's case in perspective, the supply industry in 1887 was buying around nine million tons of coal a year costing, say, 10/- per ton. If commission of 5% were to be paid on only a quarter of this, it would still amount to well over £50,000 per annum. Coal was by far the largest element in supply industry costs, but other materials were purchased as well as meters and appliances. It also seems likely that a corrupt manager would also arrange commission for himself on sales of by-products (coke, tar, etc) as well as purchases. The scope for exacting commission was very large indeed. It seems probable that the scope for concealing commission in larger undertakings with accountants and auditors, particularly those whose costs were set out in *Field's Analysis* (see chapter 9) or *Gas World Analyses*, was less than in smaller undertakings. As for them, it is not unreasonable to suggest that the cost of gas might have been a couple of pence per 1,000 cu ft lower if costs had not been inflated by commission.

Although gas managers were commercially minded when their own commission was at stake, there was no such enthusiasm to get involved in marketing their gas. Here is what a correspondent to the *Gas World* had to say in 1893.

> It is time that the directors of gas companies should
> recognise that their true function is that of tradesmen seeking
> to sell their goods to the best advantage, to supply the best

article and to do the largest trade possible. Hitherto the theory has been, 'Here is the gas, burn it; we are graciously pleased to supply it, to make the consumer pay for measuring it [a reference to meter rent] and collect the money; for the rest the public can go to the gasfitter, or the stove maker and do the best they can for themselves'.

Clearly uncertain of the reaction of his colleagues, he wrote under a pseudonym. Criticism also came from outsiders. When in 1906 the Society of British Gas Industries (SBGI) (which represented those who supplied gasworks equipment, appliances etc.) invited an architect to address them, he berated gas companies for being 'the most unapproachable people in the land... spoiled by success and calculated to snub any enquirer'.

This reluctance to get involved in trading was a particularly British reaction. American gas managers had no such qualms. Their stunts to attract more business were reported occasionally in the gas press, often with a comment that such aggressive methods would be unacceptable in Britain.

For men accustomed to dealing only with gasmaking, any involvement in trading represented a major innovation. There were practical and psychological barriers to overcome. They had little or no experience. There was also a long-standing disdain for the appliance and fitting business. This went back a long way. In the 1840s the *Gas Gazette* did not

advocate or recommend gas companies becoming gas fitters; on the contrary we discourage that, as being somewhat derogatory to the position of a board of directors; but we do earnestly recommend that gas companies *find the capital and pay the fitters* for such work... Every fitter would then become the canvassing agent of the companies.

This advice was not taken. As profits from gas were so easy to make, undertakings took no interest in building up long-term relationships with traders with a view to finding new outlets for gas. They were equally cavalier with their customers, taking no steps to deal with their reasonable concerns. Nothing was done to review the efficiency of apparatus or to set down codes of practice for installation work. In the words of the *Ironmonger* of 1875,

the companies caring not one farthing what desperately bad work may be done inside the house... (It was) disgraceful too that perhaps not half-a-dozen gas fitters in London ever proceed systematically to test the pipes for leakages before finally leaving the work.

Most workmen engaged to do gasfitting work were likely to be not a gasfitter but a Jack-of-all-trades, a blacksmith, whitesmith, glazier, brazier, plumber and bellhanger all rolled into one.

The *Ironmonger* went on to publish a very clear and accurate description (which could be used today) of how tests may be carried out safely to check for gas leaks. At about the same time in London the Plumbers' Company arranged for the City & Guilds of London Institute to organise classes for plumbers, many of whom also undertook gas pipefitting. There is no evidence that gas undertakings took any notice of these developments.

In the 1880s there was one area where technical progress seemed to offer the gas industry a significant lead in a completely new market. This was in the supply of gas engines. At a period when the only sources of motive power were muscle, wind, water or steam, there was a great potential market for a small power source. Steam engines, with their boiler, boilerhouse and stoker could not economically be scaled down to meet demands for a few horsepower or less. They were therefore disproportion-ately expensive in capital and labour costs for small loads. Gas engines were ideal for this limited role. They could be installed almost anywhere and, being semi-automatic, did not require a boilerman. For most larger installations gas could not compete on price with coal-fired steam engines. Even then, a compact gas engine might be chosen where there was no room for a conventional boilerhouse, and some very large gas engines were installed.

The idea of internal combustion engines had been around for a considerable time. As mentioned earlier, Philippe Le Bon envisaged the possibility of some form of internal combustion engine in the first years of the century, but nothing came of his ideas for many years. The first gas engine to be brought into general use was that of Lenoir (1860). In 1867, Otto doubled the efficiency of Lenoir's engine and over the next few years several thousand Otto engines were made. The next major step was the introduction of the Otto four-stroke cycle in 1876, which led to further major improvements in efficiency. By 1900 Otto had produced 55,000 motors ranging from $1/2$ to 1,000 horsepower. In the UK Crossley Bros. of Manchester, who held British rights to the Otto patents, had manufactured 17,000 gas engines by 1885.

In the years up to 1914 the efficiency of gas engines increased steadily and they remained a very important source of motive power, despite the availability of electric motors. By 1908, gas engines of up to 2,000 hp were available and there were large gas engines with an installed capacity of 575,000 hp in Europe and of 350,000 hp in USA; smaller engines of another 2,000,000 hp were in use. The demand for low hosepower motors collapsed following the invention of the 3-phase asynchronous electric motor. This was more convenient and, with suitable tariffs on offer, cheaper than gas. Electric motors were adopted much more quickly in Germany than in Britain.

Somewhat surprisingly, gas engines attracted negligible attention in the gas press. They did not benefit the gas supply industry nearly as much as might have been expected. The reason was simply that engines did not require gas of the high standards of purity and illuminating power prescribed for lighting. Almost any gaseous fuel would do. It was also the case that powerful gas engines required large volumes of fuel at pressures which the public mains were often unable to supply and, unless special anti-fluctuators were fitted, could suck so much gas out of the main that other customers would be deprived of their supplies. Gasworks and gas distribution networks were not generally designed to meet these specialised needs. Neither gas engine customers wanting the cheapest fuel nor gas engineers for technical reasons were particularly interested in working together.

As a result, gas engines were often sold complete with their own gas-making plant. They could therefore be installed anywhere, quite independent of the gas mains. Many in fact were installed in country houses to drive dynamos for early electric light installations. In 1878 J E Dowson invented a simple and cheap process for making a low calorific value gas highly suitable for engine purposes but not for lighting. As a consultant he designed many installations, the largest of which was for the Urban District of Walthamstow. One of his gasmaking plants provided fuel for 13 engines rated at 3,000hp generating electricity for the Council's street lamps and tramways. As the gas periodical press was directed towards those in the supply industry making gas for lighting or heating purposes, the lack of references to gas engines becomes less surprising. Although gas engines were still available between the wars, being advertised in trade directories, their market was effectively lost to electric motors or, where mains electricity was not available, to oil engines such as those of Petters of Yeovil, who first entered this market just before 1900, selling small engines for agricultural and dairy applications.

When serious competition first appeared, gas seemed very ill-placed to counter it. The industry was well-established but unpopular, complacent, lacking allies, lacking new technology and unsure how to proceed. There was no immediately obvious way to enlarge the market for gas lighting. Advertising might have helped, as it did at this time for Beecham's Pills, Frys and Cadbury chocolate and many other traders and manufacturers of consumer goods, both in local newspapers and, from the 1880s, weekly magazines such as *Tit-Bits* and *Pearson's Weekly*. However the gas undertakings had no new story to tell; customers knew only too well what they offered. There was no central body to co-ordinate any advertising on a regional or national scale in an attempt to change popular conceptions of gas lighting. Individual undertakings were, with very few exceptions, too small to advertise on their own, even if they had wanted to; the appliance makers could not create new markets from scratch on their own. Another possible strategy might have been to cut prices in the hopes of increasing sales. This would have threatened dividends and, unless co-ordinated with neighbouring undertakings, would have invited invidious comparisons and charges of profiteering against those who did not reduce prices. If this was ever considered as an option, no evidence of any great debate has survived in the columns of the gas press. The suspicion must be that any cut in the price at which gas was sold sufficient to encourage customers to use more would both reinforce the widespread perception that undertakings were overcharging while simultaneously destroying their profitability.

In the absence of any alternative strategy, gas supply undertakings would have to find a way to become involved in the 'stove' business. This was a strategy that carried potential risks. As mentioned above, this business had been left in the hands of the appliance makers and local ironmongers, plumbers and independent gasfitters who would supply appliances if asked by customers, just as they would supply lighting fittings or, indeed, coal or paraffin appliances if the demand were there. Because of the previous neglect of the appliance business by supply undertakings, customers had come to regard ironmongers and gasfitters as their prime source of practical advice on gas matters. Such men had built up their knowledge and skills through their experience of supplying and fitting apparatus for customers. This was something of which gas engineers by and large were ignorant.

It would not do for gas engineers to antagonise local tradesmen unnecessarily by attempting to assume a leading role in a business they had previously been only too willing to disregard. Against this risk, they had to decide just how committed they were to promoting appliances. If the efforts of local tradesmen were inadequate, they would have to buckle to and learn this new business themselves if they wished to see it grow. Such a change from traditional ways was by no means universally welcomed. Two leading articles in the *Gas Journal* in late 1880 echoed a general sense of quiet despair and helplessness pervading much of the industry.

It has with many people become rather the fashion lately to discuss the position of the gas industry when gas has ceased to be the great illuminating agent - when, in fact, that honourable vocation has been assumed by another, and gas is relegated to the still useful, but much less ornamental purposes of heating, cooking and the like... It will be the commencement of a bad time for gas makers when they have to find other outlets for their chief product, not for the sake of increasing their returns, but to make up for losses sustained in their, at present, most important and useful field.

It is not clear why, apart from nostalgia for a comfortable past, the industry should resent having to make the effort to develop new markets. Perhaps the writer was unconsciously contrasting the decorative and florid gas lamp fittings which graced the family rooms with the crude heating and cooking equipment used by the servants below stairs. Perhaps he envisaged the status of the industry and its senior men sliding if it became too deeply involved in the 'less ornamental' uses for gas.

Fortunately such counsels of despair did not discourage gas engineers. They began, haltingly at first but later with enormous gusto, to supply appliances direct to customers, largely bypassing the existing retail traders.

Tentative moves to find new markets, 1875-1890

I
f interest in new uses for gas was to be stimulated without antagonising those already involved in the business, what better way could there be than staging an exhibition? Exhibitions to show progress in the arts and industry had a notable pedigree. Much of the enthusiasm dated back to the Great Exhibition of 1851. On display there, as well as the major eye-catching exhibits, were some items in the miscellaneous metal section. Along with Lockerby & Stephenson's six-light chandelier for gas, Harvey's cooking stove or ship's fire-hearth of wrought iron and Young's Vesta lamps to burn rectified turpentine was a display by William Strode, manufacturer. This included a gas cooking-range incorporating a flexible gas torch for lighting the burners, a gas broiler for chops, steaks &c and a hot air stove heated by gas. Interestingly Strode showed a device for adding naphtha vapour to coal gas by which 'its illuminating power was nearly doubled'. Strode's description of his exhibit, published in the official descriptive catalogue already quoted in chapter 1, included his forecast that the use of gas for cooking would soon be universal. This was grossly over-optimistic. Gas appliances were of negligible commercial importance at the time. Gas was expensive and technology had not yet caught up with innovation.

Similarly at the Paris Universal Exhibition of 1867, which attracted exhibits from many countries, some cookers were shown. There were reports in the technical press to keep British gas engineers informed. The *Gas Journal* carried a series of six extended reports on gas and water apparatus on display. Four of the six related to gas works materials and one to meters, which were shown by makers from France, Britain, Prussia, Russia, Spain, Belgium and Norway. The final article was the only one concerned with utilisation and dealt almost exclusively with lighting but there was a short section devoted to cooking apparatus. This suggested that considerable interest in the possibility of using gas for cooking might develop.

> The various kinds of cooking apparatus from all countries indicate the great efforts now being made to introduce gas as ordinary fuel in kitchens... We have seen a beefsteak broiled in 10 minutes and 5 litres of water boiled in 20 minutes with a small stove.

The rudimentary nature of the equipment on offer is clear from the first regular illustrated advertisements in British trade journals from the 1860s, some of which have been shown earlier.

By the time of the 1878 Paris exhibition the quality of appliances shown was considerably improved. Several British firms were amongst the exhibitors, including Sugg, Leoni and Wright, who between them were awarded four medals. Another medal was awarded to the firm of Winfield, to which no other reference has been found; presumably it made some novelty which caught the judges' eye. Leoni's prize was for kitchen apparatus and Wright's for gas warming apparatus. The relative crudity of the British entries which were of plain cast iron without enamelling was shown up by the quality of the stylish enamelled French hotplates on display. A letter to *The Times* a few years later suggested that the 1878 Paris Exposition gave the first great impetus to the use of gas for cooking and heating. This is arguably correct, but in Paris, as described in chapter 2, gas industry attention was focussed very much more on the displays of electric lighting and the implications of competition on the gas lighting market for the industry than on appliances for other purposes.

Not all exhibitions were on a major international scale, nor were they always a commercial success, for example a general exhibition in South Kensington in the mid 1870s at which some gas equipment was shown. Some exhibitions were devoted to particular products. No doubt triggered by news of developments in electric lighting in France, early in 1877 the South Shields Gas Company announced its intention to sponsor its own exhibition for the sole purpose of promoting the use of gas for purposes other than lighting. The engineer at South Shields, W J Warner, was an influential figure at the time. He had played a leading role in the establishment of the British Association of Gas Managers (later Institution of Gas Engineers) and was elected president a couple of years after his exhibition. In staging an exhibition the company hoped to demonstrate appliances using gas for cooking, heating, laundry, water heating and motive power and invited the co-operation of 'manufacturers of gas engines and apparatus for cooking and heating by gas'. To encourage the participation of as many makers as possible, it was announced that a number of silver medals were to be awarded for the best appliances on show.

At first response from makers was rather slow; the offer of medals was not as effective an incentive as the organisers had hoped. In the absence of accepted criteria, ill-informed judges sometimes awarded medals on the basis of novelty or appearance regardless of quality, convenience or utility. In what might prove a lottery for prizes, inefficient or impractical apparatus could be rewarded, while solid goods from reputable makers were passed over. The better known makers were initially cautious about submitting their appliances for competition. It was with some relief that they learned the names of the judges at South Shields, who were recognised as both knowledgeable and independent. Among the exhibitors were firms who would become prominent in the appliance business, J Wright of Birmingham (cookers), Ewart & Son (water heaters), and C Wilson of Leeds (cookers & fires) as well as many other firms whose names quickly disappeared. As well as the expected appliances, one or two more exotic items were shown, including a cigar lighter and a burner for singeing horses' manes.

The exhibition opened with a civic banquet cooked by gas (this was to be a recurring feature of such exhibitions) and speeches. Warner's speech suggested the spirit of a revivalist meeting rather than a trade fair;

> The gas-pipes appear to be not only 'the perfection of civilisation' but the conduits of mighty forces – light, heat and power – the elements of which were created, gathered and stored by our heavenly Father through long past ages to refine, elevate and bless mankind.

The exhibition, held in a drill hall, was a resounding success, being visited by no less than 30,000 people over the course of the week that the exhibition was open. It must have drawn visitors from much of the North-East, as the company had only 5,500 customers at the time. It was the first of hundreds specifically arranged to promote gas held over the next quarter of a century. This first exhibition was arranged by a private gas undertaking; the next few were managed by municipal undertakings, Birmingham in 1878, then Bradford, Halifax, Leeds, Wakefield, Rochdale and Newcastle-on-Tyne in 1879.

Public interest did not wane. The Leicester undertaking had only recently been purchased by the Council, which enlarged the works and expanded the mains network. To ensure that the enlarged capacity would be fully used, the Council's gas committee decided to hold an exhibition and to publicise gas cooking by supplying cookers on hire. This strategy was not universally welcomed, as the local paper reported. A deputation of ironmongers and gasfitters immediately petitioned the council to reconsider their decision as 'such letting is coming into direct and serious collision with their interests as a body of traders who are also large ratepayers'. They were also worried that 'at the extremely low rates charged for the use of the stoves, it is impossible for us to compete with them'. In fact not one of the 33 traders who signed the petition was exclusively dependent on gas work. For example, one described himself as a furnishing and general ironmonger, gas fitter and cricket outfitter, another was a brazier, waterworks plumber, gas fitter and electrical bell hanger and a third an ironmonger, haberdasher, oil and general dealer. Was the future of gas in Leicester to depend on the efforts of such uncommitted traders?

The Gas Committee put up a robust rebuttal which was accepted by the Council.

> It appeared that the day consumption might be materially increased if the prejudice of the public could be removed and cooking by gas became more general practice but as the sale of gas cooking stoves had been in the hands of the memorialists [ie. petitioners] ever since the introduction of gas into Leicester [many years before the Council took over] and the limited number in use showing either how little they had pushed the trade or how largely they had failed in their efforts...

The committee pointed out that they would only hire cookers 'so that consumers might have their prejudices removed and see the advantages of using gas in preference to coal'; they had no intention at that time of selling appliances. They claimed that the rates they charged were fully economic (based on the few already hired out) but even if the rates were not, the expenditure would be fully justified by the profits on additional sales of gas, 'the primary object of the committee being to secure the consumption of gas'.

This ambivalence over whether hiring should be seen as a temporary promotional expense or as an ancillary trading activity which should be financially self-supporting was to bedevil gas industry thinking for virtually all the time up to nationalisation. It is interesting that the awareness and questioning of appliance subsidy in 1880 in Leicester should gradually cease to be a matter of general concern as the gas industry demonstrated its resilience, both creating an enormous appliance business and greatly improving its lighting technology.

Leicester Corporation put on another highly professional display in 1894 with cookery demonstrations. Despite a small entrance charge the total attendance was 49,214. This demonstrated an enormous and continuing public interest in this new labour-saving technology. People were much more ready to have a gas supply than they had been only a few years earlier as they enjoyed the benefits of generally rising standards of living.

By involving themselves in the promotion of these early exhibitions and by vetting equipment to be included, undertakings were beginning to influence what appliances their customers should use. When Leeds held its exhibition, the manager Henry Woodall arranged a series of cooking tests using the various appliances submitted for exhibition; this was presumably both to assist the judges and to help in selecting appliances for the Leeds undertaking to stock. Here is an early example of a gas undertaking implicitly accepting some degree of responsibility for the performance of appliances, a precursor of the public service ethos that was beginning to emerge. Sometimes when the local manager did not wish to undertake testing himself – no standardised test methods had been developed – an outside expert was brought in, usually a gas engineer. The *Gas World* was disgusted when Rotherham Corporation selected Miss Stopford of the Liverpool School of Cookery rather than a gas engineer to undertake testing of cookers for them and to award the certificates of merit.

> No maker will quietly submit to have his stoves tested by a cook in a drillhall in the short space of four days. If this system of testing spreads, it will soon be a recommendation not to possess a gold medal.

The size and scope of an exhibition did not necessarily guarantee that its organisation would be above board. In 1882/83 there was a major Electric and Gas Exhibition at the Crystal Palace; Livesey and other senior members of the Gas Institute (a forerunner of the IGE) were responsible for the gas section arrangements. Two of the major lighting makers were represented, Sugg from London and Bray from Leeds. After the exhibition Bray complained that he had been allocated a much worse stand than his rival and that he had been excluded from consideration for the prizes on offer by Livesey and the other organisers, who were close friends and had masonic links with Sugg. Representations to Livesey were treated with Olympian disdain; Livesey, a leading figure of the gas 'establishment', declined to justify his actions. The *Gas World* suggested that the awards for the gas lighting entries were given on the basis of 'bribery, wire-pulling and corruption' and 'wilful and shameless jobbery'. The *Financial News* asked

> whether Mr. Sugg's official friends were fair and reasonable in their championship of his interests at the expense of his competitors... It is a singular fact that wherever Messrs

Livesey, Gandon and Ohren [fellow directors of the Crystal Palace Gas Co] could get their oars in, there was nothing but backwater for Mr. Bray.

Livesey was supported throughout by the *Gas Journal*, which was owned and edited by Walter King, a masonic friend of Sugg and Ohren. The *Gas Journal* reports were described by the rival *Gas World* as 'characterised by gross animus and vindictiveness, by shuffling, suppression of truth, distortion of facts and gross misrepresentation'.

What began as a dispute between two commercial firms, Sugg from London and Bray from Leeds, soon came to have wider ramifications. Sugg and Bray were involved in a costly, long-drawn-out and ultimately inconclusive legal action over infringement of patents. More seriously, the affair symbolised a deep unease within the gas engineering profession. As he had been unable to get satisfaction from Livesey, Bray raised his complaints at Institute meetings. Engineers were drawn into rival camps. There was tension between the commercially-minded and those who saw themselves as professional engineers; the latter objected to being harangued by a trader on the activities of a respected professional. There was the question of relationships between makers as suppliers and engineers as customers; there was the murky matter of favours being solicited corruptly. Apart from this, engineers from small provincial undertakings felt that their colleagues from London and other large undertakings, who often acted as engineering consultants for small companies, were riding roughshod over them and disregarding their reasonable concerns. The subsequent controversy split the Gas Institute and rumbled on until 1899. Livesey for some years stubbornly refused to justify his actions in the Crystal Palace affair but finally shook hands publicly with Bray to signify the ending of the feud. The whole affair was rumbling on at a time when the industry was intensely nervous about the impact of electrical competition.

It must be remembered that at this time gas undertakings had no sales organisation of their own, only meter readers and in some cases technical inspectors. The first exhibitions were organised by gas undertakings but their impact and success depended crucially on the willingness of the makers to support them by providing appliances, display stands and the salesmen to man them. The appliance makers enthusiastically seized the opportunity to show off their wares. During the 1880s and 1890s, such exhibitions were very much a novelty and, as has been seen, attracted great local interest. They were only arranged during the summer months, but there could be several every week; for example in May 1893 there were exhibitions in Barnsley, Bingley, Birkenhead, Dublin, Dumbarton, Jersey, Portsmouth, Stonehaven and Westgate. As well as offering demonstrations, such exhibitions were usually accompanied by intensive canvassing in the neighbourhood in an effort by the exhibitors to win sales. 'Lady canvassers' were found to be particularly effective in persuading potential customers to try gas cooking and were employed by many makers.

During the 1880s there was some debate over who should play the lead role in promoting gas appliances. While the largest undertakings had the resources to mount their own exhibitions, this was beyond the capabilities of most smaller undertakings. It was not long before individual appliance makers began to approach them offering to stage exhibitions either on an exclusive basis or in combination with other makers. Generally such approaches were welcomed; sometimes if the manager refused to co-operate the makers went ahead anyway. Where they were involved, the makers carried all the burden and cost, put all the arrangements in hand, advertised, organised cookery demonstrations and canvassed customers. Gas engineers were uneasy about leaving matters entirely in the hands of traders who might be here today, gone tomorrow. They were afraid that, if matters were left entirely to the makers, customers might have a poor deal.

> Competing salesmen at stove exhibitions frequently frighten intending purchasers and cause embarrassment which results in driving away trade.

The engineers were of course concerned that gas itself would get a poor reputation. Their prime object was to promote gas sales but their interests could become submerged beneath those of the makers who were only concerned in selling appliances.

Direct marketing was an expensive business for the makers; it was estimated that the cost of exhibitions was £300-400 each. It is hardly surprising that makers wanted to profit as much as they could from this expenditure. When a manager did not make exclusive arrangements with a single maker, it was rumoured that an 'association' of notable exhibitors, including Richmonds, John Wright and Fletcher, Russell often attempted to take control of the arrangements. This gave them an opportunity to exclude potential outside competitors, whatever the gas manager might have wished. Other members of the 'association' were alleged to be Leoni, Davis (of Bath), Billing, Hassall & Singleton and

Wilson; of these others, only Wilson survived into the 1890s. It was not unreasonable that the organisers should be able to exert some control over who participated; they were, after all, left to shoulder all the costs. The *Gas Journal* considered this restrictive practice unsavoury but feared, from hints received from time to time, that it might be rife. Of course the makers could only act in this way because the supply industry had no marketing capabilities of its own.

John Wright & Co, on behalf of the makers, retorted that they did not mind fair competition but had to take matters into their own hands as 'disreputable practices have become so common at gas apparatus exhibitions'. Some, such as that at Carlisle in 1885 were overrun with

> sellers of pots and pans, the vendors of slag-ware, the gas-burner hawking fraternity, the retailers of magic razor strops and all the other tag-rag-and-bobtail crew who have too frequently infested gas exhibitions.

On one occasion Richmonds were summoned for selling goods without a hawker's licence; this suggests the character of some shows. Apart from the distraction, there was another reason for the makers' desire to exclude tinkers from their exhibitions; they wished to keep on good terms with ironmongers who might stock their appliances. Fletcher, Russell actually wrote to Wright in 1893 asking that the sale of kitchen utensils at exhibitions should stop in order to retain the co-operation of local ironmongers.

Not all undertakings were enthusiastic about arranging exhibitions; some at first pooh-poohed the idea that they should get mixed up in such matters. If they were already selling as much gas as they could produce, they would not be keen to increase sales if this necessitated building new gasmaking plant. This might have seemed a hazardous enterprise as long as investors preferred to speculate in the new electric companies rather than in an unfashionable industry such as gas.

It was soon found that exhibition visitors were very interested in straightforward cookery displays to show the possibilities of gas. Lady demonstrators were in great demand. Often the best were under contract to individual appliance makers; demonstrations were directed towards selling particular cookers, rather than promoting gas as such. A few acted as freelance impresarios, putting on their own shows. One of them, Agnes Kelman, described how she rented premises, 'town halls, theatres, music halls, skating rinks, drill halls, old churches...' and attracted paying audiences of up to 1,000. In the early years, she said, a successful lecturer could earn 'really large sums of money'. At first such exhibitions were 'regarded as a sort of fashionable recreation to fill an idle hour before afternoon tea' but it was soon realised that 'the ladies who attended the demonstrations meant business... and looked for substantial instruction rather than passing amusement'.

Such demonstrations helped to satisfy a real public interest in cooking by gas. Marie Jenny, the wife of William Sugg the gas engineer who had been involved in the Crystal Palace affair, wrote a cookery book which also described gas appliances, particularly those of her husband, and how to use them. The success of Mrs. Beeton's book was a manifestation of growing interest in household management; another was the establishment of the National Training School of Cookery in the mid 1870s. This had the support of a very influential committee; Princess Louise was the first president; Queen Victoria attended one of the lectures (and partook of an omelette). The national school was followed by others in Liverpool, Manchester, Birmingham, Glasgow and Edinburgh. A first class diploma from one of these could lead to a post as lady cook and lecturer. The diploma course covered theoretical and practical work, demonstration cookery and the chemistry of food. Even so, it had less of a technical emphasis than the German Continental Gas Association course for lecturers at Dessau. To obtain a certificate there, the lecturer was taught not only cookery but also about gas manufacture and utilisation, assembly of appliances and comparative cookery tests with different fuels.

Some undertakings were keen to encourage their customers to learn more about gas and engaged their own lecturers. In 1888 the SMGC arranged a series of twenty presentations, which resulted in immediate orders for 859 stoves. Manchester engaged Miss Young of Warrington to demonstrate for them. The GLCC bought 1/- tickets for Miss Ida Cameron's shows, which they gave to potential customers. Miss Edden, who had previously been contracted to Fletcher, Russell, an appliance maker, was appointed by the GLCC in 1906 at £200 pa. as their first home service adviser to visit customers in their own homes and advise on the use of gas appliances. Her services were so valuable that within a year, five assistant lady advisers had been appointed.

Cookery was being taught in Board schools by the 1890s; this 'vital but quiet social revolution' would not have been possible without the availability of gas cookers for equipping the schools. This suggests strongly that gas cookers were already spreading rapidly in ordinary homes; they were not exclusively for the better-off. Ten years later so many children had been taught how to use gas cookers that the educational value of exhibitions was being questioned. The Americans were equally interested in learning about cooking by gas. As the *Gas World* reported,

> In some of the great cities of the United States, and most conspicuously at Boston, it is now quite the fashion among clever and enterprising young ladies to take lessons in the culinary art.

Cheaper classes were put on for working class girls. Exhibitions were also arranged in Australasia to promote gas appliances eg. in Adelaide in 1887 and New Zealand in 1890.

By the end of the 1880s, the gas industry had largely recovered its confidence. Electrical competition was proving less damaging than had been feared and still offered virtually no competition in the domestic lighting market. The profile of gas had been raised in the public mind by exhibitions. There was however a considerable difference between creating an awareness in gas for lighting or cooking and converting this interest into sales of appliances. There was as yet no mass demand for gas appliances. There are a number of reasons for this. The technology for efficient gas utilisation was still embryonic. The appliances on offer in Britain lacked the style and finish of those widely available in France. Gas was still perceived as an obsolescent fuel soon likely to be superseded by electricity, both for lighting and other purposes. There was a substantial cost threshold to be surmounted, paying for the pipes, meter, fittings and a deposit before one could become a gas customer. Gas cookers cost two or three times as much as a coal range to provide an equivalent service. Crucially, gas was still too expensive.

Just how price-sensitive some poorer customers were was shown dramatically in Melbourne, Australia. The 1880s had been boom years; the population increased by 40% to half a million. Numbers of gas customers doubled to 65,000. The price of gas fell from $6/4^1/_2$d in 1884 to 4/7d in 1889. Appliances were hired out by the hundred every month. During the 1890s the economy collapsed. Sales of gas halved. In 1893 5,000 cookers had already been returned from hire and more were coming in by the week.

Britain did not face a similar collapse, but customers were acutely aware of comparative costs of different forms of lighting. In 1888 the gas engineer at Glossop in Derbyshire collected figures of the proportions of homes using oil lamps in 44 towns, mainly in Lancashire and Yorkshire, but including Birmingham and Glasgow. He found that in thirteen, 30% or less used oil; in another eighteen, 31-50% used oil and in the remaining thirteen, more than half of all homes used oil lamps. There was obviously a large potential market for gas lighting if the conditions could be made right.

In the same year a Lancashire gas engineer from Darwen carried out a survey of around 1,900 households in the town who did not use gas. Some of the main reasons given were:

332   objected to paying a deposit
120   previously customers but fittings out of order
340   fittings inconvenient or out of order
301   can pay for oil weekly but not gas quarterly
646   prefer oil; oil cheaper

A number of other reasons were given. It was claimed that gas spoiled the window plants, was injurious to health, the quality was poor, a customer had some bother once with the inspector, etc. etc. The engineer concluded that

> ... although oil, this democratic competitor, is not so brilliant as its aristocratic rival, electricity, it is proving itself to be the more formidable of the two.

What is very clear from these surveys is that, despite the problems being experienced by electricity, there was no certainty that gas would benefit. Indeed around 1890, it began to look as if the prophets of doom a decade earlier were to be proved right. Because of high cost and inadequate public satisfaction with the service offered, despite a number of very popular exhibitions it might not be possible to create a mass market for gas.

Whilst most British gas managers did not feel comfortable involving themselves in 'trade' by selling appliances, there was no such feeling against supplying them on hire on request. Irrational or not, the managers perhaps had an inkling that a commitment to marketing would mean appointing salesmen, advertising, perhaps employing gas fitters and certainly becoming more closely involved with their customers over a whole range of transactions. There would no longer be a simple supplier-purchaser contractual relationship but they would have to consider how the gas they sold was being used. They would have to consider its comparative effectiveness, advantages and drawbacks. In any event the undertaking would be a very different type of business and probably harder to manage profitably.

By contrast, no such commitment was apparently required for hiring. It was seen as a promotional activity to introduce new appliances to the public in order to encourage sales of gas. If customers liked the appliances they could buy their own either from ironmongers and gas fitters or direct from the makers; if not the appliance would be taken back, refurbished and passed on to another potential buyer. In the 1870s and 1880s while gas lighting was well known, gas appliances represented an unfamiliar and expensive technology whose merits were still unproven in the public mind. In these circumstances hiring gave customers the same confidence as buying on sale or return; if they did not get on with gas, they could send back the appliance. The difference was that gas companies were not expecting to supply appliances on sale themselves. As a promotional activity there was no need to consider hiring as a separate business in its own right. It could be undertaken without necessarily covering its full costs. In fact it could be subsidised.

Hiring had a long pedigree. In 1847 the *Gas Gazette* reported that the manager at Devonport was offering lighting fittings for hire, together with a special ventilator, the Arnott Valve, to carry away heat and smell. He also offered cookers for hire, but without much success, even though he was not charging a full economic rental. (He charged $7^1/_2\%$ of the capital cost as an annual rental; this figure included all costs of repairs). The *Gas Gazette* went on to claim that hiring is 'the universal practice of similar companies in the United States... to their manifest advantage.' If true, this is surprising, as hire was almost unknown in the US a quarter of a century later. This report triggered a discussion on the origins of hiring in the gas industry. The Henley undertaking offered light fittings on hire as early as 1834 (charging 10% of the capital cost as rental) as an introductory offer to build up customer numbers quickly. The practice was abandoned a few years later. The Dorchester company (est. 1833) had managed to sign up customers for 200 lights during its first twelve years of existence. It offered lighting fittings for hire from 1845 and within a couple of years had trebled the number of lights in use. The manager passed details of his scheme to interested colleagues, some of whom adopted it.

These schemes were mainly for lighting. After 1850 there are a number of references to appliance hire. Goddard of Ipswich 'sold and let out on hire gas fittings and gas stoves'. From the early 1870s several managers

began experimenting, including
William Wright of Lewes, who
commended hire of appliances 'on
hire at a nominal rental sufficient to
pay interest on capital invested and
to pay for repairs'. Hardick of
Salisbury started hiring cookers in
1872 to build up his daytime
business; five years later he had let
out 90, mainly two- and three-
burner cookers.

THE EAST ANGLIAN
GAS COOKING APPARATUS,

INVENTED AND MANUFACTURED BY
EBENEZER GODDARD,
GAS ENGINEER, IPSWICH.

Goddard's cooker

This trend towards hiring did not
go unnoticed by appliance makers.
John Wright & Co, established in
1866 as general ironfounders, had
begun early to specialise in gas
appliances, and claimed to be the
oldest gas appliance business in the
world. The firm at first supplied
grates, stoves and all sorts of ornamental ironwork but soon concentrated
on cookers, broilers, radiating gas stoves and other appliances. From its
advertisements which appeared regularly in the gas press, it is possible to
trace the development of appliances. By the 1880s cookers were
recognisably similar to those of today. Wright was obviously keen to
develop this new business and, from the early 1870s, encouraged
undertakings to supply cookers on hire.

One name in particular has been widely mentioned in connection with
the popularisation of hiring, that of Magnus Ohren, secretary of the
Crystal Palace Gas Co. His repute is based on a reference in *King's
Treatise*, published in 1882 by Walter King, a close friend and masonic
colleague; they belonged to the same lodge. (It will be recalled that these
two were involved in the Sugg and Bray affair.) The Crystal Palace
company fixed 600 appliances, cookers and fires, for its 10,000
customers over the decade from 1869. The issue of these hired appliances
was clearly intended to develop new markets rather than to be a separate
self-financing venture. Their total cost was £2,160, ie an average of £3/
12/- each. By 1879 Ohren had hired out 353 cooking stoves (@ 1/6d per
qr.) and 240 heating stoves (@ 1/-). His annual hire income came to
£154, or 7% on the capital invested. This had to meet the costs of
buying, installation, servicing, depreciation and ultimately replacement. It

is clear that Ohren was writing off a substantial part of his costs not covered by the rental income received.

Other contemporaries gave the major credit for building a market for hired gas cookers not to Ohren but to Alfred Colson, who was appointed engineer and manager to the Leicester Corporation Gas Dept. in 1882. He later combined this role with that of electrical engineer for Leicester! Colson himself attributed the general ignorance of the advantages of gas to 'the apathy displayed by gas companies generally in bringing before the notice of their consumers the merits of (gas)'. Within a couple of years of his arrival over 2,000 hired stoves had been supplied. He wrote a booklet, *The Economy and other Advantages of Cooking by Gas,* for his own customers which proved very popular and was used by many other undertakings. Manchester Corporation started hiring in 1885 at rates from 1/- to 4/9d per quarter, much the same as Hardick had charged at Salisbury ten years earlier; 250 were let in the first 3 months, suggesting considerable latent demand. Kendal was more generous; it lent stoves free and met half the cost of fixing, presumably as a temporary promotional gimmick.

These examples support the assertion that, very early on, subsidised hire had become the general rule within the industry. It is not clear whether Colson for example decided as a matter of policy to promote cookers by offering them at less than the full economic hire charge or whether he simply adopted the practice of the time, expecting to cover repair costs from the rental income but charging capital costs against gas revenue. This was the pattern twenty years later, when four out of five homes with a gas supply in Leicester had a gas cooker; the cost of repairs, £5,556, was just covered by rental charges, but the Corporation set aside an additional £8,285 pa. for depreciation against the capital outlay of £72,000.

An industry-wide consensus on appropriate terms for hiring seems to have emerged. In 1911 the *Gas World* could say that 'the generally accepted basis is 10% on the cost', that is, annual rental charges would amount to 10% of the initial cost of the appliance. At the time, costing methods were not sufficiently developed to calculate the true costs of renting appliances; what is certain is that the 10% charged would have done little more than to cover the cost of the capital invested, with no margin for servicing and ultimate replacement. There was therefore a considerable element of subsidy.

At the time this was of no great concern. Sales of gas and numbers of customers were increasing steadily. As described earlier, gas companies were generally reckoned to be profitable concerns and they were as yet under no serious competitive pressure. Gas engineers as a rule of thumb reckoned that they sold gas at double the cost of manufacture. They would no doubt have considered cast-iron gas cookers bought for supply on hire on a par with other gasworks plant with an estimated life of sixty years. There was at that time no problem about meeting any deficit on the hire account from the profits on gas sold, particularly as hired appliances would increase off-peak sales without adding significantly to peak loads. If an economic charge for hiring were to be calculated today, provision would be made for installation, spares and repair costs, handling costs, depreciation, ultimate replacement and indeed for a profit margin on the business of hire. The question of funding relacements for obsolete hired appliances near the end of their life was to cause the gas industry serious problems between the wars, as will be described in chapter 11.

This failure to provide adequately for the periodic upgrading or renewal of capital investment was by no means unusual in the late nineteenth century. As one historian of accounting methods has said, in the UK, 'the recognition of depreciation was frequently delayed until replacement, and since firms often paid dividends out of profit defined gross of depreciation, serious liquidity problems might arise when replacement was required'. Similarly, in America before 1900, the amount of depreciation set aside varied in practice according to the financial condition of the firm's business and only rarely was an attempt made to allocate depreciation to departments or operations.

While British gas managers may have come to accept the logic of the arguments in favour of subsidising the appliance business, this did not mean that they thereby became enthusiastic about marketing appliances themselves. Hiring was acceptable but actually setting out to market and sell appliances was demeaning; it meant becoming involved in 'trade'. Indeed, many managers not only failed to market appliances themselves but seem to have treated private installers (other than as sub-contractors) with resentment, mistrust and obstruction rather than as potential allies.

Undertakings wanted to sell more gas; makers wanted to sell their appliances. What of the ironmongers, plumbers and gasfitters? They had been accustomed to supplying lighting fittings as the undertakings concentrated on gasmaking rather than marketing and utilisation. It seemed to make sense for the independent traders to move into this new appliance business if it showed signs of growing. During the 1880s, the *Ironmonger* trade journal devoted considerable space to the gas business, providing regular reports for its subscribers. These included descriptions of new gas apparatus, reports on Gas Institute meetings and general comments on the state of the business, seen from the point of view of the ironmongery trade. Ironmongers were interested in other forms of lighting, especially candles, oil lamps and paraffin and noted that the spread of gas lighting would damage the trade in oil lamps. They were of course also interested in the reports of the new electric lighting and how it might affect their trade. The *Ironmonger* was one of the papers which warned its readers of the widespread speculation in dubious electrical shares in 1882.

In an 1882 editorial the *Ironmonger* reported that the gas stove business

> has of late assumed an important position, not only as a manufacturing industry but also as an essential portion of any respectable ironmonger's business.

The article went on to complain that the gas undertakings were entering into unwarrantable competition with regular tradesmen. They should get their profits from selling gas and should not meddle in the business of others; they should pass potential appliance customers to the local ironmonger. It was alleged that gas undertakings promoted wasteful appliances rather than efficient ones so that they would sell more gas. There was a further complaint.

> In London and elsewhere... the companies let out on hire these stoves on terms which... are quite inadequate judged in relation to cost prices... Let them by all means educate the public by means of holding exhibitions and by advertisements... In letting out stoves on hire, they are not invariably doing that which is prudent and wise.

The editorial went on to argue that gas undertakings should cut the price of gas rather than subsidise their appliance business to the detriment of ironmongers, and invited comments from readers. There was little response by way of letters from the ironmongers themselves; perhaps, as claimed by gas undertakings, the trade did not think the gas business was worth pursuing. Since undertakings could undercut them at any time by subsidising sale or hire terms from the profit on the sale of gas, this is hardly surprising. It is interesting to note that there was only muted objection to the involvement of gas undertakings in hiring appliances, which seems to have been generally regarded as a legitimate promotional activity.

One gas manager put forward an ingenuous defence to criticism from the ironmongers.

> Given a free choice, there is no question between buying and hiring. Gas companies would much rather the customer was the owner of the whole of his appliances; and they only resorted to hiring as a means of securing a large class of custom that was otherwise unobtainable. They found that many who for various reasons would not buy would hire... It is an essential of the hiring business that the rent charged should be comparatively trifling... The low hiring rate, or the cheap selling price, is regarded by the consumer as a concession that he may reasonably claim from the gas company.

There were two reasons why opposition was not more vocal. One was that the substantial discounts traditionally enjoyed by retailers were under threat and this was of more pressing concern. In the event, any attempt to defend them would prove a hopeless struggle. Discounts were commonly available; for example, co-operative societies and firms often advertised prices 5% or 10% above cost rather than at the maker's published retail price. Boots the Chemists was built upon a basis of quality goods sold at low profit margin. In the piano business the retail price list was regarded as 'a little piece of pleasantry'. By offering appliances at what appeared to be uncommercial terms, gas undertakings might well have been adopting a common practice of the period.

The other reason for ironmongers to be relatively unconcerned about the appliance business was that this did not provide a good fit with the average ironmonger's trade. The mainstay of his business was a mass of small cash transactions rather than a few sales of expensive items. He would sell pots and pans, fireirons and replacement grates but was less likely to deal in the kitchen ranges installed by the builder or of course gas appliances costing several pounds for which there was only a limited demand. Other makers of expensive items ran into the same problems. The Singer Sewing Machine Co in the 1850s needed dealers who could handle its new machines. However, especially in the earlier years, it could not find retailers prepared to finance the holding of stocks of a relatively expensive article and who could successfully market such a new appliance. As a result it was forced to develop its own retail shops which provided a base for salesmen on commission and for dealing with after-sales service.

The first known purpose-designed showroom for gas appliances was opened by the GLCC in 1894. Before then some undertakings had rooms at their gasworks to which customers might be admitted, but these were storerooms rather than retail premises. Following the GLCC's lead many other showrooms were opened in subsequent years. The fact that they were designated showrooms rather than shops for the next three quarters of a century shows how gas managers wished to dignify their retail business, implying that they were more interested in demonstrating the advantages of gas than actually setting out to sell appliances.

Here there was a major difference between British and American gas engineers. Hiring in America was almost unknown. Americans wanted to sell as much as they could, and were always on the look-out for novelties to tempt customers to buy. The contrast could not have been more marked. Typical British attitudes were encapsulated in a press report on the activities of an American manager from Syracuse, NY. 'To pitch a gas stove on the pavement and cook a joint in the presence of the passer-by may strike the English manager as a rather advanced way of pushing business'. The American handed out free baked potatoes to passers-by and, in the interests of gaining a possible sale, would fix up a cooker temporarily in a customer's home and send a demonstrator to cook the evening meal to show what gas could do. The Americans saw no conflict of interest between themselves and private traders, plumbers and gasfitters.

No evidence has been found to suggest that gas undertakings made any strategic assessments when they first decided to hire out appliances, or indeed that they fully understood the likely costs. There are very few references to appliances in the board minutes of undertakings that have been examined although details of gas sales and income were routine, suggesting that the appliance business was not considered of sufficient importance to be considered at board level. Decisions on appliance trading were taken at officer rather than director level, no doubt influenced by reports from those who had practical experience. First one undertaking began a hire business, and then another. Gas managers were able to discuss the pros and cons at their professional gatherings and reports were appearing in the gas press. In the early years there were a few references to hire charges being set at a level to cover the full costs of the exercise; this idea seems to have been quietly dropped when it became apparent just how popular the idea was with customers.

Support for hiring was not universal; John West in 1894 was of the opinion that 'the best plan is to sell stoves... but, failing this, to let them out with the option of purchase upon the 3 or 4 years' hire purchase (HP) system'. West was in a position to give dispassionate advice; he had left the supply industry ten years earlier to devote himself full-time to his own business making powered stoking machines for gasworks. His suggestion that HP terms should be offered was very much in keeping with other businesses of the time. The concept was already well established by the 1860s, particularly 3 year agreements in association with the sale of pianos. It was later available for other consumer durables. One possible reason for the reluctance of the gas industry (and indeed other retailers) to offer HP terms was some legal uncertainty over the ownership of goods covered by an HP agreement and whether they could be constrained for debt. This uncertainty was finally resolved in the House of Lords in the 1890s, by which time hiring rather than HP had become widely accepted in the gas industry.

Despite the scope for differences of opinion on the desirability of hire and the appropriate terms, there could be no doubt that the principle was well established. In 1889 the *Gas World* could report that 'ten or twelve years ago gas cooking ranges were comparatively unknown. Now there is hardly a town of importance in which... the company does not let out stoves on hire'. By the turn of the century housekeepers applying for a position could ask for a gas stove as an accepted perquisite of the post. By 1914 a practical cooker fixed with gas lights to a penny-in-the-slot meter had become a normal feature in modest rented working class houses. All of these developments were associated with the hired appliance market; appliances were available for sale, but very few customers bought their own. This was a peculiarly British response, associated from the 1890s with the prepayment supplement, whose genesis is described in the next chapter.

Prepayment meters and the growth of the working class mass market from the 1890s

D uring the 1880s the gas industry grew steadily. During the 1890s it received two boosts which dramatically changed its trajectory; between 1885 and 1895 the number of customers grew by just over a quarter but in the following ten years they doubled. The boosts were first the invention of the incandescent gas mantle which revolutionised gas lighting and will be described in chapter 7. The second boost came from the invention of the prepayment meter which, used innovatively, enabled gas to break into the mass market of working class housing. In the words of George Livesey,

> This extension of gas supply to weekly tenants is the most
> extraordinary and remarkable development of the business
> that has ever been known.

It is surprising that the gas business should expand dramatically following something as mundane as the introduction of a new type of meter, rather than some new process of gas manufacture or the invention of new and desirable appliances. A number of historians of the gas industry have noted that the sudden spurt in the growth of the supply industry coincided with the availability of prepayment meters, where the insertion of a coin allowed the passage of a measured quantity of gas. It might be imagined that one was caused by the other. The full story of how the supply of gas through prepayment meters became inextricably linked with the supply of hired cookers is rather more complex, and has not been described before.

One consequence of the general introduction of meters around the mid 19th century was that customers, instead of paying a rental for a particular level of lighting service, now paid in arrears, after the meter had been read and the account submitted. This meant that the undertakings were supplying on credit. Security for payment was an important concern, as they could not pick and choose their customers at will. In return for their monopoly privileges, all undertakings were under a statutory obligation to make a gas supply available on demand. This obligation to supply had been common from the 1850s, obligatory in London from 1860 and universal under the Gasworks Clauses Act of 1871.

To cover the risk of non-payment, undertakings insisted on a substantial deposit before a supply would be given. Manchester required the amount of an estimated winter quarter's account. In Darwen, Lancashire, when the Corporation decided to dispense with deposits, £290 was returned to 969 customers, an average of 6/- each. In 1888 in Salford, not a wealthy area, deposits of at least 5/- were required from new customers. There is no doubt that these deposits were a hindrance to the less-well-off who might otherwise have considered using gas, at least if the pipes were installed. They were 'considerable enough to stand in the way of the use of gas while oil is sold from door to door and at low prices'.

This was not the only expense a potential new customer would face. Unless a previous occupant had gas installed, there would be the cost of connection to the main, internal pipework, lighting fittings and the meter, an outlay of at least £5-7; added to this might be the cost of a cooker unless it could be rented. The need to lay down perhaps a month's wages in advance meant that most poorer households were effectively debarred from using gas by the initial cost threshold. There is also the suspicion that some managers at least preferred to regard themselves as suppliers to the gentry; they were disinclined to promote gas among the less well-off. In 1892 a gas official writing under the pseudonym "Lux" talked of a self-defeating bureaucratic approach which had the effect of inhibiting poorer people from becoming gas customers, even if they wanted to. As late as in 1904, a correspondent to the *Gas World* described his attempts to persuade his gas company to let him have a supply under the heading 'How not to do it'. With these hindrances to the spread of gas, it is not immediately clear how the invention of a prepayment penny-in-the-slot meter might help.

Various coin-operated machines were first invented in the 1880s. While their value for vending low cost items, chocolate or cigarettes for example, in the street or in railway stations is obvious, paying for gas supply in this way seems bizarre. It is rather as if the technology was applied almost at random on the off-chance that important new uses might emerge. There is no evidence that gas engineers were looking for such a device or indeed that they understood at first how significant it would become once it was available. The first prepayment meter patent was granted in 1887 but the apparatus was impractical. Brownhill's meter of 1888 was, according to *The Times*,

> based on the principle of the confectionery and other
> automatic supply stands now so familiar to the public...

enabling the industrial classes to avail themselves of the
advantages of gas lighting... an important consideration is the
suppression of the dangerous paraffin lamp which has been
the cause of so many fatal fires among the labouring classes.

Brownhill's patent was taken up by Parkinson and Glover, two major
meter makers. Other meter makers introduced their own variations and
soon prepayment meters were available from every meter maker. Whilst
they were available, at first they attracted little interest. Indeed there was
some scoffing from traditionalists, some engineers saying that, although
things were pretty bad, they had not come down to selling gas by the
pennyworth yet.

The crucial factor in the successful introduction of prepayment meters was
the entrepreneurial way in which this new technology was harnessed to
overcome several long-standing problems that previously stood in the way
of a more widespread use of gas; security for payment in arrears, as with a
monthly or quarterly bill; the unwillingness of landlords to pay for the
installation of gas; the sheer initial expense of installation of pipes, fittings
and appliances. Prepayment meters overcame the problem of security for
payment but did not address the problem of the costs associated with
having gas installed.

The breakthrough came in 1889 from the manager of the Ramsgate
municipal undertaking, W A Valon, a respected gas and water engineer
who later set up his own consultancy business and was president of the
Incorporated Gas Institute 1891/92. Valon, following the pattern of many
other undertakings over the previous decade, had arranged an exhibition
with cookery demonstrations the previous year, but the results had been
disappointing. He undertook a survey and found that half the houses in
the town did not even have a connection from the gas mains in the street,
especially cottage property with a rental value of £30 pa. or less. He set
himself the objective of introducing gas into the £15-30 houses,
disregarding for the moment the smallest dwellings.

Valon had heard, probably through reports in the gas press, that the
gas undertaking in Lille, northern France, installed replacement gas
lighting without charge following a factory fire. This was to forestall the
factory owner who had in mind the installation of the new electric
lighting; the initial outlay by the undertaking would be recouped from
profits on gas sold. Following the success of this negotiation, the manager
arranged to install lighting in private houses for a three-year trial period

without charge; the only stipulation was that customers should agree to use a specified minimum amount of gas; in fact almost all customers used more than this. The fittings were to remain the property of the undertaking during the trial but then became the customer's. 160 customers in Lille were signed up over the next 15 months.

Valon had the imaginative idea of linking this concept of free installation of lights with the newly invented prepayment meter. He could provide a complete gas installation with meter, lights and a small boiling ring to poorer homes who could not otherwise afford the initial costs of having a supply put in; the prepayment meter would provide security for the money due. As the relatively low gas consumption to be expected from modest homes would not provide enough profit to recoup the costs of the installation, his prepayment customers would pay a surcharge – the **prepayment supplement**, typically 20 to 30% on the flat rate price – for their gas. Another advantage of Valon's scheme was that it was eminently suitable for rented houses; it could even be used where there were lodgers. Owners of rented property had no objections; it cost them nothing and increased the amenities of their premises.

When Valon first floated his idea in a letter to the *Gas Journal* in January 1889, to enquire if anyone else had attempted such a scheme before and to benefit from any previous experience, he met with a very cool reaction. The demands of the cottage population, according to the *Gas Journal*'s leading article, were

> too insignificant to be worth the risk of supplying... it is worth nobody's while to go to a few pounds of expense for laying on the gas... It is scarcely to be expected that progress in extending the use of gas among these benighted householders will be rapid at first, even with all the facilities offered by Mr Valon. It will take years to bring a proper sense of such change of circumstances, in regard to lighting, home to the appreciation of people who have always looked at gas afar off, as not for them.

In any event, it went on, what succeeded in Ramsgate 'would not in fact be very likely to succeed in a different district'. With hindsight it is hard to conceive a graver misjudgement.

Despite the misgivings of the *Gas Journal*, the progress of Valon's experiment was followed with great interest by other British undertakings. As the rival *Gas World* said,

> Ramsgate is to be the scene of a double experiment which, we may safely say, will be watched by every gas manager in

the Kingdom. From it we shall learn whether the plan of charging everything in the price of gas is feasible and whether the prepayment meter is a practicable apparatus.

Valon in fact did not use a coin-operated meter; he preferred a stop meter of his own design. With this, depending on how much gas was needed and paid for, an amount of gas was 'wound on' by the inspector. When this was used up, the meter stopped the flow of gas. The inspector had to call again to collect more money and wind more gas on. Despite the inconvenience of this compared to a coin meter, the outcome quickly became clear. Within six months of the start of the scheme, the local paper reported that customers paid 'willingly and cheerfully'. At an average cost of £4 per house, Valon fitted up 800 homes within a couple of years, 'people who could never otherwise have burned gas, owing to the first cost of fitting', and within five years he had increased the number of his customers by over one third. Birmingham and Liverpool, 'in the poor localities of the City,' soon followed suit. Liverpool was the first company in Britain to use penny-in-the-slot meters rather than the stop meters used at Ramsgate. Prepayment meters quickly replaced stop meters, being more convenient both for the customer and the undertaking. When the two largest undertakings in the country introduced the prepayment supplement concept, the SMGC in 1892, followed by the GLCC in 1894, its almost universal adoption in the UK was assured.

By mid 1894, over 67,500 prepayment meters had been supplied or were on order, with Liverpool (10,000) and the SMGC (15,000) leading the way. Demand was so great that the number of prepayment installations made was limited only by the ability of the meter makers to meet orders. The GLCC, unable to get enough meters from the makers, had to suspend installations early in 1896 when 15-20,000 orders were outstanding. Gas in rented accommodation proved to be such a desirable feature that, while it was still uncommon, landlords were able to charge an extra 6d a week on the rent if it were installed. In the early years, prepayment meters were offered almost exclusively in small cottage property; only later were they a regular alternative to an ordinary (credit) meter. At first, undertakings varied in what apparatus they would offer; some supplied a cooker or ring with lights, some only the lights and some the meter only. Following the lead of the SMGC and GLCC, within a few years the supply of a cooker, rather than a boiling ring, became the general rule and, in the years just before 1914, incandescent lighting was also supplied as a matter of course by the larger undertakings.

It is interesting to note that when prepayment meters first appeared, the makers used their advertisements in the gas press to explain the commercial advantages to engineers, many of whom were apparently inexperienced in such matters. As one meter maker explained,

> The object is... to place the consumption of gas as easily within reach of the mass of the population as petroleum, candles, etc... without any initial outlay or trouble, such as deposit, references or guarantee now required by Gas Companies

Another maker put the argument on a higher moral plane:

> An important consideration which cannot be overlooked is the duty of Gas Companies and Corporations, who have a first-class monopoly, to supply the working classes with gas, without the burdens and restrictions which now exist.

It seems unlikely that such moral strictures would have much influence with the average gas manager. What was certain was that they recognised the value of the prepayment supplement in creating a mass working class market for gas where it was previously almost unknown.

The prepayment meter, cooker and two light fittings typicallly supplied.

SLOT
INSTALLATIONS
COMPLETE

There can be no doubt that prepayment meters effectively created a new market. During the 1890s when they first became available, the numbers of credit (ordinary) meter customers continued to rise steadily on the same trend as before. When large numbers of prepayment customers were added to this growing number of ordinary customers, total numbers rose sharply. Prepayment customers in cottage property would obviously use less than the larger domestic, commercial and industrial customers with credit meters. While total sales grew, average consumption per customer fell. This would have important implications between the wars when the competitive position of the gas industry relative to electricity was far less favourable than it was before 1914. This is discussed in chapter 13.

The prepayment supplement system brought substantial benefits to both customers and undertakings. As a spokesman for the GLCC put it in 1899,

> This automatic [prepayment] system has been of very special advantage... it has just come to fill up the blank caused by the great expansion of the electric light... The supply of gas to these stoves for cooking purposes... is a great boon to all gas companies; it equalises the supply of gas throughout the day.

The GLCC itself provides a striking, but by no means untypical example of the explosive growth of the appliance business following the introduction of prepayment meters and the prepayment supplement. It has been estimated that in 1892 there were no more than 6-7,000 cookers in use in the GLCC's area of supply when the company had 217,000 customers. The first prepayment meters were issued (with grillers) in 1894. Two years later when cookers were supplied to prepayment customers instead of grillers, 36,600 cookers of all descriptions were supplied to customers. This included sales, hired cookers to credit customers and, what were probably the great majority, cookers to prepayment customers. Between 1894 and 1911, the number of customers had more than doubled and prepayment customers greatly outnumbered those with credit meters. By 1911, almost half-a-million GLCC customers had hired cookers, 62% (ie. 174,776) of all credit meter customers and 74% (ie. 320,606) of prepayment customers. This compares with only around 3% in 1892. The average consumption of gas by prepayment customers was only about one third of the average credit customer (which included non-domestic users); nevertheless the sheer numbers of prepayment customers brought a very important increase to total sales of gas.

This increase of customers and gas sales was repeated throughout the country to a greater or lesser degree. Even so there were 400 undertakings in 1903 which had still not supplied their first prepayment meter; these were probably the smallest unauthorised undertakings. Generally it was the private companies who took the lead; Sheffield was one of the few private companies which failed to introduce prepayment meters. As Ramsgate Corporation introduced the first prepayment supplement scheme in the world, it is a little surprising that municipal undertakings generally were much slower in adopting the concept than private companies. In 1899, 27% of all private company customers had prepayment meters as against only 11% of municipal customers. The reasons are discussed in the next chapter. It was not until the inter-war years that municipal undertakings finally caught up, as shown in the following table.

CUSTOMERS WITH PREPAYMENT METERS, COOKERS (%)

	PREPAYMENT METERS %		COOKERS %	
1902 (all)	24		25	
	Private	Municipal	Private	Municipal
1905	40	29	42	22
1908	50	36	51	25
1911	56	43	54	29
1914	57	50	57	35
1925	58	56	66	60

The next table shows how these figures translate into average consumptions between the wars. As in the earlier table, this shows the gap between private and municipal undertakings was closing steadily.

AVERAGE CONSUMPTION (000 CU. FT.)

	CREDIT		PREPAYMENT	
	Private	Municipal	Private	Municipal
1922	48.3	34.6	19.8	17.3
1925	49.6	35.9	21.7	19.3
1929	49.8	36.5	21.2	19.5
1935	44.2	36.4	17.4	17.0
1938	45.5	40.9	16.3	16.1

1893 had been a high point for municipal undertakings; in that single year there were more municipal than private customers, although the private undertakings supplied almost two thirds of all gas sold. By the later 1890s, private companies were drawing ahead because of their greater willingness to supply prepayment installations. This was particularly true in new markets for gas, such as that for cooking.

In 1899 taking an average for larger undertakings only, 33% of private but only 8% of municipal customers had cookers. In Scotland the municipal figure was even lower, at 5%. These figures for private undertakings are heavily influenced by the GLCC and SMGC which together provide half the customers in the private group. If these two are excluded, the average drops to 17%, which is still double the municipal figure.

The following graph taken from figures in *Gas World Yearbooks* shows actual numbers of cookers sold in the largest undertakings in the country. These were the ones with 10,000 customers or more in 1899, 24 of which (with 990,000 customers) were private and 26 (1,063,000) were municipal.

COOKER SALES 1900-1940

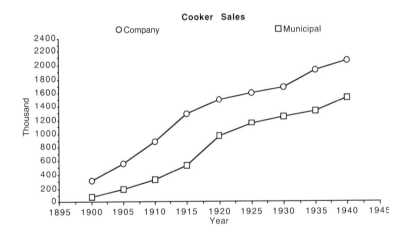

This is a clear illustration of the failure of municipal undertakings to keep pace with their private couterparts in the appliance business.

It was not only the British who were interested in the prepayment supplement experiment and its influence in opening up new markets for gas. The French, from whom the first germ of the idea of 'free' installation had originally come, were interested to hear of British experience in linking this to the new prepayment meters. In 1894 a report was made to the professional body of the French gas engineers, the Société Technique de L'Industrie du Gaz. According to the report, British companies, large and small, which had adopted prepayment meters had their highest expectations surpassed. Installations were limited only by the ability of the meter makers to meet orders. Most prepayment meters were fitted in houses with an annual rent of £25 or less, suitable for workers earning 18-30/- per week, and could be supplied to landlords who let off rooms. The French heard that the supplement was generally around 9-10d per 1,000 cu ft, that is, around 25-35%, but varied from 6d per 1,000 (Tottenham) to 1d per 20 cu ft, equivalent to 50d per 1,000 in one case (Radcliffe and Pilkington). From the context of the discussion it appears that no prepayment meters were being used in France in 1894, although they were introduced in Lille, where the idea originated, the following year.

Elsewhere in Europe, a prepayment supplement scheme was successfully introduced in Holland in 1896. Interestingly, the prepayment meter was never introduced in Belgium, despite the number of customers relative to the total population and the average consumption per customer being similar in Belgium and Holland. The first installations of prepayment meters in Germany were not made until 1896, although German gas engineers would have been aware of prepayment meters. A Danish firm made application for a German patent in 1892 but ran into problems with German industry regulators which were not resolved for several years. Prepayment meters were never as popular in Germany as in the UK and few undertakings offered them; in 1937 for example, 20% of customers were prepayment in Germany as against 65% in the UK. Possibly as a result, gas cooking never achieved the same popularity in Germany as in the UK. A German visitor in 1926 reported that more gas was used for cooking in England than in Germany, where the coal stove would be used during the winter; in Germany gas was used for cooking only when the coal stove was not required. As in Britain, German prepayment customers were supplied with cast-iron cookers; however, by the early years of the twentieth century, most German customers preferred to buy their own pressed steel enamelled cookers. In this they followed American rather than British practice.

In the United States prepayment meters were first used in the late 1890s (Seattle 1896, Newark, N.J. 1897) but only as a direct alternative to a credit meter where the credit status of the customer was in doubt; they were often fitted in bars. Early experiences were reported in a paper to the American Gas Light Association in 1899. Where a prepayment meter was fitted, there was a small supplementary charge (in Newark prepayment gas was $1.25 rather than the normal $1.20 per 1,000 cu ft) as a contribution towards the extra costs associated with this type of meter, estimated at 10-15 cents per 1,000; this however excluded any installation or appliances, and even so was insufficient to cover costs. In Newark, residents were canvassed to take prepayment meters, but there were immediate problems of security, especially in tenement blocks, and there had been a number of robberies. 3,500 were installed but they attracted a higher level of complaint and needed more repairs. There was never any question of free installation of pipes, lights or appliances by the gas undertakings; even modest changes to pipework in a house by the Newark gas undertaking aroused fierce opposition from the New York Master Plumbers' Association.

During discussion at the American conference further problems were aired. One New York company found the prepayment business unprofitable and took the meters out. Another saw them as a reasonable alternative to fortnightly reading and billing for doubtful customers; meters were usually read and bills rendered monthly, although saloons were billed weekly. During the discussion on the paper, there was a full description of the British prepayment supplement system of supplying appliances without direct charge by the manager from Toronto; this aroused no comment or interest among his American colleagues.

At the same American meeting it was reported through the German association of gas managers that ten German gasworks charged an average of 12.2 pfennigs per cubic metre for heat, 16.4 for light (presumably the standard rate) and 19.2 for gas through prepayment meters. Differential prices were also being charged by some UK undertakings at this time, discounts being allowed for non-lighting use of gas.

In Australia, which generally followed British practice, adoption of the prepayment supplement was uneven. The system was first introduced in 1903, although the British meter maker W & B Cowan sought to interest his Australian customers as early as 1893. By 1905 Melbourne had introduced prepayment meters and was supplying Fletcher, Russell grillers while the Australian Gas Light Co of Sydney was still supplying only credit meters. One fifth of all gas customers in Australia were supplied under the prepayment supplement system by 1913.

It is not clear why the prepayment supplement should have been taken up with so much more enthusiasm in Britain than elsewhere in Europe; in America a culture of self-reliance and market-oriented behaviour was clearly unfavourable to the system. The only hypothesis that can be proposed is that gas cookers provided a highly attractive alternative to traditional British cooking with an open fire. By contrast the European tradition of cooking using efficient closed stoves was less susceptible to change. Gas rings and grillers were welcomed on the continent as a source of quick heat, but only as an addition to the existing stove, not as an alternative. In 1890 it was said in the *Gas World* that

> With the exception of batteries of boiling rings, which suit the stewing propensities of the cooks, gas cooking can scarcely be said to have established itself [on the continent] in popular favour. The French housewife would regard herself as very advanced if she only boiled the traditional *pot au feu* by gas; and the German wife has hardly awakened to the possibilities even of the simple boiling ring.

Although not associated with prepayment meters, the Paris Gas Co (CPECG, Compagnie Parisienne de l'Éclairage et du Chauffage par le Gaz) introduced a scheme to provide free appliances as a means of increasing gas sales. In the 1880s the CPECG accounted for half of all gas sales in France, but was untypical of the French industry in general. It was set up in 1855 to amalgamate six predecessor companies. It was given a concession granting it exclusive rights to supply Paris for a fifty-year period; in return it contracted to supply gas at a fixed price of 30 centimes per cubic metre for normal customers but 15c. for public lighting throughout the term of its concession. This represented an immediate saving over the previous prices (40c. and 20c.) and so was welcomed. The agreement however took no account of potential efficiency savings, which would accrue exclusively to the undertaking, nor to the reasonableness of these prices by comparison with those charges elsewhere. In fact at the time the agreement was struck, prices currently ruling in London were about 50% less than Paris prices. The financiers who invested at the time of the flotation never had cause to regret their involvement.

With an extremely profitable monopoly the CPECG never exerted itself to build up its customer base, although over its first 30 years of existence its sales increased sevenfold, mainly to industrial and commercial customers and also to the residences of the wealthy, for all of whom having the best lighting was more important than the cost. As in Britain the complacency of the CPECG was shaken by the onset of competition. Around 1880 its two largest customers, the department stores of Bon Marché and the Grands Magasins du Louvre both converted to electricity. In 1887 after a serious fire at the Opéra Comique all theatre owners were required to switch from gas to electricity. Hotels, restaurants and businesses all adopted the new lighting. When at the 1889 Universal Exposition visitors could compare gas and electric light for themselves, electricity was generally considered to provide the superior lighting.

The loss of its largest and prestige customers precipitated a crisis for the CPECG. In 1885 only 5% of Paris households used gas and even amongst employees of the undertaking only one in twelve of the office clerks were customers. Reasons for this reluctance to use gas are clear. Gas was very expensive. Apart from the cost of the gas, there were a host of ancillary charges (meter and installation rent, standing charges etc.) which almost doubled the charge the customer had to pay. Perhaps most damaging of all was the cost of making the connection from the company's main into individual apartments; traditionally the CPECG had even made a profit on this fitting work, even though it was essential if customers were to be signed up. The idea of a loss-leader was completely alien to CPECG thinking.

The first step towards bringing in new customers came in 1887, when the company offered to provide free installations for customers where there was already a supply in their apartment block; this concession mainly benefited the flats of the better-off. The major move came in 1894 when the company introduced its fee-free programme, installing gas, supplying a single light fitting and cooking ring free of charge and even doing away with meter rents. Over the next ten years 227,000 new connections were made, doubling the number of customers the company had in 1889.

The introduction of the fee-free programme in Paris coincided with the widespread adoption of the prepayment supplement concept in Britain. Whilst both initiatives dramatically increased the number of middle and low income customers, there were significant differences. Gas in Paris was still much more expensive than in London and so was less affordable for the working class. Just by how much Paris customers were being overcharged was illustrated dramatically in 1903 when the CPECG cut its price by a third from 30c. to 20c. following pressure from the City authorities. This was only a couple of years before its concession was due to end and no doubt the CPECG hoped to gain some goodwill from its conciliatory gesture, probably in the vain hope of an extension to its concession.

By contrast with the CPECG's rigid concession, the framework within which British companies operated was more flexible, despite the regulatory powers of the Board of Trade. Dividend levels were controlled and it was in the undertakings' interests to reduce prices as far as they could to attract more business. Potential British customers were more actively pursued, particularly by the appliance makers, as is described in chapter 8.

The enthusiasm of British customers for cooking and lighting by gas by comparison with mainland Europe is clearly illustrated in the following table showing the position in 1936. In that year the UK supplied just over 50% of all gas made in Europe, five times as much as France and almost three times as much as Germany, which had a substantially larger population. The advantage enjoyed by the British gas industry was not limited to overall size alone, which might be attributable to bulk industrial sales. The average sales of gas (by volume) per customer were twice as high in Britain as those in France or Germany.

The appearance of grillers, sometimes supplied instead of cookers to prepayment supplement customers, changed little from the 1890s to this 1936 model.

EUROPEAN GAS SALES

	Sales; 1936 (M^3 x 10^9)	Sales per customer; 1937 (10^3 cu ft)
UK	8991	28.4
Germany	3186	15.1
France	1788	13.1
Holland	586	16.6
Italy	543	19.6
Belgium	450	17.7

This table flatters Germany's position as, in the 1930s, coke oven gas for industrial purposes was increasingly being fed into the German grid, accounting for over half the total sales by 1936. German domestic sales in 1936 were hardly more than in 1913 but non-domestic sales had increased from 6% in 1913 to 48% in 1936. British non-domestic sales amounted to around 30% of the (much larger) total, emphasising the continuing importance of the domestic market in Britain. Unfortunately there are no figures showing how sales were divided between the various uses, lighting, cooking, water heating, space heating, commercial, industrial etc.

The UK manufactured gas industry was also larger than that in the United States, although there comparisons become confusing because of the availability of natural gas alongside manufactured gas, both for direct supply and as a feedstock.

In the official American statistics, gas supply undertakings were divided into two groups; those who supplied natural gas and those who supplied predominantly manufactured gas. The latter were defined as those who sent out at least 25% manufactured gas, the balance being natural gas. The rationale for this unusual distinction was that undertakings would distribute natural gas in preference to manufactured gas as soon as supplies became available; it was far cheaper and required no manufacture. As natural gas could be used as a feedstock for manufactured gas, there was a risk that gas manufacture would be considerably understated unless there was some loading in its favour in the offical statistics.

The widespread adoption of the prepayment supplement was a largely British phenomenon; it was this, with the 'free' issue of gas cookers to a mass market, which made Britain pre-eminent as a supplier of manufactured gas.

Municipal trading in gas and electricity – early years

I t is puzzling why municipal undertakings performed less well than their private counterparts; they faced the same challenges from alternative fuels. Undoubtedly in the late 1870s it was they who were the trailblazers, sponsoring exhibitions to promote new uses of gas, rather than the private companies, and it was Leicester Corporation which first made a dramatic success of hiring cookers.

First it is worth looking at the reasons for the development of the municipal sector which from the 1880s right up to nationalisation in 1949 accounted for about one third of the gas supply industry, whether measured by sales, customers or number of undertakings. The municipalisation movement was particularly strong during the 1870s, when the number of municipal gas undertakings doubled to 120 out of a total of 450 statutory undertakings. Concern at the inefficiency of private gas company management was one of the reasons for municipalities to buy out their local companies. Private undertakings might, it was thought, charge too much; they might be poorly managed, and, not least, if there were large profits to be made, why should these not be returned to ratepayers as a whole rather than only to shareholders. Providing efficient services might also be construed as a sign of progressive municipal management, the range of provision reflecting local pride. Why then did they soon fall behind, particularly in relation to the appliance business? Were there constraints which hampered them while leaving private companies untouched? It is worth looking for reasons why they were relatively slow to react to market conditions, particularly when private companies, through the prepayment supplement, were attracting new customers by the million, tapping new markets and improving their load factor simultaneously.

One reason was that, unlike private companies, they were open to the criticism of unfair trading, whether justified or not. In the political climate of the late 1890s, such accusations were widespread, and were bound to influence the councillors who sat on Gas Committees and determined trading policy. As a Croydon ironmonger said about hiring appliances,

> it is very questionable whether when you charge all that is
> legitimate to charge against the gas stoves and cookers they

make any profit at all, but absolutely a loss; only they do not show that in the municipal accounts.

As chairman of the Croydon Gas Company he was in a very good position to comment. It is ironic that Croydon should be critical of municipal enterprise as, only a few years earlier in 1887, a vote to bring the Croydon company into municipal ownership was only narrowly lost.

Another factor may have been the inability of some municipalities to attract the best engineer/managers because they were unwilling to match salaries in the private sector. Municipal undertakings had the reputation for paying their managers badly. The gas press occasionally included letters from disgruntled municipal engineers, who were tired of hearing that managing a gasworks was a simple job, not much different from that of a works foreman. Obviously public servants could not have a completely free hand when spending public money. Nevertheless press comments give the impression that municipal gas committees regarded the gasworks merely as a routine production process necessary to meet a known demand, notably for lighting the streets. Councillors were slow to come to terms with the fact that gas lighting was now in competition with electricity, and that diversification under an entrepreneurial manager offered the best prospects for future progress, and importantly, could produce profits to keep down the burden of municipal rate charges.

Another reason for relatively poor performance by municipal undertakings could be that some gas committees interfered directly in detailed management procedures, particularly in connection with purchasing supplies. As an example, in Leeds in 1889 the city council considered a report that 600,000 of the one million tons of coal purchased over the previous five years were substandard. It transpired that several of the gas committee members were directors or proprietors of collieries supplying the gasworks. The council, unable to prove any allegations of corruption, came to the bizarre conclusion that the losses due to purchases of bad coal might be offset against better results when good coal was bought! In another case at Wishaw in Lanarkshire the municipal gas engineer was directed to place orders for coal with a Glasgow firm in which a councillor had a major interest. Coal costing 11/- per ton was invoiced to the council at 20/- per ton.

Following the Salford case and other well-publicised cases of bribery, a Royal Commission of Inquiry into the Metropolitan Board of Works was set up and the Public Bodies Corrupt Practices Act of 1889 was passed. Under the Act, bribery was a criminal offence but only in relation to municipal undertakings. Legislation may have discouraged major acts of bribery but would be less likely to change a long-standing business culture, especially among the smaller companies out of the public eye.

There is no doubt that this undercurrent of commercial corruption was a factor in the distaste of leading professional gas engineers for involving themselves in trading. Even the technical meetings of the Gas Institute became well-recognised opportunities for traders to press hospitality on attenders, 'pouncing upon every opportunity for waylaying unwary gas managers'. Meetings were 'beset by persons who only attend for the purpose of hawking... who never contribute to the technical value... They usurp the best rooms at hotels and jeer at the technical and business proceedings'. There was even a proposal that traders should be completely banned from meetings of the Gas Institute. This would however have meant foregoing the financial support of the makers towards the cost of the proceedings and associated hospitality; it was not approved.

An earlier chapter described how undertakings began to become involved in appliance trading. Another possible option, seriously considered for a time, was to avert competition by supplying electricity as well as gas. By 1878 a dozen companies had applied for authority to supply electric lighting. The leading gas engineer of the day, George Livesey of the SMGC, was strongly opposed to such diversification, fearing that it would distract engineers from their main task and weaken the long-term prospects of the industry. In 1878 he gave evidence to a parliamentary select committee appointed to consider whether municipalities should adopt electric lighting and whether gas companies should be authorised to supply it. He declared

> Gas companies... have no special claims to be considered as future distributors of electric light... electric light committed to their care might have a slow development... processes of gas manufacture are unlike those needed for electricity... I have a strong opinion that [gas companies] should not be allowed to have anything to do with the electric light.

The committee accepted his view. No private undertakings supplied electricity.

Livesey's evidence is very much that of the professional engineer. He took no account of the experience of his colleagues in purchasing, works management and the potential economies of scale in billing and administration. These might have been of considerable advantage to anyone setting up a new electricity undertaking. Most of the five hundred authorised British gas companies of the day, mainly very small, rather than taking a stand on principle, took a pragmatic view. They judged correctly that there was no imminent challenge to them from electricity in their immediate locality and therefore no urgent action was necessary on their part. In fact the potential economies of scale from combined utility undertakings are only being achieved in the mid 1990s, following nationalisation, privatisation and the establishment of a strong regulatory environment.

Diversification into electric supply was far more common in the United States, where by 1899 almost 40% of all gas companies were also supplying an electric lighting service. This certainly had no adverse effect on their growth, as the following table shows.

SALES OF GAS, 10^9 CU. FEET

	UK		USA	
	Sales	%	Sales	%
1869			9.2	
1881/2	66.6			
1889/90	90.3	+36	43.8	
1899/1900	135.8	+50	67.1	+53
1909/10	177.7	+31	150.8	+125

It seems probable that the faster American growth may be attributed to the far greater enthusiasm with which managers set about selling appliances and also to the adoption of the carburetted water gas process, which reduced the cost of gasmaking. Rapid growth was helped by the greater average size of American companies compared with Britain; there were few of the village and small town undertakings which had proliferated in Britain because of the earlier start of the industry.

In fact it was the municipalities which took a very much more active part in developing electricity supply than private gas companies. This was in part due to the terms of the electricity supply Acts of 1882 and 1888 which gave them a central role in determining the shape of the new industry. As well as giving them powers to lay electricity cables in streets, they could, after 42 years, purchase at written down value any private companies established under the Acts. Mindful of the danger of allowing the development of monopoly powers, the Acts provided for the setting of maximum prices for electricity.

The motives for municipalities to take over gas or electricity supply were mixed. In part they wished to make good the perceived inadequacies of existing private companies; in part they hoped to make a profit to support the rate income and to fund municipal building projects. Another strong motive was to promote provincial civic pride and make a considered response to the increasingly complex wealth-creating requirements of urban local government.

Between 1898 and 1902 some 62 municipal undertakings began to supply electricity and by the end of 1903 the tide of municipal development had reached its highest point; by that stage more than two-thirds of all connections to public electricity supply mains were accounted for by municipal rather than private undertakings. This meant that almost all the largest gas undertakings (with 10,000 customers or more in 1899) found themselves competing with municipal electrical undertakings. The exceptions were those in London ('where both local government and electrical utilities were poorly organised'), Newcastle (which had an excellent service from its regional electricity company) and Preston. This situation was unchanged in the 1930s; outside London virtually all towns with a population of 60,000 or more had municipally-owned electricity undertakings.

This municipal investment in electricity must have adversely affected interest in municipal gas departments, whether consciously or not, at least for a few years. No direct evidence has been found to prove that investment in prepayment installations was deferred, although the gas press suspected this. It is very clear however that municipal ownership, for both gas and electricity undertakings, was coming under closer scrutiny. The enthusiasm for municipal enterprise in the 1870s and 1880s, most notably exemplified in Birmingham under the Chamberlains, was giving ground to the exponents of private enterprise. Contemporary political debates must have constrained the scope for municipalities to act as entrepreneurially as they might have wished. In 1899 parliamentary committees of both Houses were as a matter of course striking out clauses in municipal gas (and electrical) bills which would have given powers to 'manufacture, sell and deal in all sorts of appliances required for the consumption (of gas).' This effectively prevented municipalities emulating private gas companies by promoting hired appliances in association with the prepayment supplement. The consequences are clearly shown in the tables in the previous chapter.

Lively discussions about municipal trading and municipal socialism led to the establishment of the Select Committee on Municipal Trading of 1900; the debate continued over the next few years. To counter the publicity attracted by exponents of municipal socialism such as George Bernard Shaw, the Industrial Freedom League and the Liberty and Property Defence League were set up; these supported extreme anarchic individualism. As an example of the more extreme views being expressed at the time, Lord Avebury, a respected banker, considered municipal trading would 'check industrial progress', bring a 'risk of ultimate loss' and was an 'interference with natural laws'. *The Times* published a series of articles in 1902-3 attacking municipal socialism. These were wide-ranging, covering housing as well as trading activities, although interestingly there was no specific criticism of gas undertakings' performance.

Implicitly the key issue in the debate was whether electricity generation and distribution should be in public or private hands. Proponents of private enterprise claimed that only large scale generation and distribution over wide areas would bring optimum economic benefits. The corollary was that municipalities with their restricted geographical spread would be unable to benefit from technical advance; they should withdraw from electricity supply to leave private venture capitalism a free run. This active debate came at an unfortunate time for municipal gas undertakings, just when they might have been planning to embark on supplying appliances. Although gas undertakings were not directly attacked, such articles must have influenced opinion in municipalities against embarking on an aggressive policy of promoting gas appliances, despite the excellent prospects of success.

When private companies wished to embark on appliance trading, they could use retained profits from sales of gas to finance the business. Municipal gas undertakings were not in the same happy position; they required the approval of the Local Government Board to raise capital for investment in appliances and this might involve a public enquiry. Such enquiries provided a focus for objections, whether on principle or because some local trader feared he would be adversely affected. At a more parochial level, local councillors were more susceptible to pressure from local tradesmen worried about competition and wanting to keep the business for themselves than were private gas companies.

Sometimes municipal undertakings went to considerable lengths to counter local opposition. In Birkenhead for example the Corporation organised its own gas exhibition in 1885 because the local traders refused to combine with the Corporation to arrange a joint show. It was emphasised that the Corporation 'did not want to encroach upon the business of local tradesmen. It is rather unfortunate that the whole of the local tradesmen did not heartily co-operate with the committee'. Similarly there were objections when Glasgow Corporation proposed the sale and hire of appliances. However, as one councillor pointed out, there was not a single ironmonger in the city selling gas appliances. 'If they waited until the ironmongers of Glasgow educated the people they would wait until doomsday'. Within five months of the stove department being opened, 2,000 stoves of one kind or another had been supplied. In Macclesfield, one councillor described how he had been recommended from shop to shop until at last he had to give up; 'for the sake of half-a-dozen shopkeepers, they could not let 5,000 burgesses suffer'. It was not long before the Macclesfield engineer was instructed to go ahead with hiring stoves. Not every Corporation was willing to promote the appliance business. Burton-on-Trent did not offer to hire gas stoves allegedly because no-one asked for them. Interestingly, some private gas fitters had no objection to municipal undertakings hiring appliances to promote the business; their objection was to sales, which in their view should be channelled through local tradesmen.

The minutes of the Leicester Gas Committee give a typical example of the climate in which municipal undertakings operated. A deputation of gasfitters and ironmongers petitioned the council that hiring by the gas department damaged their interests as large ratepayers. 'As the extremely low rates charged for the use of the stoves, it is impossible for us to compete with them...' The gas committee responded by pointing out how little the petitioners had pushed the trade since gas first became available in Leicester, that they had failed to take space in the highly successful exhibition arranged by the committee, that there was room for the traders to compete in a market whose potential was almost untapped and that the profitability of the gas department would benefit all ratepayers, including the petitioners. The committee produced a forecast business plan showing a steady profit accruing. In their words

> There must be no lack of energetic and vigilant management.
> The course pursued by your committee... would not be
> omitted in private business enterprise... This large
> undertaking should be managed on behalf of the general
> ratepayer on purely business principles.

This report was approved by the full council.

The extent of municipal involvement in trading activities potentially extended beyond the provision of the basic utilities, water, gas, electricity and housing into a very different sphere of activity where gas (or electricity) was concerned. If cookers were being hired out, whether or not with a prepayment meter, who should undertake the installation and servicing? Should this be done by council employees, even if private traders were not meeting local needs? If municipalities did become involved, how could they counter accusations of unfair trading?

Undertakings were however being inexorably drawn into the new non-lighting business from the 1880s through the arrangement of exhibitions, the testing of appliances, then hire and finally through the offer of prepayment installations requiring appliances, installation and servicing. For ironmongers and private gasfitters this trading activity by gas undertakings was bad enough; municipalisation was the last straw, particularly when jobbing work such as gasfitting was involved. It is hardly surprising that evidence of such local tensions is scarce. However Birmingham provides a major and well-documented example of this conflict of interests and underlying frustrations erupting.

There is evidence that in Birmingham in the early 1870s, that is, before the undertaking was taken into municipal ownership, the existing gas companies were not only doing gas fitting work but were subsidising it from the profit on gas. It is not clear why the Birmingham subsidy was deemed necessary, as there appears to have been adequate competition to avoid unrealistic pricing; 65 independent gasfitters were listed in the *Post Office Directory* for 1872. Possibly the managers were attempting to force standards up by intervening in this market; if so, judged by later complaints about poor quality workmanship, they appear to have been unsuccessful.

After municipalisation in 1874, the involvement of Birmingham Corporation in gasfitting attracted vociferous criticism from the private men. This was perhaps to be expected but it was also ironic. In fact the private gasfitters faced much fairer competition from the Corporation than they did from its private predecessors. The Corporation operated a fixed tariff for gasfitting work and refused to depart from this, even at the risk of losing the job to a competitor. Its prices must have been fair as it won orders for less than half the jobs for which it tendered but still made a modest profit. When the private gasfitters petitioned the Corporation in 1888, the gas department was able to show that there was room for both private and Corporation gasfitters. Indeed London firms were sometimes brought in to undertake particularly complex installations. Apart from the questions of competition and pricing, the continuance of the department was justified as it met a widespread public demand, set standards for good quality work and dealt with customer complaints (often proving that the problems lay with the customers' own fittings rather than 'bad gas').

Interestingly around 1880, Birmingham Corporation proposed a contract maintenance scheme for their water customers; the declared intention was to avoid waste of water. Predictably this aroused fierce hostility from the local plumbers. Later, the Corporation abandoned plumbing in the face of continued opposition from local men, although it continued its gasfitting. In 1892 the Birmingham gasfitters were still complaining that the Committee was doing a roaring trade in the supply of gas fittings and 'this should not be permitted'.

In an attempt to defuse this persistent criticism of its actions, Birmingham Corporation made enquiries of other major undertakings, 55 corporations and 26 companies. Of these 28% sold or hired stoves including fitting, 60% did fitting work (of which 36% at cost or free) and only 12% did not supply or fix equipment. The proportions in the municipal and private groups were almost identical. Birmingham's involvement in trading in 1888 was therefore in line with the practice of all the major undertakings in the UK, both municipal and private. This enquiry confirmed that the practice of subsidy was well established in areas other than the supply and hire of appliances, though far from universal.

The strength of complaint from ironmongers over both fitting and the supply of appliances and parts appears to have varied in different parts of the country, those in Lancashire being particularly well organised. Opposition was never so strong in the London area. Possibly this was because there were more specialist suppliers and there was less need for the general ironmonger who flourished elsewhere.

Municipal electrical undertakings faced the same hostility to appliance trading. In evidence to the Board of Trade departmental committee on the electrical trades in 1916 the Electrical Contractors' Association particularly opposed the sale of appliances. The Association was happy for undertakings to operate showrooms and to pass enquirers on to contractors; it was claimed that the costs of the showroom would be covered by introductory commissions paid by contractors.

In the light of this confusion of purpose, it is hardly surprising that municipal gas undertakings failed to grow as rapidly as their private counterparts where sales of gas and supply of appliances were concerned.

By contrast, municipal pride required that public street lighting should be as good as possible. When a new lighting technology based on the Welsbach mantle, described in the next chapter, became available, municipal undertakings were as quick to adopt it as the private companies.

Welsbach lighting revitalises the gas lighting market

T he rumblings of discontent amongst gas lighting customers surfaced as soon as electricity provided an alternative. Earlier chapters showed how the gas industry's dependence on lighting was being gradually reduced. However in 1890 virtually all 'convenience' lighting in Britain was supplied by gas and ten years later in 1900 gas still accounted for around 92%. If the general dissatisfaction with gas lighting was not to tarnish the idea of using gas for other purposes, which were now becoming increasingly significant, it was important that if at all possible the technology of lighting should be improved.

There had been steady progress in making incremental improvements to existing lamps. There was also a search for a radically improved technology. William Sugg was one of the first to realise that the shape of the gas flame and its temperature were crucial in determining the amount of light produced. Reminiscing in the 1880s, he claimed that

> It was certainly not known up to 1858 that there was any difference in the light obtained from any burner consuming like quantities of gas... It was generally supposed that 5 cubic feet gave just as good a light in one burner as another.

This was quite wrong; in fact the shape and temperature of the flame were of critical importance for the amount of light given out. If the gas stream was well fanned out, it received adequate oxygen to burn rapidly, producing the incandescent carbon particles that gave the light. To achieve a good flame profile an accurately machined burner orifice was essential.

The idea of fitting a non-metallic burner tip instead of relying on a simple hole in the pipe originated in Germany; tips prevented oxidisation and corrosion of the burner orifices and consequent deformation of the flame. They were first developed by Schwartz of Nuremberg and Brönner of Frankfurt am Main. Around 1860 the British makers Sugg and Bray independently produced tipped burner jets which produced a well-shaped flame. Sugg followed the Germans in using steatite, vitrified soapstone, which could be accurately machined. Bray used a ceramic insert to produce a sharply defined flame. These non-metallic tips had another advantage; they acted as insulators, preventing the flame from losing heat by conduction to the metal gas pipe. The hotter the flame, the more light was produced.

The idea of using the heat of a gas flame to produce improved light through incandescence was not new. The first brilliant limelight was demonstrated in 1826 but was impractible for general lighting. Another idea demonstrated in the 1870s was to use platinum wire mesh, which was extremely expensive but could be heated to glow white hot. However it might melt if the heat were too great and anyway it gradually lost the power to incandesce through the effect of gas on its surface. Another significant step was the invention in the early 1880s of the Clamond basket or mantle made of magnesia, in effect another form of the limelight. Suspended over a gas flame this gave a good light but proved fragile and unsuitable for general use. What was needed was some material that could withstand the intense heat of the flame while incandescing with a white light.

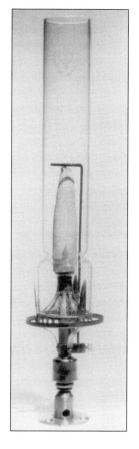

The solution to the problem was discovered by chance by an Austrian research metallurgical chemist, Carl Auer von Welsbach (1858-1929). After working under Bunsen and the famous British chemist Sir Henry Roscoe at Heidelberg where he gained his doctorate, he returned to the University of Vienna to continue his fundamental research into the rare earths, including thorium and cerium. During an experiment, he was heating a thorium solution which accidentally boiled over on to an asbestos mat which began to glow unusually in the heat of the flame. He soaked some cotton wool in his solution and put that in the flame. He found that the cotton burnt away leaving a rigid glowing thorium oxide skeleton. This was the origin of the idea for developing a new form of practical gas lighting. Instead of cotton wool he dipped a knitted fabric into his solution; later the chemically treated fabric was knitted into a tube (at first open, later tied at one end) into which the flame could play. This was a gas mantle. The first mantles were suspended over the flame on a fine wire hook, making them very susceptible to vibration. Later mantles were supplied already bonded to a

An early suspended Welsbach mantle and burner.

ceramic base; this strengthened them and made them easy to fix. The first lamps using mantles where the flame went up into the mantle were somewhat unsatisfactory as the burner assembly cast a shadow where the light was most needed. Inverted mantles, where the flame played downwards into the mantle, gave a much better all-round light.

Welsbach took out his first patents for mantles and impregnating fluids in 1885 and 1886, a couple of years after the wild speculation in electricity shares had died down. When the first reports of the incandescent mantle were received in England, they were greeted with the same incredulity as Winsor's proposals to provide London with gas light; Walter Scott had described Winsor as a madman 'proposing to light London with – what do you think? Why, with smoke!' The *Gas World* was equally incredulous at the announcement of Welsbach's patents.

> We are inclined to think that the Vienna correspondent of the *Daily Chronicle* must have been troubled recently with mental aberration. Telegraphing from Vienna, he says; A very important invention which will, it is said by some lighting engineers, completely revolutionise the present system of gaslighting, has just been perfected by Dr Auer (von Welsbach) in the chemical laboratory of the Vienna University.

After describing the system the *Gas World* went on,

> Anything more senseless than the above we do not recollect of having read. Nothing more vague or ridiculous was ever published about electric light, even in the heat of excitement about that system of lighting.

After the disappointments with other experiments in improved lighting systems, this initial reaction of condemnation was understandable and was shared by almost all gas engineers of the time.

At first the misgivings of the sceptics were justified. The early mantles proved unsatisfactory in practice. They were very fragile. The first one demonstrated to a British gas engineer crumbled into dust within 24 hours. In street lamps, mantles were liable to shatter as a heavy cart rumbled by. More seriously, small variations in the composition of the impregnating fluid caused wide variations in light output and mantle life. Because of these problems it seemed likely for several years that, despite its promise, the incandescent mantle would prove a dismal failure. The street lighting installation in Vienna using Welsbach mantles had to be taken out and replaced by electric lamps or flat flame burners. According to reports in the gas press, 'we are not yet convinced that this system of utilizing gas has come within the domain of practical lighting' and again 'the durability and the efficiency of the Welsbach light remain to be proved'.

Welsbach himself was heavily criticised by disappointed investors both in Britain and in the other West European countries where lighting companies had been established to exploit his discoveries. Nevertheless he doggedly continued his experiments, varying the proportions of various elements in his solutions in an attempt to find the best combination. He finally found that thorium with a trace of cerium gave the best results, and he patented the new formula in 1892, unchanged thereafter right up to the present day.

What of Welsbach himself? He was born into a talented family; his father was an inventor of printing machinery. He himself was a fine chemist who had studied under leading figures of the time. He was a quiet unassuming man, engrossed in research all his life. Once he had solved the scientific problems associated with incandescent lighting and patented his results he played no further part in their commercial exploitation, having sold the rights for an enormous sum; he was paid one million gulden for the British rights alone in 1886. In view of this it is hardly surprising that the investors were extremely concerned when for several years it seemed as if the patent might prove worthless.

He did not restrict his research to the gas industry. After patiently and systematically resolving the problems with his gas lighting, he turned his attention to electricity. It was reported in 1898 that he was experimenting with an electric lamp with an osmium metallic filament. This was an improvement on the Edison carbon filament lamps then available but despite seven years' research Welsbach was unable to make it viable; the osmium lamp was only suitable for low voltages. His instincts in searching for a metallic filament were right, but he concentrated his efforts on the wrong metal. By 1906 experiments by others found that tungsten was best for electric lamps. Even then it was some years before a process for making ductile tungsten filaments was perfected. Carl Auer von Welsbach died in 1929.

Following the discovery of the new solution formula, mantles, too, were becoming more robust. The first successful street lighting installation in the UK was in Winchester early in 1894, followed quickly by many others. By the mid 1890s a mantle life of 2 weeks for street lamps was not unusual and a few years later 2 months was average, and a 6 months life could be expected in the home.

To assess the importance of Welsbach's discovery, it is helpful to consider how greatly his mantles improved the lighting power of a cubic foot (cu ft) of coal gas. In the early 1880s a simple flat flame burner produced the light of 2 candlepower per cu ft of gas. The first mantles in the late 1880s gave 8 candlepower; by the mid 1890s this had risen to 18 and between the wars inverted mantles were giving 25 candlepower per cu ft. Some street lighting schemes using high pressure gas could give 50-70 candlepower. High pressure lighting was only available along a few major thoroughfares where a very high standard of lighting was required. The lamps were supplied through a separate network of pipes at a pressure several times higher than the normal street mains. Such an arrangement was expensive in both capital and maintenance costs and could be justified only in exceptional cases. A few installations were provided by major gas undertakings such as the SMGC as a practical demonstration of what could be done to compete with the best the electricians could provide.

Right from the outset, even the simplest form of Welsbach lighting was much cheaper than its competitors. The following table gives the annual cost in 1892 of maintaining 48 candlepower of lighting, covering running costs and replacements but not original cost. This was before Welsbach's improved mantle fluid was available.

Gas	Argand	93/-
Gas	Regenerative burner	41/-
Gas	Incandescent	30/-
Petroleum	Large lamps	44/-
Petroleum	Small lamps	58/-
Electric light	Incandescent	245/-

This comparison published in the gas press was no doubt intended to flatter gas but it makes the point that gas was very much cheaper than electric lighting and now for the first time was cheaper than oil. In the domestic market, electricity had the benefits of cleanliness and convenience, but even in the 1920s and 1930s it still had no large cost advantage over gas lighting.

Welsbach lighting was not universally welcomed by gas engineers, some of whom feared that customers would be satisfied with the lighting standards they already had. Because of the improved efficiency of incandescent lighting gas sales would fall, bringing reduced profits in their wake. This was an unduly pessimistic scenario. Almost everyone changing to Welsbach lighting took the opportunity to improve the standards of lighting in their homes and got a much better service for the same money. The same thing happened in shops and factories and for street lighting. The following table, based on French experience, shows how the average level of lighting (in lux) improved particularly following the introduction of inverted mantles, and how the consumption of gas per useful candle hour (in litres) fell.

COMPARATIVE PERFORMANCE OF GAS STREET LIGHTING 1878-1910

	Lux	Litres
1878; flat flame	0.1	10-15
1878-92; recuperative	1.2	4-6
from 1892 upright incandescent	1-1.5	1.1
from 1903 inverted incandescent	2-3	1.0
from 1910 high pressure	8-15	0.7

Improved robustness of the mantles meant that by 1905 incandescent lighting could even be fitted in trains. The first experiments with gas lighting on trains were as early as 1860. Lighting burners in the coaches were connected with flexible pipes to a gas storage container in the guard's van of the train. To improve standards of lighting, gas mantles were being introduced by 1905. This was obviously to forestall competition from electric train lighting using dynamos, which was first tried experimentally in the 1880s. It however proved more costly both in first cost and annual running costs than gas. Gas lighting for trains was discredited following a couple of disastrous railway accidents in 1910 and 1913, when escaping gas was ignited by burning wreckage and created a raging inferno in the wooden carriages and was a major factor in the terrible loss of life. Although precautionary measures were immediately introduced to reduce the risks, train companies moved decisively away from gas for lighting.

Despite the unsolved technical problems, in the mid 1880s there were speculators keen to exploit any potential there was in the new process. In Britain the rights were bought by a company, Welsbach & Williams, capitalised at £40,000. Before it started trading, its rights were transferred to a new company, the Incandescent Gas Light Co. On the basis of a prospectus that was, to say the least, economical with the truth, the

Incandescent Gas Light Co was floated with a capital of £500,000 in 1888 to exploit the Welsbach patents. In the words of the Gas World, 'the thought of asking half a million of money to work a gas burner patent almost takes one's breath away'. Those who rushed to invest in this new invention were gravely disappointed by the early results; unsolved technical difficulties meant that any hopes they might have had of making a fortune were soon dashed. By 1892 the company's capital had been written down to £31,000.

Investors in the Incandescent Gas Light Co in 1887 had lost almost all their money by 1892. Once the problems with mantles and fluid were finally sorted out by Welsbach in 1892-3, the opportunity arose for a financial killing to be made, not only from new investors anxious to buy a stake in this new technology but also by charging premium prices for Welsbach lighting. The directors of the British company who controlled the patents and held virtually all of the preference shares received £13-17-6d in dividends for each £1 share between 1893 and 1896. A new company, the Welsbach Incandescent Gas-Light Co was promoted in 1897 with a capital of £3,500,000 (of which over £1 million was subscribed by new investors), much of which was disbursed in fees for services of questionable value and to compensate the directors and Julius Moeller, the general manager, who was entitled to enormous sums under his performance-linked contract, no less than £24,500 in 1895-6!

With impregnable patents on both the burners and the mantles, the British Welsbach company sold its products subject to a condition that its burners could only be used with Welsbach mantles and that its mantles should only be used with Welsbach burners. Its products were expensive. The first burner on the market cost one guinea (£1/1/0d) and the mantles were 5/- each. By contrast, a Bray or Sugg jet to produce a flat flame cost 1d or 2d for an admittedly far inferior light. Welsbach prices came down steadily; in 1895 the patent burners had been reduced to 10/- and mantles to 1/3d. In 1900, just before the first patents expired, a Welsbach mantle cost $7^{1}/_{2}$d (recently reduced from 9d or 1/-).

These prices were high, but should be compared to prices of electric light bulbs which were also expensive. In 1891 carbon filament electric light bulbs cost about 3/9d to 4/6d each; by 1900 they were 2/- to 3/-. After the Edison/Swan patent expired the price came down to 1/-. The first tungsten filament bulbs introduced around 1907 cost 4/- to 6/- but were four times more efficient than the earlier carbon filament bulbs and lasted much longer. Electricity was also expensive; in the mid 1890s it cost typically around 7d per kilowatt hour while gas cost 30d per 1000 cu ft; for a penny electric customers got around 500 Btu while gas customers got 16,500 Btu. Straight price comparisons without taking account of efficiency of utilisation must not be carried too far. It is however clear that when gas was spreading fast into the homes of lower middle class and working homes, electricity was restricted to the wealthy.

There can be no doubt that the Welsbach company exploited its monopoly ruthlessly. It was making a net profit of over 20% on turnover and profits exceeded £100,000 in 1899 and 1900. It enjoyed a very much more favourable trading position than its German counterpart which had been able to obtain patent protection only for the burners but not for the mantles or the fluid formula. In consequence there was from the outset fierce competition in the German incandescent lighting market and prices were considerably lower than British prices for an identical product. German labour costs were lower but this was not enough to explain why British mantles cost three times as much as German ones in 1895, and more than twice as much in 1900.

It is hardly surprising that others sought to take advantage of the high prices achievable for lighting burners and mantles in the British market. Various companies sought to bypass the Welsbach patents with their own variants of burners and mantles but were put under intense legal pressure. As well as threatening such companies with legal action, Welsbach advertised that individual customers laid themselves open to legal proceedings if they used any incandescent burners or mantles other than Welsbach's. The company's fiercest British rival, the Sunlight Incandescent Gas Lamp Co, actually proclaimed in its advertisements that it would indemnify any of its customers if they were brought to court. Welsbach tackled the problem of competing makers quite simply: after long-drawn-out legal actions to weaken them financially, it bought them up. First the Meteor and De Mare companies fell, and finally the Sunlight company came under threat. Both companies had their own patents and each accused the other of infringement; the stakes for both were very high indeed as the outcome would determine their commercial future. In fact both managed to drag out the legal preliminaries over several years to delay the start of the action. The *Gas World* commented sharply that Welsbach should either establish the validity of its patents in the courts without any shadow of doubt or 'face all competition in regard both to price and the quality of their mantles'. In fact, just before the case was due to come to trial, Welsbach bought out the Sunlight Company for £110,000 and the action was dropped.

It was not enough for the British Welsbach company to protect itself from its UK competitors. Wholesalers and middlemen quickly realised that they could get their supplies more cheaply from the continent. In 1900 when Welsbach was charging $7^1/_2$d per mantle and Sunbeam 6d, German mantles could be bought wholesale for 2/6d per dozen. A couple of years later, after the expiry of the UK patent, Welsbach was charging $2^1/_2$-3d wholesale (6d retail) while imported mantles were 2d wholesale and $4^1/_2$d retail; there was never any suggestion that they were of inferior quality. The import of mantles was very big business. In 1903 it was estimated that British firms satisfied only half of the 50 million British market for mantles. The balance was imported from Germany, which was producing 150 million out of a world total of 350 million mantles.

Welsbach in the UK concentrated its marketing through traditional ironmongers rather than working with gas undertakings. This was a deliberate matter of policy. Possibly the company decided that after the early setbacks with incandescent lights it would test response through the local ironmongery trade rather than run the risk of having the new system held back nationally by the prejudices of gas engineers. Obviously after the early setbacks, the supply industry had to exercise some caution before endorsing the new system.

There is another possible explanation for Welsbach's policy of dealing with the ironmongery trade rather than gas undertakings; Welsbach may have calculated that it could achieve better profit margins if it dealt with small traders whose livelihood came from the markup on hardware rather than the supply industry which relied on gas sales for its profit. Welsbach may also have calculated that it could enforce its prices and control competition far more effectively if it was dealing with small tradesmen rather than with supply undertakings. It was crucial for Welsbach's strategy that its agents should not handle competitive products and especially should not buy foreign mantles. The temptation to buy imported mantles was enormous; they were cheaper to buy and could on occasion be passed off as British mantles which were trademarked **Auer**. Middlemen were well aware of this and looked for as many outlets as they could find for their cheap imported mantles, including unconventional outlets such as barbers' shops. Sometimes foreign mantles were imported in bulk and repackaged with forged labels and boxes to make them appear British; some were even given a lookalike **Aur** trademark.

Welsbach took vigorous steps to control the business, acting immediately on reports of infringements, serving writs almost like confetti. They employed their own force of writ deliverers; more than once there were violent altercations and one Welsbach man was thrown through a shop window. The company became involved in 'guerrilla warfare' with fly-by-night companies importing cheap German mantles. Even if one firm was closed down by court order, another sprang up immediately to take its place. It was noticeable that most of its actions were against small traders, who did not have the resources to set up a credible defence; in consequence a large body of case law was established to make the 1885 and 1886 patents virtually impregnable. Despite its best efforts, the British Welsbach company was unable to establish a secure ring-fence round its British market; its key strategy failed.

The Welsbach company was quite willing publicly to defend its policy of dealing with ironmongers rather than gas undertakings. In the words of its general manager Julius Moeller in 1901,

> It is only of late years that gas companies in this country have, to any appreciable extent, taken up the sale of lighting appliances, and even now, only about a third of the gas companies are properly equipped for the business. I can state from my own experience that the gas companies were opposed to the introduction of incandescent gas lighting in 1893 and 1894 and if they take an interest in it now, it is rather out of the fear of the competition of electric lighting than from any desire to push the best and most economical system of gas lighting. The business of the gas companies is to sell as much gas as possible. The Welsbach business is to produce the maximum amount of light with the minimum amount of gas. The interests of the two are not therefore identical... The gas companies want to be at liberty to sell mantles and burners without any restriction as to retail price... The trade however must sell at a profit; they live by the profit made on such sales while the gas companies who have the big monopoly of the sale of gas, disregard the profit to be made on the sale of gas appliances.

Moeller's attack on gas industry involvement in the lighting business was shrewdly phrased and he made a valid point about cross-subsidisation of appliance business, notably through the prepayment supplement system, although when he referred to appliances he was probably thinking particularly of lighting fittings. His confidence in himself and his company soon proved to be misguided.

Gas engineers may also have been privately concerned that this new equipment would expose their own technical inadequacies both as regards the manufacture and utilisation of gas. If they were to involve themselves, they would have to learn enough both to advise customers and to accept responsibility for the installation and maintenance of Welsbach lighting. As a technical commentator said, it was the advent of Welsbach lighting which

> finally constrained the gas companies... not merely to instal, but thereafter to maintain at a nominal charge, the system in good and satisfactory condition.
>
> This was a notable new departure and altogether fresh responsibility for the gas companies who had previously regarded their duty to the customer as ending with the supply of gas to the meter. In effect it has entailed almost everywhere the setting up by the gas companies of a complete gas appliance and fittings department of their undertaking, to the great gain and convenience of the public generally.

At first many gas engineers did not concern themselves greatly with the doings of the Welsbach company, but gradually came to realise that improved gas street lighting gave them a strong marketing weapon in their battle with electricity. Thanks to the incandescent mantle, gas street lighting could now be both cheaper and better than the electric lamps then available. In Glasgow, for example, it was calculated that, after taking account of the costs of conversion from flat flame to Welsbach lighting, the saving on the cost of gas would be over 25% within the first year and over 50% in subsequent years. Public lighting authorities were quick to adopt incandescent street lighting and the conversion was in full swing by 1904. Most authorities took the opportunity to upgrade standards of street lighting rather than to save money; consumption of gas did not in fact fall greatly. In a small minority of towns there were more electric than gas street lamps; very few indeed were all-electric in 1904, just Erith, Ventnor, Watford and Wimbledon.

In London the SMGC scored a dramatic promotional coup and set an example to the whole industry. In 1898 it offered to convert all the street lamps in its area from flat flame burners to incandescent burners at no cost to the local vestries (public lighting authorities). The SMGC would do the work at its own cost, around £2 per lamp. It would continue to charge the same as before for gas until it had recouped its investment; thereafter the gas charge would be cut to match the actual cost. In this way all the benefits would go to the vestries, who carried none of the risk and did not have to invest a penny. The SMGC relied on a sharp reduction in gas consumption to recoup its outlay within a couple of years at most. At that time it typically charged £3/3/9d pa. for the gas for a flat flame burner. By substituting a Welsbach burner the SMGC expected gas charges to fall to 11/9d pa. for a similar standard of lighting, a reduction of over 80%. Within a single year almost two-thirds of the 21,000 street lamps in their area of supply were converted on the basis of the SMGC's offer. A few years later incandescent lighting was universal in the SMGC area except for those few parishes which had their own electric undertakings and probably intended to convert to electricity. The GLCC also offered a similar scheme to the vestries in its area of supply. By 1900 the SMGC began to supply incandescent rather than flat flame burners to their domestic customers as a matter of routine; any prepayment customer who made the request would be supplied at no extra cost, although the customer would have to supply his own replacement mantles.

In 1898 with the SMGC deeply involved in the incandescent lighting market, it wanted to be sure that all its customers had a fair deal. In the words of George Livesey,

> What the gas companies were anxious for was that, not only as to [lighting] burners, but as to gas stoves and fires the consumers should use the most effective appliances they could obtain.

This desire for a fair deal also extended to price. Here the SMGC came into conflict with Welsbach. Livesey was not prepared to pay the inflated prices for mantles demanded by Welsbach; the SMGC bought cheap non-Welsbach mantles in defiance of the Welsbach company's claims that such mantles infringed its patents.

The opportunity for a definitive test case came when Welsbach sued the Guaranty Incandescent Light Co, due for trial in April 1902. This action was badly timed from Welsbach's point of view. Its aggressive litigation was beginning to attract unfavourable press comment, particularly as the case between Welsbach and its chief rival, Sunlight, had never come to court. Its first patents had just expired and profits collapsed from £121,000 in 1899 to £24,000 in 1901, leading to a suspension of dividend payments. There was a revolt by shareholders, concerned at the company's poor financial performance and no longer satisfied that Moeller's two-pronged policy of litigation and disregard of the supply industry was still appropriate. Moeller and the rest of the board were ousted and a new board elected. The new management discovered that they had inherited 1,600 lawsuits of various sorts and over 500 more writs were awaiting issue. Between December 1897 and March 1901 the company had spent no less than £38,856 on legal charges concerned with patents and infringements.

If this were not enough, by now some key figures in the gas supply industry, among them Livesey himself, were becoming concerned at the implications for them of the outcome of the Guaranty case. Livesey was persuaded to take an interest in this case by James Keith, a lighting engineer, who had previously campaigned for a reform of the patent laws, alleging that, for the industrialist, British law was inferior to German and American law. In 1901, Keith had written a letter to the *Pall Mall Gazette* under the heading 'A Patent Scandal' suggesting that Welsbach only took action against sellers and users of mantles who could not adequately defend themselves, while refraining from taking action against any makers who would be able to put up a proper defence. Welsbach issued a writ for libel against Keith.

Livesey reckoned that if the Welsbach patent and monopoly were to be upheld, the price of mantles was likely to remain high for a few more years, until a later Welsbach patent expired. He and the SMGC would no longer be able to import cheap foreign mantles. This would prove a major handicap in the efforts of the supply industry and other lighting manufacturers to popularise incandescent lighting for general use. As Livesey said,

> If the action is lost, at any rate we shall know where we are; and if it is won, of which there is a fair chance, we shall get mantles at a cheap rate and the system of incandescent lighting will go like wildfire.

He was well aware that in Germany, where there was no Welsbach master patent, 90% of all new lamps were incandescent. The first improved incandescent lights were installed in Berlin in 1896; by 1900, 97% of the city's 28,000 street lamps were incandescent. In the UK two factors were responsible for the slower development of the market, the Welsbach company's monopolistic pricing and its policy of dealing almost exclusively through ironmongers, while public lighting business was handled by the undertakings.

Livesey's intervention was crucial as he brought both the interests and the financial strength of the supply industry to bear in opposition to Welsbach. Through the SMGC he set up a guarantee fund with an initial contribution of £2,000 and invited contributions from other undertakings with a target of £20,000 to secure an adequate defence. It was fortunate that the guarantee fund was in place as, by mischance, the Guaranty company's factory was burnt down just before the trial was due to take place. Without the existence of the fund it would have been impossible in the circumstances for Guaranty to have put up an adequate defence.

Faced with determined opposition, for the first time the new Welsbach management was prepared to enter into negotiation with the supply undertakings, admitting that 'they had treated them so badly in the past'. In fact it was estimated that 85% of Welsbach's business had been transacted through ironmongers, leaving very little for gas undertakings. Both parties were keen to resolve the differences between them, once the threat of litigation was lifted. The libel writ against Keith was withdrawn and an undertaking was given that the wholesale prosecution of small sellers and users would cease. This was no minor concession. The undertakings agreed to pay a small royalty on every mantle they made themselves ($^1/_4$d) or bought from a non-licenced importer ($^1/_2$d). Although an agreement was reached, it was widely forecast that it would speedily collapse, particularly as unofficial importers were unlikely to pay any royalty. This was immaterial. The important outcome was that the supply industry and Welsbach were co-operating for the first time rather than being in a state of armed neutrality.

Under new management the Welsbach company attempted to restore its position in the UK lighting market. Prices were cut and major cost-saving measures introduced; modest dividend payments resumed in 1904. However without its patents it was never again the dominating force it had been under the Moeller régime. The company was unable to sustain what a subsequent chairman described as the 'absurd original capitalisation'. Its capital was written down in two tranches, back down to £265,000 in 1910. The company struggled on until 1928 when it was taken over by ICI.

Interestingly, Welsbach technology has survived the test of time. Gas mantles are still in use today in caravans, boats and camping lanterns, operating on liquified petroleum gas (LPG). They are often seen at the site of road works providing emergency lighting where there is no electricity supply. They are even used for street lighting in some city centre areas where the environment is particularly sensitive, fed from the normal gas mains and now using methane (natural gas). So widespread is their use that, according to P Crawford Sugg, of the seventh generation of the Sugg family involved in the gas business, more mantles are sold in Britain today than at the height of the gaslighting era.

The Welsbach saga epitomises the continuing dilemma of the gas supply industry and its managers. They desperately needed Welsbach technology to enable them to withstand electrical competition in the lighting field and, in conjunction with the prepayment supplement, to create new working class markets. The technology was however controlled by the Welsbach company which had a different commercial agenda, to maximise profits. As long as the patents remained valid and Moeller was at the helm, Welsbach was quite prepared to ignore the views of the gas supply industry, making no concessions whatsoever in its marketing strategy. A sales network of ironmongers and other small traders was developed and this proved adequate for the company's purpose. Welsbach's uncompromising attitudes finally persuaded the supply industry that it would have to intervene if its own interests were not to be placed in jeopardy.

Welsbach technology was so important to the supply industry that there was an even more surprising example of a gas undertaking straying outside its traditional role. The British Welsbach company made mantles and burners but relied on the Austrian Welsbach company for its supply of thorium/cerium fluid for impregnating the mantle fabric. In 1905 gas engineers heard that a group of German chemical companies had cornered the supply of Brazilian monazite from which thorium was derived and were potentially in a position to hold the whole British industry to ransom. The SMGC, where Livesey was still at the helm, decided on its own account to attempt to break the ring. It tried without success to buy a proportion of Brazilian output and in 1906 purchased a monazite mine in Shelby, North Carolina to develop its own production. This proved commercially unviable and the mine was mothballed the following year. The mine re-emerged from obscurity in 1914. With the imminent prospect of war with Germany it was feared that supplies of mantle fluid would be cut off instantly, with extremely serious implications for the nation. The SMGC offered to open up its mine in the national interest. This proved unnecessary as supplies of German mantles continued to pour into the country at least until 1917, many being re-packaged and passing through the neutral Netherlands. British mantle manufacture was stepped up but collapsed again in the early 1920s following the resumption of German imports which undercut British prices.

This is an extreme example of a gas undertaking stepping outside its traditional role. Far more common was a reluctance among gas engineers to depart from what they perceived as their proper role of managing gas manufacture and distribution to embark on marketing gas. They had discovered that when they first offered appliances on hire this did not bring them into conflict with retailers, ironmongers and gasfitters. Similarly there was no opposition when the concept of hire was extended to the complete gas installation with the prepayment supplement concept. Gas managers were however generally still unwilling to accept that their role might quite properly encompass selling, fitting and servicing appliances. They managed to draw a fine distinction between their 'professional' duties and 'trade'. They had not yet come to recognise that their business was to sell a service to their customers, efficient and economical heating, lighting and cooking, rather than merely selling a commodity.

If selling was an unattractive option, then the development of technical standards by the supply industry might provide an alternative lever to exert control over the market. Engineers might if they wished ensure that customers got a fair deal. In 1896 for example the *Gas World* noted that Huddersfield Corporation was applying for powers to inspect all gas pipes laid in new buildings, 'which may be taken as the insertion of the thin end of the wedge'. It went on,

> Gas... is brought to the consumers' door in the most scientific manner, and then is left to shift for itself under conditions provided by an ignorant user or a careless or incompetent plumber.

It went on to suggest that the gas engineer's

> contract with the consumer should be not to supply a certain quantity of gas which, if used in a certain way, will give a certain amount of light, but it should be to provide a certain amount of light... the fittings and burners should be under the care of the supplier, if not actually his property.

These comments made little difference to general perceptions in the supply industry. After all, the appliance makers by selling their own products were already busy selling gas for the supply industry, and this development is considered in the next chapter.

8 The role of the appliance makers in creating new markets before 1914

In a curious way the willingness of the makers to become actively involved in marketing appliances allowed the majority of gas managers to defer any wholehearted personal commitment to sales and service for a quarter of a century or more. The makers acted as salesmen, fitters, repairers, surrogates for the supply industry; because of this the cherished 'professional' attitudes of engineers were not put in jeopardy. As already described, there was a flurry of marketing activity from a few large undertakings, particularly municipal ones, around 1880 in response to the electrical threat, especially in the sponsorship of exhibitions. Municipal undertakings later encountered great opposition when they wished to expand their trading activities to include selling and fixing appliances. A few of the largest private undertakings began to develop marketing organisations in the early years of the 20th century but these were the exceptions. There can be no doubt that most promotional activity before 1914 was initiated by the appliance makers rather than the undertakings; in the case of medium and smaller-sized undertakings, the dominant role of the makers lasted very much longer.

It was unsurprising that gas engineers should have looked to the makers for help. There existed very close relationships between gas engineers and their suppliers, and as most undertakings were small, there were typically no intermediaries. A system of mutual obligations grew up, cemented in part by payment of 'commission', and in part through social networks. Within the gas industry the payment of commission by seller to buyer to win new accounts or to retain customer loyalty had a very long history. The meter trade had a particularly bad reputation, stretching back as least as far as the 1840s; for instance one leading maker, William Parkinson, was noted for his generous hospitality and kept open house for gas engineers. What has been described as 'the pernicious practice of tipping' was by no means restricted to the gas business. In the grocery business it was widespread, even extending to Co-operative Societies. In the 1870s

> not only [shop] managers but whole [Co-operative] Committees were ready to take a tip, and at many places the trader who tipped was the only man who could do business with them.

Close trading relationships between suppliers and customers could be cemented in other ways, as formal tendering was the exception rather than the rule. George Livesey recalled how his father placed SMGC business with William Sugg as a matter of course because on one occasion Sugg reduced prices after a fall in costs without any prompting. Thereafter the Liveseys considered Sugg a firm to be trusted. William Sugg also enjoyed close relations with the GLCC; W H Makins, later Governor of the GLCC, became a director of William Sugg Ltd in 1887. This meant that Sugg had effectively closed the large London market to his great rival, George Bray of Leeds. Makins' son Paul Makins was later a director of Glover & Main, meter and appliance makers, who co-operated closely with the GLCC in developing new cookers in the 1930s.

There were other ways of cementing relationships even without the direct payment of commission. John Wright allotted shares at par to gas engineers with whom the firm did a lot of business at a time when Wright shares were standing at a healthy premium in the market. Social relationships could be reinforced in masonic lodges. The Evening Star Lodge 1719 of Freemasons established in 1877 was exclusive to the gas industry; members were to be 'directors, auditors, secretaries, engineers, managers of gasworks... or contractors for the supply of gas material'. This restriction to a single business led a mason from another lodge to describe the Evening Star Lodge as 'a trade association of the most odious character'. Another commented that... 'its very constitution shows it must have been founded for trade purposes... of a vile character'. The Northern Star 3053 and Murdoch 3480 Lodges were also exclusively gas industry lodges. Masonic functions following annual Gas Institute meetings were extensively reported in the gas press; Walter King, of the *Gas Journal* and *King's Treatise* was a prominent mason. Such close business and social relationships help to explain why gas engineers could happily look to appliance makers for assistance in matters which were outside their normal area of competence at the time.

By the 1880s one or two makers had experience in the operation of showrooms, ten years before the first GLCC showroom. They were also selling appliances and installing them, notably Sugg with his large lighting business. In the early 1880s the firm had branches in Paris, Liverpool, Portsea (in premises leased from the local gas undertaking), Charing Cross and at the Crystal Palace. All of these were probably shops with a small factory/workshop behind, except for the Crystal Palace, which was a sales point only. To bring people into the Liverpool showroom, Sugg established the Liverpool School of Cookery in 1887; this operated for seven years until the lease of the premises expired. This initiative may well have been prompted by Sugg's French wife Marie Jenny, whose book, *The Art of Cooking by Gas,* has already been mentioned. Sugg was also allowed to show his equipment in the offices of the GLCC, SMGC and Brentford undertakings. This facility could prove a mixed blessing. At Brentford the air at the gasworks was so polluted that the Sugg chandeliers on display quickly became corroded and decorative glassware spoilt.

One of the most dynamic in developing the appliance business was Edmund Richmond (1864-1902). He started as an apprentice with John Wright & Co sent to assist at the Leicester gas exhibition of 1880; he made such an impact that he was immediately appointed an area sales representative although he was only sixteen years old. In 1890 he left Wrights, who employed over 400 people and were making annual profits of over £18,750, to set up his own business in a Warrington foundry with five employees. By the time of his untimely death in 1902 as a result of a cycling accident when he was only 38, the firm employed 1,200 men and was making profits of £20,000 per annum.

Richmond was determined to use his skills as a salesman to build his own business 'by means of advertising and exhibitions in bringing the company and its manufactures well and favourably under public notice'. He called on all the major undertakings to solicit orders for his cookers and showed at exhibitions. In the first year he attended 25 singlehanded. With assistance he was at no fewer than 39 in the following year. In that year no less than £3,837 was spent on advertising, exhibitions and other promotional activity to publicise the firm and its products out of total sales of £20,000. By 1893 Richmond had a group of six lady lecturers giving demonstrations and organising competitions and other events to attract the public. These included lectures with lantern slides. Richmond had special slides made up to show disorganised and feckless households still using coal while the homes that used gas were happy and prosperous! To make their shows more interesting, Richmonds combined with various manufacturers to give cookery demonstrations featuring their products; these included Lever Bros, Bovril, Anglo-Swiss Milk Co, Brown & Polson, Van Houten's Cocoa and the Maypole Soap Co.

Some exhibitions featured the wares of several makers but sometimes a single maker was given exclusive rights to supply appliances to an undertaking. Where Richmond had an exclusive agreement, he offered the services of canvassers, 'lady interviewers' to call on all gas customers on behalf of the local gas undertaking. He found they were much more effective than men in gaining the confidence of housewives. These women were able to advise on the use of cookers as well as merely taking orders. Richmond's initiative in using women was quickly followed by other makers. After the flurry of exhibition activity for the first few years, Richmond then eased off for a few years to allow production to catch up with orders. When advertising re-started he engaged Phil May, one of the foremost illustrators of the day for lively and topical pictorial advertisements and, some years later, engaged chef E P Veerasawmy, gold medallist of Madras, who lectured on oriental cookery for the firm. In 1897 his daughter Lillie Richmond wrote a cookery book for the firm. While smaller undertakings often made an exclusive arrangement with a single supplier, others maintained a restricted list of appliances they would stock, their 'hire list'. It was a major marketing objective of the makers to get their goods on such lists. Richmonds in 1893 were prepared to pay their London representative an additional commission of no less than £100 if he persuaded the GLCC to include Richmond cookers on their list.

In the 1890s there were several hundred separate gas undertakings in the UK alone and it would be impossible to arrange for all of these to be visited without an army of salesmen; many of them were tiny and placed very small orders which would not justify the cost of a regular visit. Such undertakings had to rely on London agents who would arrange the purchase and despatch of whatever was wanted. Similarly, foreign firms relied on London agents for their needs. This included not only appliances but coal, pipe and all gasworks equipment. It was essential for firms such as Richmonds, just starting up, to have a London base if they were to stand a chance of being considered as suppliers for these undertakings which were individually small but in total represented a substantial market. Richmonds opened their own London office and warehouse in Cheapside early in 1892; this replaced an earlier temporary London office. Several other makers had prestige premises in the City of London which combined the function of a London base for their representatives with offering hospitality to gas undertaking buyers, a shopwindow and warehouse. Apart from London being by far the largest market for appliances, there were London agents who placed business on behalf of gas companies. Fletcher, Russell opened their showroom in Cheapside in 1892 near Richmonds' premises; later they both expanded and moved to Queen Victoria St. where Davis also had a showroom. Wright moved from Cheapside to Queen Victoria St. in 1898. Even the GLCC recognised the value of these City shopwindows; they arranged and maintained a special lighting display and paid commission on all lighting orders taken on their behalf.

Another field in which Richmonds were active was in the fitting of gas installations and servicing appliances, particularly for companies with whom they had exclusive arrangements. This was of enormous assistance to undertakings offering prepayment supplement installations, most of whom had no organisation for selling, fitting or servicing. Richmond was able to offer customers a complete service as he had an agency with the Welsbach company for incandescent lighting and had bought the businesses of his meter suppliers, the old established firms of George Glover and George Newton. He successfully quoted for dozens of major contracts such as installing gas in flats for the London County Council in blocks such as Navarino Mansions with 310 meters and cookers fitted. By 1907 the firm had fitted out 130,000 houses and flats and had a permanent fitting staff of 120-150 men for this work. In 1906 Richmonds also began to provide finance for appliance purchase. The firm entered into an agreement with the South Coast Gas Fittings Co to supply cookers & fires on 3 year HP terms, the SCGF to act as agents in Southampton & Southsea to collect the 12 instalments due and forward the cash in bulk to Warrington.

Representatives were expected to establish good relations with buyers; this would include offering presents to secure orders. There was a delicate line to be drawn between what was acceptable, such as gifts, and straightforward bribes which were not, particularly after the Salford gas scandal. A press cutting in Richmond's minute book reports a case heard before the Lord Chief Justice who said the illegitimate offer or acceptance of commissions 'sapped commercial morality; they corrupted both employers and employed... and they set great premium on dishonest trade'. Obviously someone in the firm thought this forcefully expressed judicial opinion was of sufficient import to safeguard it.

Edmund Richmond was a great believer in incentives for his staff and himself; his own contract provided that his salary would be reduced from £450 to £400 if the declared dividend in any year fell below 5%. Salesmen were paid commission and senior men in the factory received bonuses if they achieved good results. In addition the workmen were not forgotten; subsidised outings to Blackpool were arranged, starting in 1892. There had been a long strike that year; it is not clear from the records whether the first outing was arranged before or after the strike. In later years Richmond also entertained the workforce to tea as a personal gift. He was greatly influenced by the ideas of George Livesey of the SMGC (and Livesey was, incidentally, one of his most important customers). In 1898 Richmond introduced a co-partnership profit-sharing scheme based on that introduced in the SMGC. The workforce would receive a 5% bonus on their wages (half in cash and half in shares) when the company paid a 10% dividend. Livesey himself was present to make the first presentations to workmen under the scheme. The scheme was not renewed after Richmond's early death.

Incentives extended to major customers. At the outset all the capital required by Richmond was raised privately without recourse to public subscription. Much came locally, some from Richmond's family, some from local businessmen who joined the board (members of the board held 60% of the shares in 1892) and some from friendly gas managers; these included the managers at Warrington, Widnes, Blackburn, Colne, Belfast and others, all of whom subscribed and were given preference in the allocation of shares.

A few undertakings entered into formal agreements to pass all responsibility for appliance trading over to individual makers. Edmund Richmond was a pioneer in this field, operating showrooms for the Plymouth, Bournemouth and Dublin companies. It is worth setting out in full Richmond's offer which was accepted by Plymouth; this shows to what lengths some undertakings were prepared to go to delegate complete responsibility for marketing and customer service to makers.

In accordance with my conversation with you we beg to submit a special scheme for the supply of slot [ie. for prepayment supplement customers] and ordinary cookers to your company. The arrangement we suggest below will obviate any extra work on the part of your company in developing the business and further it will entirely meet the difficulties of repair and maintenance which is, as you are doubtless aware, a serious factor in the adoption of the hiring out of gas stoves.

We are prepared to supply you with slot cookers, as sampled, at 20/- net delivered and our ordinary model cookers at current list prices less 20% net delivered. In addition we are prepared to maintain and repair these goods for 10 years for 5% on the net cost price. The maintenance and repair is to include the disconnecting and removing the stove for cleaning and repairing, redelivery and reconnecting the same either at the same or other consumers' houses. At the end of ten years we make the stoves as good as new.

The repairing shop we suggest you shall find, we supplying all machinery, tools, boilers, ovens, repairing plant and men. In addition to this we undertake to open, provide and run a central showroom in Plymouth for stoves, gas fittings and all gas appliances, the shop to be under your name, although the expenses to be defrayed by us. The Plymouth Gas Company to have the option of exhibiting any appliances they may desire. In return for this we are to be the sole firm from whom stoves are purchased by the Plymouth Gas Company.

I think I may venture to state that I mentioned to Mr George Livesey [of the SMGC] the figure at which I was prepared to undertake this work and he said he considered it a very fair and equitable arrangement and one which could not be done at a lower price even by the Gas Company...

As this offer is entirely outside the ordinary terms allowed by the Stove Makers [see below], we ask that these terms be kept private.

Similar terms were offered to Bournemouth and Dublin and, early in 1901, Richmond was running showrooms for all three companies, under their names rather than his own. It is not known whether this practice was common to all makers; in any event it was banned by the Board of Trade in 1907. In Hull and Leek, Richmonds arranged for shops to be leased by arrangement with the municipal authorities and also had shops in Liverpool and Cardiff. In Preston the local undertaking invited makers to tender for the right to operate the gas showroom. In some cases makers combined to share the running costs; Richmonds combined with Wrights and Fletcher, Russell at Stalybridge, with Wilsons at South Shields and Mains at Inverness. Mains had showrooms in Glasgow, Huddersfield, Manchester, Bristol, Dublin and a prestige London showroom. Wrights had a showroom in their home city of Birmingham. Wrights had an agreement similar to Richmond's with the Cork Gas Consumers' Co; Wright provided salesmen to 'work the business of the Company in Cork', and in 1907 agreed to provide a showroom. Similarly at St Annes on Sea, Wrights undertook responsibility from the local undertaking for the working of the 'slot installation scheme' and managing a showroom. Wright minutes, like those of other makers, include many other similar agreements for supplying and fitting slot (prepayment supplement) installations. These particulars are based on references found in the minutes of the makers concerned; it is possible that more showrooms were operated and more fitting work undertaken by these or other makers but details have not come to light.

Richmond did not confine his marketing efforts to the home market. In 1898 representatives were appointed in Australia and South Africa. In 1900 he went himself to assess the prospects for setting up a factory in the United States. He found there was no market for his solid cast-iron cookers, Americans preferring light pressed steel cookers incorporating the latest features, despite their short life expectancy. On his return Richmond attempted to interest British undertakings in such appliances but could arouse no enthusiasm. British managers thought only of the requirements of a rental market where simplicity, long life and minimal maintenance were far more important than style or the latest technical features. It was only in the 1930s that such appliances finally appeared on the UK market.

Richmond was only one of a number of forceful entrepreneurial makers whose efforts in marketing and installation made possible the growth of the market for gas associated with the prepayment supplement concept. The makers proved that they had the vision to expand their sphere of activities as necessary and the financial strength not only to cope with their own expansion but also to offer deferred payment terms to their customers if necessary. Given the stimulus of the prepayment supplement concept, it is no exaggeration to state that it was the makers, typified by Richmonds, who drove forward the growth of the working class market rather than the activities of the supply undertakings themselves. The undertakings in most cases were bemused onlookers, astonished at the developments they had unleashed. The UK market was given such a boost by the makers before the first world war that it never lost its pre-eminent position in world manufactured gas supply.

Municipal undertakings were hampered from developing commercial policy as actively as private undertakings. However they were more active in providing a fitting service and regulating standards of service for customers. The case of the municipal fitting department of the Birmingham gas undertaking has already been mentioned. In 1883 the Manchester Gas Committee took a different line. It strictly prohibited its 'servants' from 'trafficking' in gas meters or fittings. The committee nevertheless kept tight control. Customers had to go to private gas fitters, of whom over 600 were officially authorised. These men were required to comply with the Committee's standards for installing pipes etc, and to certify that they completed their jobs in a 'workmanlike' fashion. Fitters failing to keep to the standards laid down were struck off the list. The

Committee even laid down mandatory fixed charges for running pipes and installing appliances. Authorised fitters were permitted to hire out and install gas meters, but many customers bought their own; all meters privately fixed were inspected by the Gas Dept; from 1891 the Corporation had its own meter repairers.

By contrast, the largest private undertakings were relatively slow to become involved in such activities, being satisfied to leave them in the hands of the private sector. Why this should be the case is not clear from references in the gas press. Possibly it was a practice dating from the earliest years of the industry. When the GLCC received its original statutory powers, it was required to use independent fitters rather than its own staff, despite the fact that such men often proved incompetent. Fitters at the time had no experience of handling gas or of making joints gas-tight, and any ironmonger or handyman could enter or leave the trade at will. Certainly towards the end of the 19th century there is nothing to suggest that major private undertakings were less concerned about safety matters than their municipal counterparts.

The GLCC had a long history of using private contractors for its fitting work, for repairing public lamps and the supply, repair and maintenance of gas meters, usually on three- or five-year contracts. In the mid 1890s the instant popularity of the prepayment supplement system imposed a huge and costly burden of installation work on the undertaking requiring the use of six special contracting firms for the work in addition to at least as many others for fixing meters. In fact the financial demands of prepayment supplement work were so great that the GLCC was forced to suspend installation for two periods purely on grounds of expense. In 1902 when installation was restarted, the engineer responsible was instructed by the directors to undertake part of the work with direct labour to obtain comparative cost data. As a result, the GLCC was able to negotiate lower prices when contracts were next renewed. This was the start of the GLCC's direct labour fitting organisation. Right up till the 1914-18 war, contractors completed a proportion of the GLCC's prepayment installations and in 1922 the GLCC was wondering whether to renew long-running contracts for geyser maintenance or to undertake the work with its own fitters.

William Sugg was not only an inventor and maker of lamps; he was also one of the first to establish a fitting force to install his own street lamps. On occasion these were supplied on a trial basis and were not always acceptable to the lighting authority. The Sugg board minutes have several reports of discussions with undertakings over who should pay for the gas burned during such trials. Some undertakings not only expected Sugg to bear the full cost of installing and removing lamp columns but also of paying for the gas used during the trial period. Whether this showed a hard-nosed commercial attitude or was symptomatic of a generally prevailing unwillingness to become involved in trading must remain a matter of opinion. Sugg were not alone in supplying a lighting maintenance service. Welsbach serviced its own lamps for the GLCC among others.

H & C Davis were gas fitters in Camberwell, south London who set up in 1875. They quickly established good relations with the SMGC, who at the time were not general gas fitters and did not sell gas fittings. The SMGC had its own facilities for repairing cookers, presumably only for those it had supplied on hire, and was considering making its own cookers, because there was 'difficulty in obtaining stoves of the quality and construction they prefer'. Davis made up cookers from bought-in castings from Falkirk and soon was in a position to supply the majority of SMGC needs as well as selling to the general public.

In the mid 1870s the gas appliance business was still a relatively small-scale affair. The business was in the hands of a close-knit group of suppliers. When Davis needed castings to make cookers for the SMGC he turned to a specialist. The castings came from a group of foundries owned by Malcolm Cockburn, ironmaster of Falkirk. Sugg was another who for some years made up appliances from bought-in components as well as manufacturing his own lighting fittings. Davis bought a Falkirk foundry in 1900 and transferred it to Luton in 1907 when a new factory for appliances was built. (Jackson electric cookers were made by the firm at Luton from 1912.) Apart from supplying others in the business Cockburn had three nephews who specialised in gas appliance work. Mathieson supplied castings to the Leeds tinsmith Charles Wilson and after setting up a foundry in Leeds the two combined in 1899 to form Wilsons & Mathiesons. W & A C Russell were two other nephews who set up a foundry in Pendleton and worked closely with Thomas Fletcher of Warrington. Fletcher was fascinated in small gas furnace technology and became a recognised expert on gas burners. He combined with the Russells in 1892 as Fletcher, Russell & Co. Major foundry businesses such as Coalbrookdale and the Carron Company considered moving into the fast-growing cast iron appliance business. Both produced and advertised cookers around 1900 but clearly decided this was too narrow and specialised a market for their attention and soon withdrew.

There is no doubt that the growth of the appliance market for gas was largely managed by the makers. They organised exhibitions, showrooms, canvassing, fitting and service. Even the largest supply undertakings were at first preoccupied with meeting additional demands for gas and were unable to tackle the myriad other roles which makers could fulfil. If the largest undertakings were unable to handle selling and customer service, smaller ones would certainly find it impossible. While undertakings at first welcomed the assistance of the makers, a sense of unease over their possible undue dependence began to surface. This concern was heightened by suspicion that the makers were colluding to regulate competition between themselves. When prices or discount structures changed, it was normal for all members of a Makers' Conference to subscribe to a common published announcement. This proved that makers co-operated closely, even if they did not actually regulate competition.

The first reference to collaboration over pricing came in 1894; Wright, the largest specialist appliance maker, approached Fletcher, Russell with proposals for combined action by all the gas appliance companies to agree a standard set of discounts which they would all operate. The intention was to reduce price-cutting by later entrants to the appliance market such as Cannon and Parkinson for the benefit of all. Nothing came of this. In 1898 Wrights made a further proposal for a gas stove makers' association, or a full amalgamation. As one of the Fletcher, Russell directors put it, 'amalgamation was the ruling passion at the present time'. Wright argued that a closer union should reduce costs of advertising, shows, travellers and general selling costs; prices could be maintained, bringing increased margins of profit. Existing trade names and lines would continue but there would be a central fund and common dividend. Central buying could save money. If the various firms arranged matters themselves, 'in buying the various businesses and arranging the whole affair, no promotion money, no company promoter and no underwriting would be necessary'. A central board would control overall policy but branches would have considerable autonomy to work their businesses without competing with each other.

Fletcher, Russell were probably typical of most makers in being happy to subscribe to agreements on discounts, carriage, exhibitions etc, but would not contemplate amalgamation. As their board realised, the loose confederation structure implied in the proposals from Wright could not achieve the desired economies of scale and rationalisation as long as there were still untamed entrepreneurial proprietors controlling their separate branches of the business. Such men had seen their firms and profits grow rapidly over the previous few years and would never willingly surrender control. There could be no comparison with the example cited by Wright of the four old-established meter firms who were persuaded to amalgamate as Meters Ltd in 1897, enriching the promoters but otherwise making no impact on the way the four operated their businesses. Similarly when two other old-estabished and similar sized meter makers, Parkinson and Cowan, combined a few years later in 1900, the board regularly split on family lines when future policy was under discussion; no rationalisation was possible until, under pressure from their bankers, a non-family chairman was appointed thirty-two years later.

It was clear that what Wrights had in mind was some form of tightly disciplined cartel under their leadership which would cover all aspects of commercial practice. One suggested rule was that 'new goods of all makers to be submitted to the meetings of members of the Association before fixing the price; also that all shall adhere to their list prices'; this Fletcher, Russell would not accept. They could see that if they played by the rules they would be forced into an untenable competitive position if other members were less than scrupulous. Fletcher, Russell's deputy chairman had some sympathy with the proposals. 'If he could see that the business of the Association would be worked on honourable principles, he would have every confidence in going forward with the matter but that we ought to wait a short time before committing ourselves'. By contrast Thomas Fletcher was in vehement opposition, disliking Wright's trading methods and their ambitions. 'He would have nothing to do with the question whatever and that in no circumstances would he be in any firm in which Wright & Co were connected'. Fletcher, Russell were not alone in their misgivings; the Davis Gas Stove Co shared their doubts about the Association and declined to join. The firms that joined were Wright, Richmond, Parkinson, Wilson, Main and the Coalbrookdale Co.

Within a short time the Association collapsed. Main severed their connection 'owing to want of faith in J Wright & Co and Richmond & Co... Coalbrookdale had withdrawn because they could not trust Arden Hill & Co and the Cannon Hollowware Co [both these firms were reputedly the worst offenders for price-cutting]... there was want of confidence and [Parkinson] should not join any such Association unless the whole of the makers were willing to join'. With the departure of key members and the total lack of trust, the Association was dissolved in March 1899 after less than a year in existence. It soon became clear that despite formal agreements on discounts etc, some members at least were not going to allow Association rules to stand in the way of business. One gas undertaking manager, who happened to be a personal friend of a Fletcher, Russell director, had been visited by a senior man from Richmonds. When asked about discounts the Richmond man had said 'that they were precluded by the Association from offering better terms but there would be no difficulty in arranging extra discount privately'. That this was regular company practice was clear from the agreement between Richmonds and the Plymouth Gas Co. quoted above.

Such close working together was very common at the time. It ranged from the 'gentlemen's agreement' depending solely upon the honour of the members and seeking only the determination of prices on the one hand to a closely organised association which regulated prices, fixed the amount of output and allotted to each member his share of trade while loyalty was enforced through penalties on backsliders. By 1900, the gas meter and appliance firms had agreed standard terms of trade within price associations or Conferences. Co-operation went no further for the appliance firms; an experimental pooling scheme was tried for a few months in 1912 but abandoned. In the meter business competition was much more severe and profits under great pressure. Even so it was not until 1910 that the meter makers' Conference agreed a pooling scheme; those makers who failed to make their quota of sales were compensated by those who had managed to sell more than quota. This scheme was renewed in 1918 and survived until 1924, by which time falling prices reduced profit so much that there was nothing to distribute.

Although attempts to establish a gas stove cartel foundered on mutual mistrust, the turn of the century was notable for a series of smaller-scale amalgamations between makers. Most of these were between firms engaged in the same business, eg. Wilsons and Mathiesons, both foundrymen (1899), the Davis Gas Stove Co with two other foundry companies (1900), John Wright, Arden Hill and Eagle Range, making gas appliances (1900) and Sidney Flavel and the Imperial Stove Co, foundrymen (1902). Wright attempted to buy the Cannon Co in 1899 but the Cannon directors considered the likely terms inadequate; they were doing very successfully as an independent firm. Parkinsons and Cowans, who merged in 1900, were both predominantly concerned with meters although Parkinson had a small cooker business.

Some groupings were of a different kind, particularly directed towards the special needs of the gas industry, which was preoccupied with supplying complete prepayment installations. Where a single firm could supply both meters and cookers, it would be in a better position to provide a service to gas undertakings. It would be in an even stronger position if it could also offer an installation service; it could then quote an all-in price per 'slot installation'. The three largest cooker firms were all considering this. Fletcher, Russell considered the possibility of starting the manufacture of meters when they heard that Richmonds and Wrights had this in mind but decided against it. Shortly afterwards they were approached by the Thorp & Marsh meter company with a view to an amalgamation with three or four other meter companies. This would have created another firm like Meters Ltd but with cooker manufacturing capacity. Marsh undertook to arrange financing; Fletcher, Russell were unimpressed and decided not to get involved. Marsh also approached Richmonds, again without success; there was some doubt about his commercial acumen although he had the reputation of always meeting his engagements.

Richmonds had the capacity to provide complete slot installations by the end of 1898 and claimed to be the first appliance firm to be able to offer this service. Richmonds did not make their own meters; probably they considered this unnecessary as two of their substantial shareholders were the meter making firms of Thomas Glover and J Braddock. Even so, when approached by George Glover, another meter maker, they agreed to buy his business for £68,000. John Wrights also had links with a meter firm, the Sutherland Meter Co. The amalgamation of Thomas Glover, who made meters, and R & A Main, who made cookers, (1897) was between two firms of roughly equal size. This made no difference in practice to the way the firms operated. A holding company was set up with directors from both companies on its board. The practical business of running the two branches was completely delegated to the two predecessor companies who retained their own boards of directors and a large measure of independence for many years.

Not every gas manager was satisfied with the generally accepted commercial practices of the day. George Livesey of the SMGC was quite prepared to use his personal prestige and the financial strength and buying power of his company to counter anti-competitive tendencies which might adversely affect the gas industry. In 1877 he wrote to *The Times* to condemn the practice of giving commission. At the time of the great Salford gas scandal ten years later, Livesey attempted to outlaw the practice of paying commission within the gas industry, insisting that all suppliers to the SMGC should promise not to give commission. A few meter firms publicly stated that they would give up the practice, but they were in a very small minority and it was notable that there was no groundswell of support for their stand. In 1894 Livesey initiated another campaign, this time against trade rings. He had noticed that tube makers, gasholder builders and meter makers, when invited to tender competitively, had started submitting identical prices. Livesey's view was that in restricting competition by operating a ring, the makers would stifle all incentive to reduce costs and improve quality. He was determined to oppose anything he considered unfair practice. In 1899 he was quite forthright;

> There is a combination of meter makers, and I believe what
> keeps them reasonable is the knowledge that the companies
> would make their own meters if they used the combination
> unfairly; but they do not use it unfairly.

He was ready to use the expertise within the SMGC to produce his own requirements; in 1901 for example, he again suggested that he might set up his own meter factory within a year or two, possibly in conjunction with other gas undertakings. In support of the idea Livesey cited the example of the Co-operative societies and flour-milling; he also mentioned how the railway companies undertook the building of much of their equipment without recourse to outside manufacturers. The SMGC did later set up its own meter manufacture and repair works and even a gas mantle works, both of which were still operating in the late 1950s. In 1899 the GLCC considered setting up its own company to supply its requirements of meters and fittings, although it is not known whether this was to counter anti-competitive practices by makers and indeed whether the makers were ever made aware of this proposal.

Livesey's stand seems to have been the first instance of a gas undertaking publicly putting pressure on the appliance makers by threatening to set up in direct competition. There was another instance around the same time. The cooker makers published a combined notification of identical price increases; Livesey considered the increase unjustified and thought the makers were taking advantage of the enormous demand for cookers to put up prices. He threatened to set up a group of undertakings who would make all their own appliances. At this dire threat, the makers immediately withdrew the price increase. Ten years later, simultaneous price increases led to more talk of

> a very nice little conspiracy.. run by the gas stove makers... if
> it is not possible to get a foreign-made cooker which will

answer our requirements, it will certainly be possible to combine and run a home-made article which will be satisfactory.

The SMGC was quite prepared to act. From the 1920s it had appliances made to its own specification by a small foundry which had never previously made complete appliances; this was Flavels of Leamington. Obviously a financially and technically strong company such as the SMGC could act in ways not open to medium or small companies. Even so, makers must have been aware that larger companies could act as focuses of resistance if their actions seemed to press too hard on the supply industry, and must have influenced their commercial strategy over the long term.

A record has been found of one occasion when the meter makers combined to protect their mutual interests. In 1912 a German firm, Haas began to import its meters into Britain, undercutting the prices the British makers had agreed between themselves. The British meter makers first suggested that Haas should raise prices to prevailing British level, but Haas refused and suggested that their British business should be bought out for £20,000. This was refused and the British said they would spend a similar amount competing with Haas' existing home customers. Finally Haas was bought out for £5,000. This was the only known serious incursion by European makers into the British market until the arrival of Ascot between the wars, described in chapter 11.

There are obvious difficulties in trying to establish the exact level of co-operation between competing firms. It is unlikely that records of conversations at informal or formal association meetings would be kept, but if at all, then only in strictest confidence; none are known to have survived. Knowledge of such arrangements is confined to occasional comments in board minute books which are often cryptic and unenlightening. The records of the various trade sections of the makers' society, the Society of British Gas Industries (SBGI), established in 1906, are uninformative although it is certain that the infrequent formal meetings were also the occasion of informal and unminuted gatherings. As an example, when nationalisation was imminent, the makers wished to avert the threat of appliance manufacture by the new Area Gas Boards, who in turn were concerned that they might be held to ransom by the makers. The makers gave a formal undertaking that they would not discuss prices at their meetings; what they did not say was that in future they might meet informally at other times to discuss such matters.

It is arguable that an understandable tendency towards collaboration between makers was reinforced by the attitudes of some gas undertaking buyers looking for the cheapest product regardless of performance or quality. As Thomas Fletcher said, if he were in a minority raising prices 'several of our best accounts with Gas Companies would be closed immediately'. As a result, every maker was careful not to step out of line and price announcements tended to be accompanied by phrases such as 'along with the other Gas Stove Firms'.

Appliance buying policy purely on the basis of low cost had another consequence; technical advance might be hindered. In the absence of common standards for appliances, there was the ever-present risk that the supply industry would continue to buy inefficient appliances as long as they were cheap. This would doubly penalise any maker who spent money on research to produce better, if rather more expensive, appliances. This danger had long been recognised. H J Yates of Wrights, speaking as chairman of the SBGI, put it as follows in 1911:

> In the natural desire, on the one side, to buy in the cheapest market, and on the other to sell in the dearest, the ultimate advantage of the gas interest at large, in which both sides have so much at stake, is sometimes overlooked. Makers of gas apparatus have too often directed their energies to designing, not the article that would do best justice to gas and popularise its use, but the one that would sell cheapest or show most 'talking points', and so capture a contract, a course which may make for present advantage, but is bound to yield a harvest of trouble. Makers of gas, on the other hand, do not always remember that the technical knowledge and scientific methods are the thing that cost money – indeed very often money will hardly buy them – and if that expenditure of time and brain and cash is not to be recognised and allowed for, then obviously such efforts will languish under the discouragement, and gas will be far poorer and weaker in the struggle with its rivals than it should or need be. It is not unreasonable to suggest that the matter of price ought not to be made the only criterion of comparison in those numerous cases where some of the apparatus being passed under review have scientific research and method behind them, and others are without such advantages.

As Yates said, too many makers were satisfied with turning out a 'workmanlike' product and too many undertakings were willing to buy them regardless of quality. Yates wanted the supply industry to set basic standards for each type of appliance, and to refuse to accept anything less. Of course he had his own axe to grind as a maker who was also deeply interested in research and making more efficient and more attractive appliances. However in the absence of a lead from the supply industry he would have to continue to supply what was demanded, however much he recognised the shortsightedness of such a policy. The emphasis on hire which was to persist for most of the inter-war period left a legacy which was to hinder the progress of the industry right through the 1940s and 1950s.

9 Financing expansion; was the appliance business profitable?

As a general rule managers reckoned to sell gas at double the direct cost of manufacture, the balance covering distribution, administration, profit and promotional activities. As already described, hiring particularly in association with the prepayment supplement and Welsbach lighting proved an astounding success, attracting new customers in their millions and bringing steady increases in sales of gas. Hiring and the provision of prepayment installations were originally seen as a normal promotional activity and so failed to attract the careful attention that a similar investment in gasworks plant would have merited. Although hiring and prepayment installations formed the basis of their improved performance, gas managers would have been prudent to pay more attention to the associated costs. The provision of millions of appliances as a central component of the business was of a totally different order of magnitude from providing a few appliances for promotional purposes. In fact undertakings embarked on providing appliances without having seriously considered the ultimate financial commitment this might entail.

When the appliance business first began to take off, one or two reports in the gas press purported to show that hiring was self-financing. For example in 1880 the Leicester gas committee were 'fully satisfied that the income from rents will cover interest and depreciation'. There was no mention of installation and repair costs. The committee reckoned that 'in any case the profit on gas consumed will be so considerable that if no rent whatsoever were charged the committee are sanguine that benefit would result to the department'. The Leicester report was based on an average of 40 days' experience of the first 58 customers. Such reports could not give a measured long-term view but gave undertakings the confidence to proceed. As matters turned out in the long term, the appliance business was subsidised from profits on the sale of gas.

How were managers to calculate the costs of appliance hire? The statistics collected and published annually by the Board of Trade as a part of its regulatory function were completely unhelpful. The required form specified in the Gasworks Clauses Act of 1871 was determined long before appliance trading became an important part of the business and therefore took no account of hiring. It must also be remembered that at the turn of the century cost accounting was in its infancy. In 1909 an attempt by the London County Council to have the 1871 format amended to take account of prepayment supplement business was rebuffed by the Board of Trade. In 1921 an official report declared that the statutory form of accounts was

> such that it is not possible for gas undertakings to ascertain from their accounts, thus kept, what are the total costs and profits arising from the hire and repair of gas apparatus as distinct from the rest of the business.

For twenty years in the case of the prepayment supplement and even longer for hiring, managers had been happy with the consensus that promoting gas sales by means of appliance trading was a good thing. With little competition, increasing sales and stable prices the presumption was sustainable. In the 1920s the cost of the subsidy became for the first time a matter of serious concern.

It would have been helpful in assessing the potential cost of the subsidy to be able to quantify how many appliances were actually in use at various years, even more so to show how many hired appliances were in use and how many prepayment supplement installations had been provided for customers. Unfortunately no such figures are available either from official figures or from the makers themselves. There is no information on the number of appliances manufactured each year, the market share of the various makers or the proportion destined for export. Few if any appliances were imported before Ascot water heaters in the 1930s. Whilst almost all new prepayment customers were supplied with a cooker, a simple count of new customers would omit the fires and water heaters as well as cookers, supplied to 'ordinary' customers, ie. those who had credit meters. In the absence of information on appliance numbers, one way to attempt to quantify the costs of appliance trading is to look at the experiences of a few individual undertakings even if absolute figures are not available.

As described below the GLCC was obliged to suspend its prepayment supplement installation programme twice purely on grounds of cost. Concerns first surfaced in 1897-8 when the board decided to investigate the size of the capital investment committed in connection with the prepayment system, and when it might be paid off. Their investigation showed that the average initial outlay for an installation (including meter, cooker and lights) was £7 to £9; a credit meter would have cost £2 to £3. The problem was that there was no firm basis for estimating how this outlay might be recouped, as this depended on how much gas the average customer would use. Prepayment supplement customers paid around 25-35% over the standard rate for gas; this together with the normal profit on gas would contribute towards defraying the costs of the system. The costs would include revenue costs (servicing and spare parts) as well as costs of capital. The problem was that prepayment supplement customers were those who could not previously afford to have gas installed; they were working class customers whose average consumption of gas would be less than that of 'ordinary', who included commercial and industrial as well as domestic customers; no distinction between the various categories of ordinary customers is made in the official statistics collected. Only after nationalisation in 1949 were non-domestic sales separated out. As expected, the third of domestic customers with credit meters used more on average than the two-thirds with prepayment meters, 15% more in 1956/7. It is probable that this difference between domestic credit and prepayment usage would be considerably greater in the early days of prepayment meters.

Apart from the question of repayment, there was also the problem of finding the capital to finance the installation programme. For each thousand new prepayment supplement customers the GLCC had to find around £7-9,000, and new customers were signing up not in thousands but in tens of thousands each year. Every other undertaking offering prepayment installations faced the same problem.

The first intimation of strain on resources came in 1899 when, for a short period, the GLCC suspended all prepayment installations. One of the GLCC's appliance suppliers, Fletcher, Russell became aware of the problem. In an effort to be helpful, the makers offered £5,000 credit for 12 months at a low rate of interest; they had gained the impression that the GLCC wished to negotiate deferred terms for buying slot cookers pending parliamentary approval for an increase in their capital. When the firm made its formal offer, it seemed to embarrass the GLCC, although Fletcher, Russell certainly thought that the suggestion originated with GLCC officers. The GLCC promoted a private Bill in 1900 to raise £2.5 million, of which no less than a quarter, £640,000, was for meters, stoves and installations. The Bill at first failed to gain Parliamentary approval and the GLCC was again forced to suspend all prepayment installations from April 1901 until September 1902. Despite its status as the largest undertaking in the UK, the GLCC had to ask Parkinson & Cowan, who supplied meters, to accept deferred payment until its extra powers to raise capital were approved. Another meter manufacturer Thomas Glover, hit by the loss of business, actually offered to finance installations for the GLCC for a 3 year period on deferred terms to ease their cash flow problems. This offer was not taken up but stung the GLCC into restarting installation as soon as capital could be raised.

Twenty years later in 1920 it was estimated by George Evetts, a consultant engineer who wrote a textbook on the administration of gas undertakings that no less than one sixth of the total capital of the GLCC was sunk in the hiring business. This level of investment in prepayment installations was not untypical. Information is also available for another major company, Wandsworth. During an investigation into its costs in 1921, the company stated that a total of £350,000 was invested in stoves and meters. At the time the company had a total issued capital of £1.3 million (including loans of £229,000). If the figure quoted by Wandsworth in its evidence was not overstated, no less than a quarter of its total capital was invested in gas appliances and meters. Wandsworth also admitted that two-thirds of the expenditure shown in the accounts for 'distribution of gas' properly related to stoves and meters. Such a misallocation of costs may have arisen because the statutory form of accounts made no provision for expenditure of this nature; another possible explanation is that fitting staff were in the distributing engineer's department, as they were in the GLCC some years earlier. In either event it seems likely that there may have been a fairly general understatement of costs on fitting and servicing work, lulling engineers into a false sense of security as to the full extent of the costs of their commercial activities.

The problems of financing prepayment supplement installations were not restricted to large undertakings or to private companies; municipal undertakings also had their problems. In 1899 Perth Council was supplying hired cookers at a faster rate than it had provided for and quickly exhausted its borrowing powers. Under its 1900 Provisional Order it applied for £7,388 for its hire business but was only allowed £4,388. To resolve the continuing cash-flow problem the Council decided to move away from its policy of hiring; it would in future only sell appliances either on cash or HP terms. It is not known for how long this policy was continued. It seems likely that Perth's application may have been scaled down because of the general opposition to municipal trading at the time. It is also possible that restrictions may have been placed on central funding for investment in what was arguably not a core activity.

With this very substantial capital investment in appliances, it might have been expected that the question of depreciation and obsolescence would have attracted some attention. As the *Gas World* pointed out as early as 1906,

> There is no asset or chattel on a gas company's books that perishes as fast as gas stoves and fires. It is therefore imperative that they should be properly depreciated; but where they do not return any direct revenue (some undertakings lend and fix without charge) it is difficult to write off enough on this account. Indeed, what with depreciation and interest on cost, maintenance, storing, etc, it would not be difficult to pile up such a total charge as to raise the question whether it might not pay better to give the consumer something in cash, and let him buy himself a stove to his liking.

This is a fascinating comment; it is unfortunate that it was not repeated in the early 1920s when its significance might have been more clearly appreciated. In fact only one piece of evidence has been found to suggest that depreciation was even considered. The Maidstone Gas Co first charged depreciation on its meters and stoves in 1909; in that year the appliance revenue account moves from apparent profit into loss. By the late 1920s rentals covered less than two-thirds of costs, of which depreciation represented a fifth.

The gas industry was not the only one whose prospects were seriously affected by a failure to provide appropriately for depreciation. There is a close parallel with the tramway industry which grew rapidly in the early years of the 20th century. Municipalities took out Public Works loans typically of 40 years' extent to fund the construction of tramways. Because the trams were profitable, instead of ensuring that adequate provision was made for depreciation to cover replacement of track and vehicles, large sums were diverted in aid of rates, over £½ million in total in 1915. This led to a financial crisis, as the tramways were wearing out over 20 years or so, a much shorter timespan than the life of the loan with which they had been financed. If the tramways were to be modernised, more investment was required before the original debt had been repaid. Either another debt burden would have to be assumed or municipalities would cut their losses and move to buses.

No detailed work has been undertaken on the financing of the gas appliance business and in the absence of hard data on the numbers of appliances involved, it may never prove possible. It is however tempting to speculate that after 1918 the failure of the gas industry to upgrade its appliance stock was at least in part due to the lack of adequate provision for a depreciation reserve. Debts, whether in the form of public loans, share or loan capital had to be serviced even though the assets no longer had any value. Indeed they might even have had a substantial negative value because of a continuing liability to provide a maintenance and spare parts service. This situation was aggravated by the Gas Regulation Act of 1920 which froze the prepayment supplement in cash terms, effectively at its 1914 level. The supplement remained at this 1920 level until the nationalisation of the industry in 1949 and even thereafter. This price freeze was extremely serious. During the 1914-18 war prices of labour and materials had risen two- or three-fold. Prices of replacement appliances or spare parts were out of line with revenue, and the costs of keeping an obsolescent stock of appliances in reasonable order were steadily increasing. At the same time, competition from electricity was beginning to bite in the aftermath of the war, particularly in the lighting market. It is hardly surprising that senior gas managers were reluctant to embark on costly commercial initiatives against this gloomy financial background.

In the absence of any official and comprehensive figures on trading, as distinct from gas manufacture, *Field's Analysis* is an invaluable source of information. J W Field, accountant of the GLCC, began in 1869 to produce an annual summary of the accounts of the principal gas undertakings in London which was soon extended in scope to include major provincial undertakings, both private and municipal. This was on a consistent basis including some management ratios (eg. cost per thousand cubic feet of gas made or cost per £1,000 of capital employed) and allowed valid inter-firm comparisons to be made. He included details of capitalisation, costs of raw materials, of gas making and distribution, and administration. Details of income from sales of gas and by-products were given. He also gave a breakdown of the income from rental, both meters and appliances, and the directly associated costs. The 30-35 undertakings included in *Field's Analysis* varied slightly over time, affected for example by amalgamations, but may be taken as typical of the larger undertakings as between them they accounted for more than half of UK gas sales. These large undertakings are likely to have included the most efficient and forward-looking; it is a reasonable assumption that the performance of the others for which no figures are available would have been worse.

A warning should be given about interpretation of *Field's Analysis* data; it is tempting to draw conclusions about relative costs, efficiencies and management, especially between municipal and private undertakings. Such comparisons could be misleading. The aggregate data take no account of numerous factors which could influence the outcome; local wage rates; cost of coal; charging policies; social policies. Some municipal undertakings intentionally kept prices and profits low rather than making substantial profits to offset the costs of local government. In other cases profits were milked for major municipal projects; for example the building of Strangeways prison was financed from the profits of Manchester gas department. This practice of transferring profits in aid of rates became far less common between the wars. Lastly it must be assumed that all undertakings compiled their costs on a standard basis. That this was not so became clear when the Wandsworth undertaking was investigated for alleged profiteering, as described in the next section.

Field's Analysis gives no details of capital or depreciation charges for appliances; the clear implication is that these were treated like any other gasworks capital expenditure and submerged in the overall total. Some might argue that it was appropriate to treat such rugged cast iron apparatus like other gasworks plant and write them off over sixty years. It is certainly true that many old appliances remained in use long after more efficient appliances were available. Indeed many survived up to the time of conversion of the industry from manufactured to natural gas (1967-77); in the course of the preliminary survey, many weird and wonderful appliances were discovered.

Field's Analysis data show that gas prices tracked the wholesale price index until the early 1900s. Gas prices then became relatively cheaper, especially as they did not reach the heights of the inflationary surge which peaked in 1920. This favourable climate corresponds with the great expansion of business associated with the prepayment supplement. From around 1930 gas became relatively more expensive; unfortunately for the industry this was at a time when electrical competition was intensifying.

Profits had been falling since 1910 and, particularly after 1918, it was clear that the relative equilibrium between income and costs which had persisted before 1914 could no longer be relied on. Gas undertaking profits were squeezed steadily between the wars.

In the aftermath of the 1914-18 war when price inflation invalidated the basis of the sliding scale, gas price rises had been authorised, even if these were insufficient to match the rise in wholesale prices. Revenue was being squeezed and there was a serious backlog of maintenance to be tackled, arising from wartime shortages of labour and materials. Dealing with this large volume of work would be costly, not least because of increased wages.

One way of increasing revenue considered by the supply industry in the immediate aftermath of the war was to raise appliance rental charges and perhaps even the prepayment supplement, neither of which were then statutorily regulated. (The supplement was frozen in cash terms in 1920). The larger undertakings took the lead in raising charges and imposed increases averaging around 50%, smaller undertakings following suit. Whilst many customers accepted the increase passively, others did not. Objectors failed to see why they should pay more for old appliances and fittings, especially as they had been paying rental charges in some cases for twenty years or more. With no sign of modern appliances being supplied to replace their old ones, they questioned whether they should still be paying anything at all, let alone higher charges. Some undertakings handled the problem sensitively. The GLCC for example, defused any criticism by offering to sell outright all the 270,000 rented appliances then on hire at 4 years' rental, less than half the cost of new stoves; under this offer 100,000 stoves were bought by customers. (This was a good bargain for the GLCC as the rentals received were insufficient to cover the costs of maintenance.) This offer did not include cookers supplied under the prepayment supplement scheme.

Higher gas rental charges were only one of many post-war price increases which gave rise to official concern at the possibility of widespread profiteering; the government sought to control it through the Profiteering Acts, 1919 and 1920, under which independent investigations could be ordered. While most gas rental increases escaped official scrutiny, when the Wandsworth company sought to raise hire charges it was referred for investigation. Evidence from the company and others was taken by independent accountants, despite claims in the gas press that outsiders could not understand the industry. The accountants immediately ran into a problem; neither Wandsworth nor any other undertaking produced basic accounts which could identify the appliance hire business separately. As mentioned above, the report found that the statutory form of accounts was unhelpful.

As regards the Wandsworth company, the investigators found that it was under 'a misapprehension... as to the costs and profits... which had been actually realised on that part of the business'. The Wandsworth company claimed that many of the expenses of appliance trading were misallocated, appearing under the heading of distribution of gas. This would have made appliance trading appear in a more favourable financial light than was justified in reality. In the end the findings of the report were not too damning in that the charge of profiteering was found 'not proven'. Another finding of the inquiry, hotly disputed in gas press comment at the time, was that 'ordinary [ie. not prepayment] gas meter and gas stove rentals have hitherto been charged at a rate which was sufficient to cover the upkeep and maintenance and show a reasonable return on the capital invested in gas meters and stoves'. The fact that this apparently favourable finding was criticised shows just how sensitive the industry was becoming over the cost of its hiring business.

During the course of the inquiry information was also collected from ten other gas undertakings which had a wide range of charging practice; a general acceptance of subsidy for the appliance business was noted. Of the two municipal undertakings, one made no charge at all for the hire and repair of equipment; the other charged 10% of the original cost of the equipment as rent but made no charge for fixing or maintenance either of appliances or meters. The eight private undertakings all charged rent and seven had raised their charges since the end of the war. However, only two out of the ten were able to quote a total net profit or loss from the sale, hire and repair of stoves etc. One of these was the GLCC which considered prices should have been increased by two hundred per cent in 1920 rather than the fifty per cent requested. In 1921 the GLCC prepared a statement for the London County Council to show that, during the previous 36 years, there had been a deficit on repairs, without taking into account any interest on capital or depreciation and without providing a sinking fund.

The Wandsworth report failed to address what were essentially structural problems in the appliance business as managed by the supply industry. When hiring and the prepayment supplement system were first introduced in the late 19th century, it was optimistically hoped that the business would be self-financing in the long run as promotional costs were set against increased gas sales. Because of its success in building new markets and delaying the impact of electrical competition before 1914, the industry had no incentive to examine closely the economics of the business and to consider alternatives. After 1918 there were the new problems of obsolescence and inflation. Historical costs were now out of line with replacement costs, even on a like-for-like basis. In the immediate aftermath of the war there was no question of the industry starting a fundamental reappraisal of the hiring business; it was concentrating on getting back to what it regarded as normality. A great opportunity was lost.

The protestations of the industry that it was not profiteering would have been more convincing if there had been a rolling programme of upgrading appliances or if it had made a practice of supplying the latest appliances on hire. Differential hire charges could have been justified for modern appliances with improved features but not where obsolete appliances were still being supplied, renovated but still basically obsolete. A rolling programme of upgrading, say after fifteen or twenty years of use, would have been reasonable; the GLCC told the Wandsworth inquiry that the average life of a cooker was sixteen years and seven years for a fire. As far as 'free' appliances were concerned, the industry was continuing to supply obsolete appliances of the cheapest possible grade for prepayment supplement customers who were in the majority. Buying policy remained fossilised both to reduce capital outlay and to avoid invidious comparisons between one customer and another.

Field's Analysis data were used in 1920 in a book by George Evetts to identify the possible pitfalls in calculating economic charges for hire. Although he was strongly in favour of offering hired appliances, he pointed out that, taking all costs into account, there was still likely to be 'a loss on running this portion of the gas company's business'. In some cases the policy had been 'to undercharge... customers'. Not everyone accepted the conventional wisdom. A few managers were unconvinced of the necessity of subsidising the appliance business, or indeed getting involved at all in this area of trading; in consequence they were able to sell gas at a very attractive price. 'In order to reach the low figures of cost... the stove, meter and general fittings business is completely eliminated from their calculations'. Evetts disapproved of this; 'the experience of the gas industry during the past 20 years is overwhelmingly in favour of the retention and development of this hiring business'.

Evett's view was almost universal in the industry. Here was an example of what the historian Donald Coleman described as '..enduring habits of thought and action about such matters as ... marketing or technical innovation continued well into the twentieth century long after they ceased to be appropriate'. Unfortunately, while Evetts set out evidence of inexorable change, more expensive appliances, rising costs and statutory limitation of prepayment supplement charges, he did not appreciate that problems in the wider economic field, particularly price inflation, might force the hiring business into heavy loss. The profitability of gas supply had taken a sharp turn for the worse after around 1910. This was certainly not helped by a failure to identify correctly the costs of the appliance business and by ignoring depreciation. Undertakings found it almost impossible to replace obsolete appliances and harder to continue to subsidise hire, hire purchase and sale of appliances.

A few years later in 1927 the SMGC made a statement to the Board of Trade in response to critical comments in the daily press about London gas charges. This demonstrated that the undertaking was making a loss on supply to prepayment customers as the extra costs, over and above the basic charge for gas, were 2.14d per therm, 0.53d more than was received. The company's figures are confirmed by *Field's Analysis*.

Taken together, the evidence presented in this chapter, although variable in quality and not susceptible to rigorous quantification, suggests very strongly that the appliance business was subsidised to a considerable extent from the profits on gas. Doubtless the supply industry would have argued that any element of subsidy was justified as a promotional expense to protect the market for gas. This argument has some validity, particularly if no alternative courses of action were open.

What alternatives were open? One option to raise revenue, though unattractive, was possible. Could the industry charge more for gas? Although undertakings had considerable freedom to vary charges, the threat of competition made them cautious. In 1932 the *Gas World* felt able to criticise them forthrightly; undertakings were able

> to raise or lower the price of gas at will, a condition that
> eliminates the element of chance from profit earning... The
> gas industry is its own worst enemy. We fear its complacency
> much more than we fear electrical competition.

This comment is not supported by the evidence of the prices charged by the major undertakings, who were acutely aware of competition from electricity. It might have been valid for small isolated undertakings (possibly still the majority in numerical terms) faced with competition from equally small electrical companies as yet unlinked to the grid. It would be wrong to take seriously the comment about gas prices, although the criticism of complacency should have touched a raw nerve for the supply industry.

What other options were available to limit deficits on the appliance business? There were certainly some.

* The industry could have offered simple hire of modern appliances at realistic charges as an alternative to the usually obsolete appliances provided from the supplement.
* A better option would have been to concentrate on the sale of appliances either for cash or on hire-purchase terms, giving customers a choice of type of appliance. Britain would then belatedly have followed the American lead.
* It would have been helpful to calculate hire-purchase terms on a basis that fully covered costs. Evetts had recommended that HP terms should be calculated by taking the cost price of the appliance, plus interest and a notional 10% for overheads and profit (but no allowance for showroom or selling expenses or the costs of installation); this figure he then divided into quarterly instalments. The total HP price he comes to is rather lower than the maker's list price. This was undoubtedly a common method of calculating HP terms.
* Clearly, if gas undertakings offered prices lower than list prices even with hire purchase over five years, as was common, there was no chance that any retailers would bother to promote appliances. This situation, closing the appliance trade to outsiders, seems to have evolved by chance rather than as an industry policy; it was not inevitable.
* It might even have been possible for neighbouring undertakings to combine in setting up a common specialist marketing organisation; this option was apparently never considered, although there had been a precedent. Something along these lines was done in New York to counter the threat of electricity in the 1880s. Several undertakings combined to promote gas for cooking; they subsidised the establishment of three retail outlets to sell stoves and contributed to the installation costs.

The reluctance of the British supply industry to change marketing practices with the times suggests a serious entrepreneurial failure at a crucial turning point, when the growth of the domestic electricity market was about to take off.

10 Making better appliances; the role of research

A lthough other options to develop the gas market were available, the supply industry concentrated its attention on lighting, hiring appliances and prepayment installations. Despite the steady growth of the industry, the need for improved appliances had been recognised long before 1914, even if not by gas engineers. The *Gas World* writing in 1890 gave a stinging critique of the appliances then available, particularly the design of the burners which produced an all-pervading smell throughout the house. Three years later, a letter in the *Gas World* suggested that it was the responsibility of undertakings to ensure that customers had efficient appliances. The undertakings should test the efficiency of appliances and should publish the results. The writer reported that he had bought a fire of pleasing appearance; tests with a thermometer showed that the fire had no effect at all on the temperature of the room. The suppliers and fitters were unable to suggest any remedy so the fire was scrapped. There was no redress for the customer.

In the UK in the early 20th century there was virtually no systematic research on gas utilisation or the design of appliances. An honourable exception was the work by Dr Charles Carpenter of the SMGC on lighting burners. As the gas industry did not undertake testing, others had to move in to fill the need. In 1893 the *Lancet* had tested some gas fires; in 1906 it combined with the Smoke Abatement Society to arrange further trials. The *Lancet* investigators had to devise their own test methods to establish the thermal efficiency of various fires and their ability to discharge all the products of combustion (fumes) up the chimney without creating a smell or dryness in the room (or, at worst, poisoning the occupants). They were fortunate that they were able to make use of a series of rooms in public offices in Westminster which were in process of construction, almost ready for handover by the builder to the client; these rooms were used for simultaneous comparability tests. Their report made certain recommendations to improve the fires tested; there was no indication that these particular gas fires were more efficient than those tested by the *Lancet* in the earlier trials. Nobody in the gas industry had any idea. As the *Gas World* pointed out at the time, it was far from creditable that the gas industry should have to look to such bodies for independent and systematic testing of gas equipment.

Some months later, the *Gas World* seemed to change its tune; the self-critical comments of its correspondent were forgotten in the worst kind of obscurantism. It reported a series of tests undertaken by the American Gas Institute to determine the thermal efficiency of cookers and water heaters. These were disparaged by the *Gas World* on the grounds that the tests were devised by chemists 'of the severest laboratory brand, scientific to their finger tips but scarcely of this common workaday world'. In its view such scientific tests were less valid than those of an experienced cook grilling steaks or chops. However in an illogical *volte face* a couple of months later it commended the rules for installing gas fires prepared by a committee of the German Gas Association with Professor Rietschel and regretted the fact that there was no comparable authoritative guide available to the UK gas industry.

In 1898 Professor H E Armstrong was to comment that

There had been too much of the engineer and too little of science in the gas industry; too little attention had been given to methods of burning gas by the consumer. There was too little research work in the educational system of this country; and as an illustration of the effect of this, there was not a single English name connected with the scientific development of the Welsbach light.

Not all members of the gas engineering profession were unaware of what was happening elsewhere. References in the trade press at the turn of the century recognised that the UK was behind Germany and France in the training and employment of scientists and the use of scientific methods to measure and improve working methods. This was due in part to attitudes of mind resulting in inadequate support for research facilities, especially by comparison with Germany. At the annual meeting of gas engineers in 1901, one speaker suggested that the better technical education of the continental engineer (who was likely to have graduated in a recognised public engineering school) gave him a scientific status and social standing far above that of his English colleague.

Abroad, freer scope is given to chemists and experimenters, and their scientifically prosecuted investigations lead to better results in the higher branches of research than can be shown by enquirers at home. Continental works are the more sensitive to answer to the calls of modern necessities, while British works plod ponderously along in their old conservative methods.

British engineers could show a long history of empirical work improving plant and machinery and were notable consultants and contractors for gasworks projects world-wide, like railway contractors before them. However the major technological breakthroughs had come from elsewhere.

In Britain there were no long-established centres of technical expertise, whether for gas manufacture or utilisation. The training of engineers was somewhat haphazard, relying heavily on the experience of senior practitioners rather than on research-based knowledge. There had been an association of gas engineers since the 1860s with membership by election. Members placed greater emphasis on gaining practical experience under the supervision of professional seniors rather than through academic engineering training. A few trainees were articled to managers or consultants but most learnt on the job, where skill at team games was often regarded as a more important attribute than a formal educational qualification. This is clear from the potted biographies of newly appointed managers which appeared periodically in the *Gas World*. Admittedly the following for 1900 were for small works, but formal training programmes are notably absent.

> ... employed as a meter inspector and has, like his predecessor, benefited from the improvement class conducted by the engineer... acting as assistant to his brother... served an apprenticeship to the bricklaying trade; was trained in the work of a gasworks by his father... was in the service of the GLCC for a number of years, latterly foreman... first employed as a clerk and meter inspector... holds certificates in building construction, drawing and electricity... served his apprenticeship under his father and on completion was appointed assistant manager.

Some came into the industry under the wing of a relation; family connections could be important. The two foremost gas engineers in the early 20th century are by no means untypical examples. George Livesey was brought up on the Old Kent Road gasworks of the SMGC where his father was general manager; he was succeeded as chief engineer by his brother Frank; his uncle became deputy governor of the GLCC. Corbet Woodall was the son of the manager of the Liverpool gasworks; as a young man he went to work under one brother, who was manager of the Burslem gasworks in the Potteries, before he came to London. Another brother Henry was manager at Leeds. Four of his five sons also joined the gas industry. In Northampton three generations of the Eunson family managed the undertaking between 1845 and 1948. Given this background of family and tradition, it is hardly surprising that academic qualifications and pure research were not highly rated in the industry.

Specialist technical staff were few and far between in Britain. Rather than commissioning research at home, the supply industry tended to look overseas for technical expertise, especially to Germany. It is necessary to mention only the Bunsen burner, the carburetted water gas process, inclined retorts for carbonisation and Welsbach lighting to gain an idea of the technical debt owed to continental Europe. Mention has already been made of problems measuring the candlepower of gas. Photometric investigation could have been carried out by the National Physical Laboratory but the NPL attracted virtually no sponsorship or commissions from the gas industry. As a result, ad hoc work on photometry continued right through the inter-war period, undertaken mainly by makers such as Sugg who supplied street lighting. Another technical problem was the determination of levels of sulphur impurity in gas which required a chemist, but he was often considered a long-stop: according to the *Gas World*

> the chemist is supposed to give an eye to matters when the rule-of-thumb man has failed, possibly after wasting a chemist's wages a dozen times over.

Where engineers needed assistance they were more likely to turn for expert advice to one of their senior colleagues acting in a consultancy capacity than to a scientist. Senior engineers were not averse to forwarding their own interests by setting up consultancy firms; these included many of the best known figures in the industry, Valon, Colson, Livesey, West, Woodall and others.

There was no substantial core of theoretical physical or chemical knowledge available to the supply industry which might have been applied to utilisation as well as manufacture. There were a few exceptions; Dr Harold G Colman who trained at Manchester, Strasbourg and Würzburg before taking a post of lecturer at Mason College, Birmingham was chemist at Saltley gasworks, Birmingham. He later left the Birmingham undertaking to set up his own consultancy practice; he was engaged as scientific advisor to the Richmond Stove Co. Another exception was Professor Vivian Lewes of the Royal Naval College at Greenwich; he was a frequent lecturer and consultant on gas lighting matters in the years before the perfection of Welsbach lighting.

There are three main reasons for this neglect of what scientific research might offer. Gas engineers were suspicious of scientists *per se;*

such men in their view would not be 'practical men'. Secondly, there was a prevalent view that it was the responsibility of the customer to make sure he got value from his gas installation; it was not the responsibility of gas engineers to concern themselves with gas utilisation. Lastly they assumed that their shareholders would be unwilling to meet the costs of supporting fundamental research if this would affect the level of dividend. This was never seriously put to the test. Occasionally shareholders were asked to approve contributions for special projects with a clearly defined objective such as the exhibitions at Crystal Palace in 1883 and Earls Court in 1904. Before the early 1930s there were however no national or regional research centres operated and funded by the supply industry to which interested undertakings or makers might subscribe; large undertakings could follow their own research agenda and smaller ones had to rely on whatever they could glean from makers or consultants.

Attitudes towards research and development were very different in the other countries with sizeable gas industries. The Société du Gaz de Paris set up a research establishment under Henri Sainte Claire-Deville in 1861. The Société Technique (the French IGE) organised a research fund as early as 1877; prizes were given for useful research projects. In 1910 there were five research committees, one of which was concerned with utilisation of gas. In Germany research was particularly associated with the Karlsruhe Institute and the two professors Bunte, father and son who taught there. Hans Bunte (1848-1925) had been a student of Bunsen, and was appointed professor of chemical technology in 1887 with special interest in gas manufacture. He developed close links with German gas engineers for teaching and testing. Karl Bunte (1878-1944) was head of the Karlsruhe Institute, inaugurated in 1907; he was interested in both manufacture and utilisation of gas.

It was to Germany in particular that 'gas engineering pilgrims' travelled, particularly the Karlsruhe Institute. This had facilities for experimental scale gas manufacture and analysis, coal analysis, photometrical experiment and trials of new machinery. Students intending to become gasworks managers were able to attend. Other countries had courses for gas students, but none had the practical facilities available at Karlsruhe.

It was not only in university departments that scientific progress was made. The German Gas Association had established technical and practical schools for supervisors at Dessau and at at Karlsruhe for advanced courses; further schools were planned. There were schools for technicians, fitters and lady demonstrators at Dessau. Individual undertakings had their own research programmes; in Berlin for example they worked on the distribution of light from Welsbach mantles and developed holophane prisms, reflectors and diffusers to increase the useful light where it was needed, both for street and interior lighting. Similar theoretical work was being done in America. A degree course in chemical engineering was established at the University of Michigan in 1898; in 1900 the Michigan State Gas Association funded a gas fellowship, which provided a flow of graduates into the industry. Shortly afterwards, the American Gas Light Association set up correspondence courses for engineers. The first attempt to emulate the Karlsruhe course in the UK was in Scotland; students of chemistry at Heriot-Watt College could spend a period in the laboratories at Granton gasworks, Edinburgh.

In the light of these foreign examples of centres of technical excellence it is hardly surprising that there were belated calls for Britain to emulate them. At the 1911 meeting of the Society of British Gas Industries H J Yates of Wrights urged his fellow appliance makers to recognise the case for careful research and quality control to develop efficient and economical appliances. Some makers, including Crossleys the engine makers already had research departments with a special interest in gas combustion (Crossleys began research in the 1870s) but there were still many who merely professed to turn out a 'workmanlike' product. Yates also had a message for gas undertakings; he asked them to consider the best interests of the industry as a whole and to buy well-designed equipment, even if there were a slight cost penalty, rather than insisting on the cheapest goods regardless of quality. He suggested that the best possible appliances would not work well if the undertakings did not supply their gas at a higher, constant pressure and constant calorific value. Finally he suggested that the supply side might consider determining a certain minimum standard or quality for each type of appliance, refusing to promote anything that fell short of this level. This would have required the establishment of gas industry laboratories such as were then operating in Germany and the USA. Nothing came of this rallying cry, the *Gas World* rightly commenting that such a scheme would founder on the parsimony of undertakings.

In 1912 Yates made a more concrete proposal, this time for a central laboratory for the whole gas industry to test and 'hall-mark' approved apparatus. He suggested the endowment of appliance research collectively by the industry

which may bear such fruit as certain Continental establishments for the advancement of gas science and technic have already borne. Our national shortcoming in this respect has been more than once lamented in these columns. To put it plainly, there is no British peer of the Buntes and Sainte-Claire Devilles of contemporary European science.

Even the Institution of Gas Engineers was deaf to this plea. It had previously attempted to mount its own research programme but, lacking dynamic leadership or commitment, found this expensive and difficult to manage; the experiment was abandoned. It also found that some of its senior members resented technical criticism from makers, however well-founded. The following comment from an old-style manager was particularly unfair as Yates, his target, had undertaken much research which was incorpoated into the appliances he supplied.

Things have come to a pretty pass if a gas engineer who has an inclination for looking at the scientific aspect of things cannot present his views to a technical association without being made a shuttlecock of traders who may consider their particular interests prejudiced.

Universal appliance testing to British Standards had to wait until nationalisation in 1949 and the national 'seal of approval' label first appeared in 1958.

This unsatisfactory situation with regard to research into gas utilisation was matched in gas manufacture. In 1901 there was a suggestion by the chairman of the Plymouth Gas Co that the IGE should establish an experimental gasworks funded by all undertakings for the benefit of the industry as a whole. This idea came up again in the presidential address to the Institution in 1904, allied with a suggestion that laboratories should also be set up under a consulting chemist. It is clear that, at heart, the president did not believe in theoretical studies as a basis for practical design work; in his words, 'incomparably the best designer is the experienced works manager – the gas engineer'. In the following year the lack of funds to make any progress was bemoaned and, again, nothing was done.

The first courses in gas manufacture were provided by the Royal Society of Arts in 1873; responsibility for the lectures and exams was taken over by the City and Guilds of London in 1879. Leeds was the first university to show commitment to fuel engineering; in 1905 it appointed a Professor of Applied Chemistry (Fuel and Metallurgy). A department of coal gas and fuel industries was set up in 1907; this concentrated on fundamental work on gas manufacture and combustion, rather than utilisation. The department had no initial endowment, very different from other departments of applied science which had attracted substantial financial support for research into cloth manufacture and dyeing, tanning, engineering, mining and agricultural science. George Livesey suggested that the gas industry should raise £500 pa to contribute to the work of the department and sought to find subscribers. Allied to this effort, a couple of years later the IGE agreed to endow £100 pa for a post-graduate research fellowship. It was Livesey's death in 1908 that finally ensured the funding necessary. The industry agreed that his memorial should be the endowment of the Livesey Chair of Gas Engineering at Leeds. By then Leeds was offering an undergraduate course in gas engineering but it attracted a meagre response. In a diplomatic effort to attract more interest, the university awarded degrees of honorary DSc to Corbet Woodall, Charles Carpenter and the doyen of gas engineers, Thomas Newbigging. Sadly this was not enough. Year after year successive professors bemoaned the lack of interest of the supply industry in what the department could offer, both in terms of research and the production of skilled scientists. As the *Gas World* said, 'it will take us some time to get us accustomed to associating a degree with a gas manager'. Sadly, the establishment of the department at Leeds gave the IGE an excuse to abandon its own research efforts; as mentioned above these had proved difficult to manage, had not been systematically directed and had not proved fruitful. It was not until the 1920s that the concept of an experimental gasworks finally came to fruition when a test centre was endowed at Leeds University, again as a memorial, this time to Corbet Woodall.

The first signs of awareness that Leeds might be able to help with appliance design came in 1910. Appliances were still inefficient and often smelly and noisy. The Institution's research committee asked Leeds to undertake a programme of basic research into mechanisms of gas combustion that could be applied to the design of appliances, particularly fires. It was thought that the cooker market was close to saturation but that there might be an immense market for fires, whether hired or sold. The results could then be taken up by makers, with benefits both for them and the supply industry. Interestingly the report from Leeds

The Gas Miser fire: over 1¹/₂ million were sold.

emphasised the role of convected heat in improving appliance efficiencies. However the makers considered that radiant heat contributed more to comfort, possibly on the analogy of the open coal fire, and devoted their energies to improving radiant efficiency. A few radiant-convector fires were made in the late 1930s but it was only in the 1950s that the concept really caught on after the introduction of the Cannon 'Gas Miser' fire. This was attractive and efficient (it was advertised as being cheaper than coal), the first gas fire to catch the public imagination.

In great swathes of industry, notably electrical engineering and the chemical industries, large gaps in British industrial capability were exposed by the 1914-18 war, which cut off supplies and technology which had previously been imported from Germany. The gas industry lost direct access to its main source of mantles, essential for incandescent lighting, although German mantles still came in via the Netherlands. Scientific instruments and glassware, ball-bearings and many chemical products were no longer available. As a practical step to remedy shortcomings during the war the government established the Department of Scientific and Industrial Research to sponsor research and to encourage industry to do likewise.

It is perhaps characteristic of attitudes within the gas industry that Dr. Charles Carpenter of the SMGC was fiercely opposed to state support of research if the price were the risk of falling under 'bureaucratic or political control'. In his view the industry's research centres 'should remain free to develop along their own lines and in friendly co-operation with the industrial world'. This Panglossian optimism disregards the reports, appearing regularly in the press, of progress in Germany and elsewhere outstripping British industry. As late as 1947 the Advisory Council on Science Policy bitterly remarked that

> the primary reason why our industry as a whole does not make more use of scientists (including technologists) is not because their numbers were, and are, insufficient but because large sections of industry, being conservative and complacent, have neither missed them nor asked for them.

Even if there was no industry-wide centre to promote research into gas utilisation on the American and continental model, some faltering steps had already been taken to remedy the widely recognised shortcomings. Birmingham Corporation found that its efforts to develop industrial and commercial sales were handicapped as its potential customers were unable to get the specialist advice they needed on the design of furnaces, heat treatment of metals etc. A specialist industrial heating department was established around 1910, backed up by a laboratory which could undertake work on the constitution of metals and alloys, physical testing and chemical analysis; it was a local 'National Physical Laboratory'. This laboratory played a major role in undertaking tests for the Ministry of Munitions during the 1914-18 war, and it was able to provide heat treatment on a commercial scale. Furnaces designed there in conjunction with Gibbons Bros of Dudley, a leading furnace maker, became standard in industry, not only in the UK but in other countries. The laboratory was frequently asked to give consultancy advice and even sought Board of Trade approval for its own registered test mark. Around 1910 both the GLCC and SMGC were providing technical training for lads. The SMGC set up its own laboratories in 1912. This coincided with similar initiatives in America. In 1911 the Consolidated Gas Co of New York set up its own industrial laboratory/showroom. Much gas-fired equipment was installed for demonstration; potential customers could use the facility and appliances to make their own experiments.

When at the end of the 1914-18 war the government was planning its housing programme, it wished to encourage the installation of efficient and economical solid fuel cooking ranges in cottage property. It commissioned a consultant, A H Barker (from University College, London rather than from a fuel industry), to test available appliances and to examine comparative costs. Coal was the cheapest fuel and so most of the appliances tested were solid fuel but Barker included a couple of gas cookers to see how they compared with the solid fuel apparatus. As no standard methods of testing appliances had been discussed or agreed, Barker had to develop his own. Even then, he was unable to devise appropriate tests for what he described as 'open air cooking', ie. toasting and frying. Some years later the IGE attempted to develop a method for testing cooker performance; this was unsuccessful partly because of the difficulty of setting up standard test conditions when gas quality varied so widely.

Barker's tests showed that, for continuous heating, gas was an expensive luxury, costing about three times as much as solid fuel and even used intermittently for cooking was somewhat more expensive. He found that electric lighting was more than twice as expensive as gas, although incomparably more convenient and safer. Apart from lighting, he reckoned that electricity might only be considered in the home if expense was no object.

Particularly interesting about the results in the present context were the comments about the efficiency of gas appliances.

> The construction of modern gas plant [ie. appliances] has not
> made the degree of progress in economy in the last thirty
> years that might have been expected... The gas oven today is
> fundamentally the same device as that of thirty years ago.
> Certain improvements have been made in the efficiency of
> the hotplate but the improvements are not fundamental.

Barker found that gas appliances were capable of great improvement at small cost; in particular, ovens were far too freely ventilated for efficient operation. In part this was due to the persistence of the Dutch oven tradition in gas cooker design. Dutch ovens for roasting in front of an open fire were open on the side facing the flames. When early gas cookers were made with the flames at the bottom, the oven was open at the bottom, with a drip tray for the fat placed on the floor. As well as sheet metal cookers, cast iron cookers such as the Horseferry, introduced around 1903, were made in this way. There were still large numbers of these semi-open ovens around in the late 1930s. As late as 1938 and to meet London City Council fire regulations, the SMGC was obliged to fit tinplate bases to those of its rented cookers which were open, but only when they were returned for renovation. This is a telling comment on the average standard of cookers supplied to prepayment customers between

An 1870 cooker showing the semi-open oven.

the wars and the reluctance of even the largest companies to invest in modern appliances. It is also a comment on the laxity of safety regulations generally.

Whilst the British supply industry was slow to develop criteria for appliance performance, other countries were progressing fast. The criteria for efficient cookers developed by the Hamburg gasworks were subsequently adopted as a national standard by the German Gas Association. The Karlsruhe Institute was testing individual appliances in the early 1920s. In the USA, the American Gas Association opened its own laboratories at Cleveland in 1924. The work included testing individual appliances, establishing test methods and standards and the preparation of appliance specifications based on best practice; these after a period of grace became mandatory on all makers. One of the reasons for the effectiveness of the AGA Cleveland centre must be that its managing committee included equal numbers of undertaking and maker representatives; it also included representatives of the US Bureau of Standards, Bureau of Mining, Public Health Service and the US Master Plumbers' Association. There was none of the insularity shown by the different factions in Britain which prevented the establishment of a similar British centre. By 1934 the following countries either had their own certification of approval for gas appliances or had adopted another country's standards; Austria, Canada, Denmark, France, Germany, Holland, Sweden, Switzerland, USA.

The first British Standards for gas appliances were BS 1115 of 1941 for domestic gas ovens and the important BS 1250 of 1945 covering domestic gas appliances. The impetus for BS 1250 came not from the industry but from the government, planning for a post-war Britain. The Ministry of Works wished to place orders for cookers for the Portal prefabricated house but insisted that these should be in compliance with an appropriate British Standard. Possibly worried about being excluded altogether from the post-war housing market, a standard was speedily prepared by the gas industry to satisfy this preremptory demand.

It is surprising that the scope for improvements to cookers had not been recognised or rather, acted on before Barker's careful work. It can only be suggested that the preoccupation of the supply industry with buying the cheapest cookers for hire had diverted the attention of many appliance makers away from cooker research. One whose attention was not distracted was Harry James Yates (1873-1955), whose views were quoted earlier (pp156,176). He was an example of that rare breed, scientist and dynamic entrepreneur. He was the leading light in the creation of the Radiation group, described forty years later by Dr A Rees-Jones, chairman of Parkinson Cowan, who had known him, as 'a titan'. When he was twenty his father, a Birmingham edge tool manufacturer, bought him the business of Arden Hill, gas appliance makers and foundrymen to which he brought outstanding technical and entrepreneurial qualities. Within ten years his business was bought out by John Wright & Co, the oldest and largest gas appliance maker, but Yates quickly became the dominant figure in the combined firm. As attempts in the early 1900s to form a cartel or pooling scheme with other makers had failed, Yates negotiated an amalgamation of three of the largest makers, Wright, Richmond and Davis in 1919 as Radiation Ltd; these were joined by Fletcher, Russell and Wilsons & Mathiesons the following year. An attempt was made to persuade Glover & Main to join Radiation but they, Parkinson & Cowan and Cannon determined to remain independent. Yates was chairman of Radiation from its formation until he retired in 1939, and presided over consistent profit growth from £160,000 in 1922, £292,000 in 1931 and £327,000 in 1937.

Though without formal training, throughout his life Yates was interested in research; his father set him up in his own workshop when he was twelve. His interests tended first towards electricity then gas, photography and possibly even X-rays. Within a year of taking over Arden Hill he introduced cookers with removable burners. He continued to introduce technical innovations and both undertook and sponsored research throughout his career, giving a number of papers around 1905-10, particularly on improving the performance of gas fires. Wrights set up their own technical laboratory around 1910 and managed to attract outstanding scientists, notably Harold Hartley, the first academically trained research chemist from the new department of gas technology at the University of Leeds. (Glover & Main took on the second). Hartley like Yates combined outstanding business acumen with his scientific interests; he later became chairman of Radiation. Hartley for many years contributed to discussions at the IGE but was not permitted to become a member because he was a chemist rather than a practising gas engineer; this was finally put right and he was elected president of the IGE in 1947-8.

In the early 1920s there were two significant developments which could have dramatically changed the cooker market, one technical and one organisational. The major one was the introduction of the 'New World' range of cookers by Yates's Radiation group. The design team under Hartley were required to meet several criteria; the new cookers should use 25% less gas than comparable cookers on the market. The oven should be able to reach a temperature of 400° F within ten minutes. The cookers should be safe and they should make cooking as simple as possible for the housewife. Radiation introduced the oven thermostat (Regulo) to Britain on the New World range. This had been available on cookers in America for a number of years. The cookers being fully enamelled were far easier to clean than earlier black cookers. On some models there were duplex burners for high and low heat settings. Other makers hurried to follow Radiation's lead, and soon they were all making appliances far removed from those destined for the hire market.

Despite the availability of such advanced appliances, the attention of the supply industry was still

One of the New World range of cookers, enamelled and with oven thermostat.

focussed firmly on the rental and prepayment market. The second development was surprising in view of the previous history of the supply industry, fragmented as it was. Through an initiative undertaken under the auspices of the National Gas Council (NGC), established in 1919 under David Milne-Watson in the aftermath of the war (see p. 199 below), it was decided collectively to collaborate in the design of 'national' appliances, the first to be a basic cooker suitable for the rental market. The national cooker was to be the forerunner of a complete range of appliances, intended to cut down the excessive variety which had grown up over the previous thirty years or so. A widespread view within the industry was expressed by the chairman of the Northern Gas Salesmen's Circle who

> was surprised that companies [ie. undertakings] did not restrict the makes of cookers put out on hire. They made a big mistake in giving customers several makes to choose from, where no choice was really necessary. If they had one make of cooker it saved a great deal of time in the showroom waiting on customers to make up their minds.

This variety was rather unfairly blamed by the NGC on the makers who were accused of

> more or less "dumping" gas apparatus down on the various gas undertakings, with a very small regard to what the consumer actually required.

If undertakings had effectively abdicated control of their appliance business in favour of a particular maker as many did, it was hardly surprising that makers chose to put their own interests first.

The proposed standard cookers, if they were to be truly national, would have to work satisfactorily with gas whose properties, specific gravity and calorific value varied enormously from undertaking to undertaking, eg. calorific values ranging from 200 up to 625btu per cubic foot. The wide consultation necessary to establish the requirements of different managers, accustomed to dictating their own, was very time-consuming. Although it was well known that many existing cookers suffered from smothering and extinction of oven flames because of inadequate ventilation – smelling foul and making them potentially lethal – no research had been put in hand to establish the causes and to seek remedies. Some undertakings solved the problem by rule of thumb, for example the Brentford company patented its own technique and made its own cookers, which seemed completely satisfactory. A similar problem had been experienced with gas fires some years earlier. This had been referred to the University of Leeds and the causes elucidated; in consequence all new gas fires benefited from the improved technology.

The NGC thought that a group of experts from undertakings could design a series of appliances; these could then be adopted with confidence by every undertaking, even those which had not been involved in the design. The NGC standard cookers were designed from the outset with hiring in view, the priorities being standardisation, simplicity, cheapness of first cost and ease of maintenance. The smallest standard model was even unlagged, although it was well known that lagged ovens used 40% less gas and cooked more quickly. The NGC intention was that, once the specification was published, all makers could produce them if they wished, although the NGC would specify maximum selling prices. They were not intended to displace the proprietory models produced by individual makers which might incorporate special features and command a premium price. The *Gas World* clearly thought that customers might wish to have the option of hiring something more than the most basic standard cookers and suggested that it might be 'good business to also include a proprietory article on the hiring list in addition to the standard model'.

There were no industry standards for appliances and no generally agreed test methods to measure efficiency, although in view of Barker's recent work he was co-opted on to the design panel. It is hardly surprising that problems were soon encountered. These arose because a whole series of questions which should have been answered before the programme was put in hand were not considered. Apart from the theoretical desirability of standardisation, was there any demand for national standard appliances? Would any undertakings commit themselves to buying national appliances if they were available? How could the industry reconcile the conflicting demands of different undertakings? What design experience could the industry call on that was not already available (and being used) by the makers? How would the industry find answers to intractible technical problems whose existence was already well-known without first commissioning research and waiting for answers to be found? Most crucial of all, was the NGC falling into the error of many technically-driven industries, trying to find a engineering solution to what was essentially a commercial question? Would its efforts merely ossify a backward-looking technology rather than develop new markets?

The NGC blithely assumed that makers would be happy to produce appliances to the national specification for the benefit of all. It announced that it would raise no objection if makers wished to produce their own more expensive proprietary appliances. It is hardly surprising that the appliance makers showed little enthusiasm for this NGC initiative. The NGC did not consult them, either individually or through the SBGI, or even invite their co-operation in a collaborative research effort for mutual advantage. In this, the NGC failed to follow the example of either Germany or America. It is just as well that the British makers were not involved, as it was to prove a frustrating business for all concerned. The cooker was four years in the planning, and appeared a year later than Radiation's New World cookers which were truly innovative and performed far better.

Only a couple of companies actually applied to make the NGC national cooker, which was never a major success although by the end of 1926 14,000 had been sold. This in the words of the *Gas World* hardly demonstrated a 'superabundant enthusiasm' amongst undertakings for such a basic cooker. This level of production represented less than 5% of cookers supplied, clearly falling far short of the hopes cherished when the scheme was first propounded. Even the offer of full or partial enamelling, only available in 1928, four years after the first NGC cookers appeared, did nothing for its popularity.

Despite its representation in the highest councils of the supply industry which had approved the scheme (eg. Institution of Gas Engineers, British Commercial Gas Association and NGC), the GLCC did not purchase the national cooker when it finally reached the market. Large undertakings such as the GLCC were powerful enough to dictate terms to their suppliers and to insist on appliances to their own specification. The first example of this was the GLCC's Horseferry cooker, (named after one of the GLCC's earliest gasworks) and first produced around 1903 to meet the needs of prepayment customers. Various makers tendered for the very large orders in prospect, which were often split between various suppliers. It was an absolute requirement for makers wishing to participate in the programme that all parts should be interchangeable. After GLCC needs had been met, makers were allowed to supply other customers under licence. In 1933 there were still 400,000 old-fashioned Horseferry cookers in use in the GLCC area.

When the decision was taken to provide a replacement, the national cooker was not even considered as a possible option. Two completely new cookers were developed jointly by the GLCC's own laboratories and the makers, Main with whom the GLCC had long had close links. (One of Main's directors, Sir Paul Makins, was the son of a former governor of the GLCC). The GLC '0' and GLC '1' were the result. Both were made with vitreous enamelled steel pressings, the first mass-produced steel cookers to be made in the UK. By 1939 well over half a million GLC '0' and 200,000 GLC '1' cookers had been produced. These were followed in the 1950s by another pressed steel cooker developed jointly with Main, sold in the GLCC area as the 'London' cooker and elsewhere as the Main '20th Century'.

The SMGC took a similarly idiosyncratic line. It had a long tradition of first-rate engineering, first with Livesey and then Carpenter. It had set up its own laboratories in 1912. Its gas was of constant quality. This led Carpenter to design its excellent 'Metro' light fittings without any means of adjustment. The rationale was that it would be impossible for unskilled fitters or customers to tamper with the setting, and risk jeopardising the performance of the light fitting. Later the SMGC followed the same policy with appliances; it had its own Metro appliances made and calibrated at the SMGC depot before installation. On purely technical grounds this was understandable; in marketing terms it was potentially disastrous.

None of the established gas appliance makers were prepared to make cookers to match SMGC specifications; these would have been unsaleable anywhere else where the gas quality differed. Carpenter grumbled publicly at 'the unsympathetic attitude of some manufacturers who cannot be bothered with our exacting requirements'. Consequently in 1920 the SMGC turned to an old-established firm of kitchen range makers, Flavels of Leamington. Flavels, foundrymen established in 1777, made their name with their patent kitchener, exhibited at the 1851 Great Exhibition; this was awarded one of only 17 gold medals awarded with approbation. Between the wars under a new managing director, Percival Flavel, the firm was looking for opportunities to diversify from its traditional coal ranges; a link with a major gas undertaking offered the prospect of a steady flow of large orders. The business relationship suited both parties. The SMGC invested in Flavel financially and technically to ensure that its requirements would be met precisely; indeed in 1928 the SMGC contemplated taking a controlling interest in the firm. For their part Flavels were happy to benefit from SMGC expertise, to produce goods to SMGC specifications and to have SMGC auditors inspect their books to agree prices and profit margins. By the later 1930s orders from the SMGC represented two-thirds of Flavels' business.

One unforeseen aspect of a close relationship between maker and customer was that undertakings were insulated to some extent from market signals. The SMGC was further hindered by the strongly-held opinions of Dr Carpenter, its long-time President (chairman). His comments at SMGC annual general meetings show a gradual softening of attitudes over the years.

In 1923 Carpenter reported:– In this matter one of our difficulties has been to find new manufacturers. We have to find new people who will take up the work and will be content to supply us with the articles which a long experience has told us we require and in accordance with specifications which our experience has qualified us to prepare.

In addition to this, we have to provide methods of research and manufacture such as our competitors enjoy through the splendid equipment provided by the manufacturers of lamps and fittings. We have had to find our own scientific and technical staff whose business it has been to work out the various requirements of gas appliances whether for lighting or heating purposes; and having done the fundamentals we have to set to work to produce them on a large scale. All this work we have had to do ourselves because we cannot depend on getting it done outside.

In 1928:– The consumer has relied on us not only to recommend but in many instances to design and produce the appliances best suited to his requirements. But as these are nearly all hired, we have to maintain them in an efficient condition. Owing to the large capital expenditure involved, changes to improve efficiency have to be made deliberately and carefully or evolution in design might involve greater instead of less expenditure in the long run on the part of the user.

In 1934:– One of the pressing difficulties lies in the fact that many cookers would be better for replacement by more modern types. There are so many changes in the requirements of the public that the standard article which we were in the habit of supplying for many years is not today suited to everybody's tastes and requirements.

By 1936 Carpenter had come to realise that his attitudes were out of touch with the demands of the market:– Somewhat late, I admit, it was realised that mere efficiency only partly interests the public in their domestic requirements and that black cookers and black fireplaces no longer satisfy them, whatever their efficiency may be. We are therefore getting going as rapidly as possible with appliances in which enamels of various tones and colours are drawn upon to make attractive appliances.

Despite the benefits there were also disadvantages in such a close relationship between undertaking and maker. Carpenter's change of heart precipitated a crisis for Flavels. As well as asking for coloured enamels, Carpenter also urged the firm to develop pressed steel appliances to ape those which had been developed collaboratively by Main and the GLCC technical laboratories over several years. Flavel had just invested heavily in additional foundry capacity to make appliances which were now going out of fashion and the firm could not afford more investment. When the SMGC cut back its orders in the late 1930s, from £329,000 in 1936 to £164,000 in 1938 as a result of the widespread political uncertainty, a severe cashflow crisis was precipitated, leading to the suicide of Percival Flavel and the failure and takeover of the firm. Mains, despite their close relationship with the GLCC avoided Flavel's problems. They were old-established makers with a national reputation for quality. They were far less dependent on the GLCC than Flavel on the SMGC.

The first mention of an individual British undertaking taking a scientific interest in the operation of gas appliances as distinct from lighting comes from the GLCC. When the St. Pancras works was closed, the works chemist, J G Clark, was given permission to spend some of his time examining practical problems then being experienced 'on the district', ie. in customers' homes rather than in a test situation. This work was adopted by the gas sales department in 1908 and linked with acceptance testing of appliances as an adjunct to the stores and training functions.

Interest in research within the GLCC was stimulated when Harold Brewer Hartley, a distinguished Oxford chemist, became a director. (He must be distinguished from the Harold Hartley of the Radiation group mentioned above (p. 182)). Hartley's prestige helped to attract several Oxford graduates to the GLCC research staff. [The most distinguished of these was Sir Kenneth Hutchison, FRS (1903-89) who retired in 1966 as deputy chairman of the Gas Council.] A new research laboratory was set up in 1926, named Watson House after David Milne-Watson (1869-1945) the Governor of the GLCC. We are not concerned here with Watson House's work on gas manufacture and distribution, nor the appliance testing and

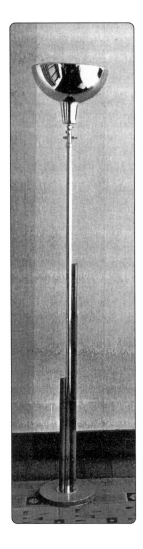

Gaslamps in the latest fashion were still being made in the 1930s.

training of fitting staff which also took place there, only matters which concern the growth of the market for gas. In the early years of Watson House much effort was put into revitalising the gas lighting business, including flood-lighting by gas. The first technical film, in 1932, was on the testing of street lamps. This British pre-occupation with gas lighting surprised foreign visitors. Some years earlier in 1926 the manager of the Munich gasworks reported that 'gas has retained its hold on lighting in England to an extent unknown in Europe... and has practically lost its hold upon America'. Only after a reorganisation in 1930 was more effort devoted to appliances, their testing and development. At this time Watson House was working exclusively for the GLCC, even though a number of senior men in the supply industry had called for the establishment of a national testing centre. At first the GLCC's attitude was ambivalent, not wishing to hinder work by other undertakings independently. A significant change came in 1933. Milne-Watson announced agreement with the National Gas Council (of which he was also chairman), the Institution of Gas Engineers and the British Commercial Gas Association (whose leading lights were GLCC staff) that Watson House should become a development centre for the industry. Other undertakings could subscribe for membership; this would keep them fully informed of the work at Watson House and allow them to make use of its staff and facilities.

At first it was envisaged that only industrial uses of gas would be involved, along the lines of the industrial gas centre set up by Birmingham Corporation in 1910. In 1936 the scope was formally extended to include the domestic use of gas (and gas lighting). By then 76 undertakings were subscribing members. Other major undertakings set up similar groupings for promoting research into the use of gas; these included Birmingham (with 50 subscribers), Cardiff (17), Liverpool (22), Manchester (18), Newcastle (11), SMGC (10) and Yorkshire (51). Bristol and Scottish undertakings were in process of setting up similar centres, which in total covered the supply of almost 70% of gas made in Britain.

The results of Watson House testing were published in the *Watson House Bulletin* from 1931. This at first was restricted to GLCC staff but later went to all subscribers. In this way, despite the absence of formal industry co-operation and nationally agreed standards, reports from Watson House came to be regarded as unofficial industry standards; even undertakings who were not subscribers came to regard them as best practice and would not go against their recommendations. Appliance makers would disregard them at their peril.

The authority which attached to pronouncements from Watson House had disadvantages as well as benefits. Watson House existed primarily as the GLCC's own research centre and its recommendations were geared to the needs and priorities of the undertaking; any wider role was subordinate to its prime function. It thus differed completely from the Karlsruhe Institute or the laboratories of the American Gas Association. These were geared to the needs of the industry as a whole. In the case of the AGA, standards were drawn up jointly by supply industry, makers and government regulatory authorities. This comment should not be construed as a criticism of Watson House standards, which were of the highest order. The criticism is reserved for the possibility that the Watson House system could filter out ideas and innovatory practice which ran counter to GLCC ideas.

Senior members of Watson House presented a paper to the IGE in 1935 making the case for greater collaboration in matters of gas utilisation. Surprisingly however they were opposed to any formal certification system, such as the development of a British Standard. Their argument was that, with the prevalence of hiring (and sale) of appliances, insufficiently robust apparatus would create problems for the undertaking. In their view 'personal judgement based on preliminary tests and general experience is considered sufficient to control this factor'. They pointed out that the Board of Trade seemed satisfied with the periodic reports it received from the industry's Central Gas Advisory Board, or at least had not commented adversely and pressed for change. The *Gas World* appeared to endorse this view with a jingoistic comment.

In other countries supervision of the manufacturers' goods may be desirable or even necessary but conditions in Britain are different... British products have reached such a remarkably high standard that already they fulfil all possible requirements.

It then moderated its tone and reported that the appliance makers would prefer a system of testing acceptable to the majority of undertakings; this would then protect the makers from having to comply with individual engineers' hobby horses.

A few examples of supply industry insularity may be cited. Radiation cookers were designed with a single oven burner which gave a sharp temperature gradient in the oven. This allowed a variety of dishes to be cooked simultaneously and was made a major selling point by the industry. Another maker, Main, considered that two oven burners gave a better performance overall, though without the sharp temperature gradient. Because of the weight given to the sales argument rather than purely performance criteria, Watson House approval required the achievement of this gradient. As virtually all appliances were sold through industry outlets, there was no opportunity for customers to express their preferences. Main had to redesign their ovens if they wished the industry to stock their cookers.

There is today a widespread view that the best cooker would combine a gas hob with an electric oven. In 1928 Parkinson Cowan (P&C) proposed such an appliance to both fuel industries. P&C could have produced dual-fuel appliances as they had made a short (but unsuccessful) foray into the electrical appliance business; they also had a flourishing business making oil lamps and cookers. To avoid any risk of putting their good relations with the gas industry at risk, P&C marketed the dual-fuel concept through a subsidiary company, Charnley Manufacturing, whose great advantage was that its notepaper did not include any names which might link it with P&C . The idea of a dual-fuel appliance was anathema to the gas supply industry, preoccupied as it still was with its struggle to hang on to the lighting market. A similar proposal by Cannon to introduce their Fifti-Fifti cooker in the early 1950s was no more successful. Retailing (and servicing) of cookers was still largely in the hands of the gas and electricity boards; neither was prepared to have anything to do with such a hybrid appliance.

The gas industry was unwilling to contemplate the use of mains electricity on gas appliances even where it might have made technical sense, eg. for controls, timers, thermostats etc. Considerable ingenuity was expended in the 1930s trying to use gas as a universal alternative to electricity for purposes for which it was unsuitable. There was a gas radio relying on gas-heated thermocouples to produce a tiny electric current. Considerable effort was put into outside floodlighting of buildings. The Watson House bulletin illustrates many other curiosities and novelties including a gas-heated drier for ladies' hairdressing salons.

The preoccupation of the industry with its traditional cooker business made it slow to adopt innovations in technology and design. The oven thermostat was in widespread use in the USA before it was introduced by Radiation into Britain. By the late 1920s most American cookers were enamelled in attractive colours and had thermostats. In 1934 in America hotplate ignition was almost universal and clock control for timed cooking in the oven was appearing. These features were still rare in Britain a quarter of a century later.

Even in the early 1930s black paint was still the main finish on new cookers in Britain. The records of Parkinson Cowan show when the shift to enamel occurred, linked to the greater use of pressed steel for cookers.

	Black	Enamelled
1932	61%	39%
1934	19%	81%
1935	8%	92%

Technical backwardness limited the prospects for selling in overseas markets. Between the wars there was a small trade in cast iron cookers to Australia, which had adopted the prepayment supplement concept to a limited extent. Elsewhere there was no market for British appliances, importers looking either to European countries or more especially American firms.

The gas supply industry between the wars

In retrospect the years before 1914 were a golden age for the gas industry. Gas undertakings enjoyed monopoly powers within their own areas. Gas provided cheap and convenient lighting. It provided an alternative to solid fuel for cooking and heating, albeit rather expensive. It was used to power small engines. Regulation was not onerous and undertakings had sufficient latitude in setting prices to achieve satisfactory profits without attracting unwelcome attention from the Board of Trade, the regulator of the industry. Sales were increasing steadily. Gas served a mass market; in 1919 it supplied over 7 million customers. By contrast electricity, despite its convenience, remained far too expensive for all but the wealthiest domestic customers; only half-a-million homes were wired for electricity in 1919. This situation was too favourable to survive long in the post-war years.

Various factors conspired to bring it to a close. These included a changed competitive environment, higher customer expectations, regulatory changes, new technology and problems arising from the fragmentation of the industry. Other factors included the financial effects of appliance trading on undertakings' profitability, examined earlier, and price inflation which was particularly damaging as many charges could not be raised.

Gas would have appeared to considerably less advantage if the electricity supply industry had been been better organised. In London, for example, there were still 70 generating stations in 1914 with a wide variety of systems and controlling authorities. In the years before the war the situation in Britain had been contrasted unfavourably with that in Germany and elsewhere by experts. In many other major cities, Detroit, Boston, Hamburg, Berlin, Paris and others, electric supply had been concentrated into few hands or even a single undertaking. The consequences of legislatively-encouraged fragmentation in Britain were exposed during the 1914-18 war. Shortages of generating capacity hindered the production of munitions. Under wartime conditions the government adopted an interventionist policy, at first under the auspices of the Ministry of Munitions and later through a separate Department of Electricity Supply. After the Armistice the government remained determined that electricity should play as important a role in the economy of the country as it did for its strongest competitors, Germany and the United States. This meant that change in the structure of the electricity supply industry was inevitable; this has been chronicled in Hannah's *Electricity before Nationalisation*.

Regulatory change in energy supply was not exclusive to the electricity industry, but made much less of an impact in the case of gas. Gas was less vital for the modernisation of industry than electricity and it was regarded as a strong and financially sound industrial sector. The economics of gas manufacture and transmission at the time militated against the creation of regional or national gas grids. The PEP report of 1939 reckoned that there were no really substantial economies to be made by increasing the size of manufacturing plant above a minimum of perhaps one million therms per annum, equivalent to the demand in medium-sized towns such as Stoke, Maidstone or Torquay. Similarly long distance transmission over 20 or 30 miles would only be economic for very large quantities, equal to the whole consumption of Glasgow. Away from the large cities, sending gas to small markets even a few miles away was almost always uneconomic. With any gains to be made from amalgamations likely to be modest, it is hardly surprising that the average manager had a parochial outlook. By contrast throughout the inter-war period long-distance transmission of electricity at high voltages was viable, making a national grid possible.

The 1920 Gas Regulation Act made various useful changes in the legislation. It introduced charging for gas on the basis of its calorific value rather than candlepower. This gave recognition to the changes which had taken place in the industry; most lighting was now by mantle (using the heat of gas) rather than open flame (which relied on the luminosity of the gas) and much gas was sold for heating rather than lighting purposes. The Act also facilitated the amalgamation of undertakings (but this still involved an expensive legal procedure) and mutual co-operation including the buying and selling of gas in bulk. This latter power allowed gas undertakings to buy supplies from the coke ovens of the metallurgical industries of the Midlands and North either for direct supply to large industrial customers or for blending with gasworks gas for the generality of customers.

There were further changes in the 1930s. In 1933 the Board of Trade's Gas Legislation Committee commended the concept of holding companies which could provide technical, financial and commercial expertise for small subsidiary undertakings which otherwise could not have afforded access to the best advice from specialist consultants. The

THE OBSTACLE RACE

Not a level playing field!

holding company movement had limited success in the years before 1939 but the advantages it claimed to offer became universally available when the industry was nationalised in 1949 through the twelve regional gas boards. Another recommendation of the Board of Trade's Gas Legislation Committee was incorporated in the Gas Undertakings Act of 1934. This allowed undertakings to offer promotional two-part tariffs similar to those which had proved enormously popular with electricity customers from the mid 1920s on.

There was however one very significant difference between the tariffs offered by gas and electricity. The gas industry never had the right, enjoyed by electricity, to levy a quarterly minimum charge so that the industry could recover the costs of maintaining a supply for customers who used little gas or kept a supply only as a standby for emergencies. Such uneconomic customers could not be shed as the industry had an absolute obligation to supply, and could not pick and choose between applicants. This discrimination between gas and electricity had no basis in logic but was based purely on political calculation. The Parliamentary Secretary to the Board of Trade admitted as much to the Joint Committee on Gas Prices in 1937.

I am not attempting to justify the exclusion of the minimum charge on any ground of logic or technicality. I am doing it entirely on the political argument that the Government are not prepared to face the opposition that would necessarily come from people in scattered places amounting to millions in total, who would never understand the reasons behind a clause of this kind.

It is impossible to quantify the overall cost of such uneconomic customers to the gas industry between the wars when competitive pressures were intensifying. Likewise the loss to the industry because it could not offer promotional tariffs is incalculable, though reason suggests it would have been very large. When contrasting the relative performance of gas and electricity in promoting their energy, it is always as well to remember that in regulatory matters concerning prices and tariffs, gas and electricity were not competing on an entirely level playing field.

It is worth considering why this was so. The importance of electricity in making British industry competitive has already been mentioned. By contrast gas had managed to give the impression of being a monopoly which cared little for the convenience of its customers and was inclined to overcharge for its product. Possibly the industry was disappointed at the relatively little support it received from civil servants and politicians. It should perhaps have done very much more to lobby for support than it did. There were a handful of members of parliament with gas connections; these were largely local politicians from constituencies involved in municipal gas supply rather than senior industrialists or major shareholders from the industry. They did not therefore have a strong voice when gas matters were under discussion. There was nothing to compare with the lobbying capabilities of, say, the railway companies or the brewers. Without a strong parliamentary lobby on which it could call, the industry was thrown back on its own resources. Here it ran into a major problem; there was no single body capable of speaking on its behalf.

The fragmentation of the industry has already been described. Just before the 1914-18 war there were over 800 independent statutorily authorised undertakings, of which a third, being municipally owned, had differing priorities from the privately owned companies, many regarding the supply of gas as a social obligation rather than as a commercial business. This certainly contributed to the persistence of the prepayment supplement and the 'free installation' between the wars, although prepayment installations were as common in private as municipal undertakings. Apart from the statutory private and municipal undertakings, there were a couple of hundred others which operated without statutory powers.

Even if ownership was fragmented, there were other opportunities for collaboration. For engineering matters, undertakings and individual engineers were part of well-developed networks. Gas managers first set up an association as early as 1863; this had over 800 members in the late 1880s and over 1600 in 1936. The gas press was a fount of information, with the *Gas Journal* and *Gas World* both published weekly and understandably giving greater emphasis to engineering than commercial matters. Engineers could also look to senior colleagues or outside consultants if they needed technical support. The masonic lodges exclusively for those with gas interests have already been mentioned.

Common interest in commercial matters was slower to develop. Most undertakings relied heavily on the appliance makers for marketing expertise and, with the almost universal emphasis on hiring rather than selling, saw little need to develop their own commercial skills. The first documented reports of setting up permanent marketing departments come from the two large London companies, the GLCC and SMGC. In the early years of the 20th century within a couple of years of each other they both recruited salesmen and opened showrooms. Unfortunately this did not lead to a common approach to marketing in the industry. Instead there was a long-lasting antipathy between the boards of the two companies, which spread down into the ranks and hindered the development of industry-wide structures which might have given the industry more political clout when it was most needed in the inter-war years.

The rivalry between the two companies had its roots in the last quarter of the 19th century. The GLCC under its capable governor Simon Adams Beck pioneered the building of a large riverside gasworks from which the company was able not only to meet its own needs but to offer cheap bulk

The new Beckton gasworks built on a green-field site.

supplies to its neighbours. The opening of Beckton works in 1870 triggered a spate of amalgamations which increased the GLCC's share of London's gas supply from one seventh to two-thirds at the time of Beck's retirement in 1876. His successors lacked his finesse. The young George Livesey, who at first had been sympathetic to the idea of amalgamation with the GLCC, became disillusioned and instead amalgamated the other South London companies under his SMGC umbrella. He quickly proved himself a more capable engineer and businessman than the leaders of the GLCC of the day. His gas was substantially cheaper. In the light of the public disquiet this caused, the 1898-9 Select Committee on Metropolitan Gas Charges was set up to investigate the higher charges of the GLCC compared to those of other London companies. Livesey's evidence provided a stinging critique of the GLCC's shortcomings. The criticisms were taken to heart and under Corbet Woodall, governor from 1906 until his death in 1916 and more particularly under David Milne-Watson, governor from 1919 until 1945, the GLCC became the unquestioned leader of the British industry, based both on size and technical efficiency.

David Milne-Watson (1869-1945) was the outstanding figure in the industry between the wars and until his death in 1945. He trained as a barrister but joined the GLCC in 1897 and made such an impression in the commercial management of the business that in 1903 he was appointed general manager with responsibility for tariffs, by-products and coal buying (where the GLCC's poor performance had been lambasted by Livesey a few years earlier). One of his first initiatives was to set up a sales department under Francis Goodenough who, as well as recruiting salesmen and opening showrooms, began to promote gas sales through advertising from 1905. Goodenough soon realised that much of the advertising paid for by the GLCC was benefiting other neighbouring undertakings. With Milne-Watson's backing, in 1911 Goodenough established the British Commercial Gas Association (BCGA), an industry-wide body to promote co-operative advertising, discussed later.

Goodenough's success with the BCGA demonstrated that initiative and active leadership could produce results even in an industry as fragmented as gas supply. This paved the way for Milne-Watson to set up and chair other bodies to speak for the industry. The next was the National Gas Council (NGC) in 1919 followed by the National Joint Industrial Council and others. The British Gas Federation set up in 1934 under his presidency brought together the IGE, Gas Companies Protection Association, SBGI, BCGA and NGC. Milne-Watson was widely recognised as the leader and spokesman for the industry; he was knighted in 1927 and received a baronetcy in 1937.

By contrast with the GLCC's high profile, the SMGC remained distinctly parochial in outlook. Livesey's successor in the SMGC was Charles Carpenter, an outstanding engineer. He elucidated the optimum design parameters for Welsbach burners in a brilliant paper to the Institution of Gas Engineers and pioneered a gas purification process to remove organic sulphur, a major cause of appliance corrosion. He was however an autocrat who disparaged the opinions of others. Instead of examining alternative methods of gas manufacture such as the use of vertical retorts for carbonisation or the introduction of the carburetted water gas process, he committed the SMGC to producing a standard high quality of gas of 560 cv, far higher than the industry average, from traditional horizontal retorts. The quality of the SMGC's engineering meant that the standard of gas delivered to customers was unvarying (see p. 187 above). Carpenter had his own Metro lighting fittings and appliances designed and made for SMGC customers; as these had no provision for adjustment they were unsuitable for use anywhere else in the country where different conditions pertained.

Carpenter was unwilling to enter into dialogue with anyone, most particularly anyone from the GLCC. In consequence, despite his efforts to create a sphere of influence based around SMGC practice, he became isolated from the mainstream of the industry which tended to follow the GLCC. It cannot have escaped the notice of those in the Board of Trade responsible for gas matters that any attempts to secure a common front within the gas industry against the threat of electrical competition were doomed to failure as long as in London the leaders of the two largest companies in Britain would not even sit down at the same negotiating table.

Carpenter's autocratic and idiosyncratic ways were by no means unique in the industry. The engineers of even the smallest undertakings had great scope to pursue their own fancies regardless of mainstream opinion in the industry. This meant that many sensible cost-saving measures were never followed up because of the intransigence of a few individualists. A couple of examples are sufficient to illustrate the problem. In the late 19th century and again in the early 1900s the Board of Trade proposed that meter connections should be standardised (as they were in the United States) so that meters from any maker could be used by any undertaking; the suggestion found no support from the industry. There must be a suspicion that some makers and engineers preferred the existing arrangements (which were no doubt financially advantageous for themselves) rather than accepting a free market. Similarly there was an officially-inspired proposal in 1934 that the plethora of different declared calorific values (cv) which ranged between 200 and 625 should be rationalised into a series of steps at 25 cv intervals between 400 and 550 cv. Such a move would have simplified appliance manufacture and adjustment and would have had minimal practical or cost implications for the supply industry, as virtually all undertakings were close to one or other of the proposed steps. Nevertheless it failed to gain acceptance. The debacle over national appliances has already been described.

These examples demonstrate the potential problems to be overcome if a national body to speak for the supply industry were to be set up. Some sectional interests were already catered for. The engineers had their Institution of Gas Engineers. The Gas Companies Protection Association, inaugurated in 1898, existed specifically to safeguard private company interests. The Society of British Gas Industries, established in 1905, provided a forum for makers of plant and appliances. There were long-standing tensions between the SBGI and the IGE. The IGE excluded SBGI members, fearing the 'taint of commercialism might demoralise the proper consideration of scientific problems' and suspected that the SBGI might be a body 'for fixing of prices and the exploitation of purchasers, its members being looked on with suspicion as potential malpractitioners'. The IGE were echoing Adam Smith's sentiments when he said,

People of the same trade seldom meet together, even for merriment and diversion, but that the conversation ends in a conspiracy against the public or the contrivance to raise prices.

Despite the existence of various representative bodies, there was no forum for definitively resolving awkward questions.

What was the impact of electricity in the domestic market, where gas was particularly strong? In 1910 only about one in fifty houses was wired and in 1919 only about one house in twenty. Even as more and more houses were connected, (almost two-thirds of the total housing stock was connected by 1938), competition was at first almost entirely restricted to lighting, as the wiring was not designed to serve other appliances. As late as 1935 the British Electrical Development Association commented that

> Houses were not automatically wired for full use of electricity, ie. over and above lighting purposes. Frequently mains were laid only sufficient for the lighting requirements of the houses.

The fact that only few British homes could use electricity meant that gas lighting was still very important. In the early 1930s lighting accounted for about 15% of all gas made and still 10% in the late 1930s. In America 8% of homes had been wired by 1907 and 34% by 1920; there gas lighting disappeared rapidly.

Just as gas undertakings found customers slow to adopt gas in the 1880s because of the costs of having it installed, this was also a problem for electricity in the 1920s; the cost of a modest electric lighting system was £11-20 in 1919 and still £5-6 in the 1930s. By the mid 1930s twice as many new electric meters were manufactured as gas meters, though because of the near saturation of the market, gas meters would be replacements rather than for new installations. Even the availability of assisted wiring (reminiscent of 'free' gas installations) was not enough to displace gas lighting in many poor urban homes. This meant that for cooking and heating in most homes, there was no serious competition from electricity in the 1920s and for most of the 1930s. Competition came from solid fuel. The first electric cooker was made around 1890 and was as much a curiosity as gas cookers of the mid 19th century. In 1923 there were only 5,000 electric cookers in use although because of the poor image of gas cookers, numbers rose rapidly. By 1931 there were fifteen firms making electric cookers and together they produced 30,000 in that year. By 1939 almost 1.5 million electric cookers had been supplied to the 8 million electric customers. This total was still short of the total of gas customers but as the average consumption per gas customer was beginning to fall, the suspicion must be that some of the additional gas meters being fixed were in subdivided premises rather than representing completely new customers.

By the end of the inter-war period, the price differential in favour of gas had shrunk. Comparisons of cost or relative efficiency between gas and electricity for cooking purposes are not straightforward; they are complicated by the characteristics of the fuel and the way it is used for cooking. For instance, a purpose-designed electric kettle may give better results than a pan of water on a gas cooker burner. Nevertheless, several authors suggest that gas was still cheaper in the late 1930s. A PEP report on the market for household appliances implied tentatively that cooking by electricity was generally more expensive than gas. The main factor holding back the growth of the market in electric appliances was the relative cost of using electricity as against gas in the home. The implication is that, in normal domestic use, gas was cheaper for cooking and heating for most if not all the inter-war years. Cost of course was not the only factor; electricity had other perceived advantages of cleanliness and modernity which helped its penetration of the domestic market. There were also applications where gas could not compete; the vacuum cleaner, the radio and the electric iron which was so much more convenient to use than the clumsy gas

Removes the Hard Work of Ironing

Gas irons were clumsy and heavy.

irons available. As far as room heating was concerned, subjective factors were of less importance for most customers than cost. There, electricity cost perhaps four times as much as coal and twice as much as gas for regular room heating. An American report of 1930 commented,

> Until recently electrical appliances in Great Britain were considered a luxury. When they were not sold as a luxury they were sold as a novelty. In fact the word electric used in describing an appliance seems to have been a synonym for expensive in the minds of the public generally.

The role of Francis Goodenough in the establishment of the British Commercial Gas Association was mentioned above. He was appointed to take charge of the GLCC's newly-formed sales department in 1903. From the outset he was determined to change the perceptions of traditionalist engineers, in particular their dictum that 'dividends are earned in the retort house'. The attitude that only engineering was important had implications for attitudes towards the selling of gas; too many were inclined to think, 'take it or leave it, but if you take it, pay for it first'. In 1907 he carried his campaign to the heart of the enemies' territory, giving a paper to the Institution of Gas Engineers. After describing the GLCC's sales organisation, he proposed that undertakings should combine to sponsor a joint advertising fund which would produce press and poster advertisements and leaflets. This was not an entirely new concept. The American Gas Association set up its own National Commercial Gas Association in 1905, but this did not attract much financial support and had still not begun major national advertising in 1913. The Germans also set up a gas promotion centre around 1910, which prepared advertising literature, provided lecturers and demonstrators and organised exhibitions.

Nothing came of Goodenough's proposal for a joint advertising fund until three years later, when the *Gas World* drew attention to proposals by the Associated Municipal Electrical Engineers of London for a programme of co-operative advertising. In the first instance their undertakings contributed 0.1 per cent of their gross revenue for publicity and the preparation of informative leaflets. By the middle of 1910 their hard-hitting advertisements were appearing. This stirred the Tottenham company to offer to contribute 2s 6d per million cubic feet of gas sold for advertising, guaranteed for 3 years, provided 50 other undertakings would do the same; this was roughly equivalent to the electricians' 0.1 per cent. The *Gas World* took a cynical view; it was unlikely that British undertakings would combine for the common good.

> Show the followers of a British trade that combined action...
> would be to their advantage and you are yet as far as the
> poles are asunder from persuading anyone to move a finger.
> Point out a private profit and they are all on it like bees
> round a sugar hogshead. Co-operative effort in
> manufacturing or marketing is repugnant to the British spirit
> and no foreign examples serve to commend it.

Despite some initial reluctance and fears that municipal undertakings in particular would be unwilling to subscribe at that level, the initiative was approved by the Institution of Gas Engineers in May 1911; participation was of course voluntary. Even so, the idea was not universally welcomed.

Dr Carpenter of the SMGC wished to draw a distinction between publicity, which he supported, and advertising, which he did not; he thought the level of subscription deemed essential by the publicity committee was unnecessarily high. Others stood aloof to watch the progress of the scheme. The committee noted a 'current of vituperative misrepresentation' with which their actions were met. Nevertheless they decided to press ahead. The British Commercial Gas Association was formed in 1911 under the auspices of the IGE. Support was promised by 201 undertakings and the Society of British Gas Industries promised financial support from the makers. The SMGC finally joined in 1913.

During its first year the BCGA produced 700,000 leaflets and brochures, attracted 3,000 enquiries from its advertisements and started a regular bulletin for subscribers; total expenditure was around £12,500. The greatest testimonial to the effectiveness of the BCGA came from the *Electrical Review*, which compared the puny efforts of the electrical industry at advertising with the BCGA Frankenstein.

> The support which they are in a position to give to the electricity supply industry in combating the activities of the monster will be as serviceable as a pea-shooter in the hands of a man opposed to an adversary armed with a Mauser pistol.

Gas was not only cheaper than electricity;

> the apparatus can be hired, and the gas company's officials take an intelligent interest in what (the customer) is doing. They prove to him that they really want him as a customer. The exact opposite is too often the case where electricity is concerned.

Ironically this was the same criticism that had often been levelled at the gas industry.

At the end of its second year the BCGA had over 400 subscribing members representing over three quarters of UK gas output. The main emphasis of its advertising effort was devoted to water heating. It received thousands of responses to its advertisements. Unfortunately many of these were from individuals who had been unable to get any information from their local undertaking. As Goodenough said,

> Judging by some of the evidence, it would seem as if some managers even resent having business created for them,

whether because it involves the trouble of supplying the demand or because they think it is a reflection upon their own enterprise, it is difficult to say.

Sales of BCGA literature continued to rise, ultimately to 6 million items a year. A new periodical publication, *A Thousand and One Uses for Gas*, was introduced, aimed especially at non-domestic industrial and commercial customers. Campaigns were masterminded to inform and influence professional people, doctors, architects and so on. Virtually all undertakings in the country were subscribers.

It must be questioned whether the BCGA was in fact a marketing organisation or rather, a public relations office. At its meetings and in many talks by Goodenough, the importance of salesmanship was emphasised. However when he spoke about the activities of the BCGA it is clear that he was concerned more about the dignified dissemination of general information than masterminding hard-hitting campaigns. He talked about supplying editorial matter to be offered for inclusion in local papers and advertising matter suitable for concert or theatre programmes, in church or chapel magazines and so on.

The BCGA reinforced local sales campaigns; on the lorry are cookers, fires, a geyser, irons and gaslights.

Goodenough claimed that the BCGA
has never taken up an aggressive attitude. It has always
sought to be rather pro-gas than anti-electricity or anti-
anything, believing that it is soundest commercial policy to
talk about your own goods rather than to criticise your
competitors.

Goodenough did not restrict his activities to the gas industry. He
became president of the Incorporated Sales Managers' Association and
also of the Incorporated Society of British Advertisers. He was closely
involved in educational schemes for technical and commercial staff and
the development of scientific skills in management and selling. When the
Board of Education set up a committee on education for salesmanship in
1928, Goodenough was appointed chairman; he received a knighthood in
1930.

The symbol adopted by the industry was the versatile and friendly
figure of Mr Therm, designed by the commercial artist Eric Fraser in
1931-2 as a rush job for the GLCC's advertising agents. He displaced the
unmemorable 1920s image of Mr G A Service. This was at a time when
the industry was increasingly concerned at competition from electricity.
Mr Therm was quickly adopted as a universal promotional symbol by
other companies and for national advertising by the BCGA. His slogan,
'**Mr Therm burns to serve you**' was almost as memorable as the character
himself. Fraser was paid five guineas for his original drawing and when he
sought further payment for the widespread use of his image, he was given
another 25 guineas; this was for one of the most long-lived and
memorable of all
advertising images,
probably surpassed
only by the Michelin
man who dates from
1898. Mr Therm
was finally retired
from national
advertising in 1962
to be replaced by the
'High Speed Gas'
flame motif. Mr
Therm was instantly
recognisable,
homely, amusing and

Mr Therm.

versatile; he generated great public goodwill. In the words of *Advertising World*, 'this advertising is of the welcome rather than the intrusive kind'.

The electricians took a different approach to promotional activities and marketing, according to the *Gas World*. They did not leave electricity to speak for itself. They were aggressive in their salesmanship and were quite happy to disparage gas as a fuel, quoting comparative costs which perhaps would not stand up to impartial scrutiny. By contrast the gas industry, attempting to portray a dignified image, only managed to look stuffy and old-fashioned, and gave the impression that it was unable to rebut the claims of electricity. Certainly it had nothing with which to counter the simple appeal of an all-electric house, promoted by the electricians. In the public mind, gas was on the defensive, a Victorian relic that would wither away. There can be no doubt that the efforts of the gas industry in the 1930s to retain the lighting load, when the advantages of electricity were established beyond doubt, reinforced this perception. In addition, the industry's emphasis on hiring old appliances would put off upwardly mobile families wanting the best for themselves.

The gas industry often failed to portray itself in the most favourable light. It liked to use statistics of relative performance and cost, which might possibly interest men, rather than attacking the domestic market from the women's point of view as the electricians did. The Electrical Association for Women (EAW) was set up in the late 1920s to provide a social framework within which women could inform themselves on the tremendous changes taking place around them, particularly those associated with electricity. The EAW was strongly backed by the Electrical Development Association; lectures and demonstrations were arranged to 'educate' the members and, by word of mouth and example, the general public. A correspondent in the *Gas World* in 1933 described the response of the gas industry to the EAW as 'petrified apathy'! There was no talk of setting up a competing women's organisation with gas as its driving force. The EAW had managed to attract an air of social superiority, with several titled ladies as members; perhaps the gas equivalent should concentrate on the common housewife? If the gas industry failed to put over its case, it gave the impression that it was unable to rebut the case for electricity.

Needless to say, nobody took up the cudgels; the gas industry seemed preoccupied with defence rather than attack, and concerned more with the low first cost of appliances than meeting customer wishes. In conventional marketing wisdom, this policy of inertia and short-termism was madness, despite the much greater penetration of gas in the domestic cooker market. In the mid 1930s there were perhaps fifteen gas cookers in use for each electric cooker. However by 1938 one-and-a-half million electric cookers had been supplied. Once again the gas industry, mindful of past success, was resting on its laurels.

By the mid 1920s the consensus amongst senior gas managers for appliance subsidies was beginning to crumble. David Fulton of Helensburgh pointed that the real test of a policy of subsidy was not the number of cookers supplied but the return on capital employed and the effect on the price of gas. By these criteria he had seen nothing to suggest that the free cooker policy had resulted in cheapening the cost of gas. Indeed he feared that customers would not appreciate an appliance they did not pay for, would not keep it clean and would not take care of it. Some customers took cookers only because they were free. 'It is not unknown for a consumer to have a gas cooker simply because the next-door neighbour has one, and after getting it, use the hot-plate only, the oven being a useful store cupboard for boots or firewood or vegetables'. Free issue was no longer justifiable.

Predictably the comments on his paper fell into three groups;

* the supporters of free appliances and installation. The Dundee municipal undertaking was a notable exponent of this approach. There they took the view that the majority of their customers were poorly paid and would prefer a reasonable all-in service. They recognised that such a policy would not be appropriate in wealthier areas. Scottish municipal undertakings tended to provide the cheapest possible gas tariffs; unlike some English municipal undertakings, they did not consider making contributions in aid of rates an important policy objective.

* those who favoured hiring, with charges set to recover as much as possible of capital and service costs. This included the GLCC and SMGC and probably the majority of managers.

* those who, with Fulton, believed the appliance business should be fully self-supporting.

The *Gas World* hoped that Fulton's paper would stimulate an industry-wide debate on this important topic but was disappointed.

The two large London undertakings were still wedded to the concept of hire. Carpenter's paternalistic attitudes were matched in the GLCC at least until the later 1920s. The 'settled policy of the GLCC for many years past' was to offer cookers, fires and water heaters on simple hire, according to Stephen Lacey, its Distribution Engineer, speaking in 1927. Lacey actually wanted 'to prevent the manufacture, sale and installation of gas appliances by those whose only concern is to make quick profits'. Goodenough thought that many undertakings preferred hiring to hire purchase, both for their own benefit and that of the customer. Others were beginning to take a different view. The municipal undertaking in Birmingham decided in 1923 to switch away from simple hire towards hire purchase; there was no special advertising but customers were weaned away from an expectation of hiring towards purchase. In 1929 Newcastle adopted the same policy. Burnley favoured hiring only for wash boilers and sold most appliances on HP. Manchester inaugurated its sales department in 1929, even though in the words of its commercial manager, 'at its inception [it] meant fighting our own "free" service'; free appliances were still available on request.

It was only in the early 1930s that the main opinion formers in the supply industry began to turn against hiring, or at least, hiring of appliances which gave the industry a poor image in the minds of the public. A correspondent in the *Gas World* in 1934 emphasised the importance of getting rid of old black cookers. They were

> out of joint with fashion and desire... It seems a queer turn of fortune's wheel that the undertakings which displayed most enterprise in past days by affording consumers the privilege of simple hire and... "soaked" the districts with black cookers before those of more pleasing appearance had been made dependable should have to suffer.

The writer almost implies that this is the fault of the makers. He proposed that the makers might give the smaller and more backward undertakings the same favourable trade terms available to larger undertakings as an inducement to replace all old hired cookers. Some such offer was necessary to 'tempt conservative undertakings out of their somnolence'. In the words of David Milne-Watson to the National Gas Council in 1934, 'Ruthless scrapping may appear, at the time, to be expensive but it will undoubtedly repay handsomely those who undertake it'. He practiced what he commended to others. These words were spoken just as the GLCC began introducing its pressed steel GLC '0' and '1' cookers to replace the thirty-year old Horseferry and other obsolete cast iron cookers. During 1935, 92,000 old cookers were replaced and a total of 364,000 new cookers were supplied.

Some incentive was certainly desirable for the weaker undertakings, most of whom were small and with very restricted financial resources. The option of a major replacement programme such as the GLCC's was not available to smaller, less financially strong undertakings. The manager of the small Basingstoke undertaking, for example, gave a paper describing how he rebuilt cookers, using his own employees; 'the intelligent worker can quite easily do the work'. Other undertakings did similar work. The following comment, made in 1929, suggests the extent and persistence of the general problem.

> Many works had less than 30% of their consumers using cookers before the [1914-18] war. On the other hand there were companies which embarked on the cooker campaign and had up to 60% of their consumers with cookers at that time. Now they are paying the penalty for forging ahead – ahead of their time. They now have little scope for introducing cookers of modern design, and are loaded with a load of rather antiquated cookers still too good to scrap. We are still waiting for a really cheap cooker suitable for free fixing but capable of standing up to hard work for a reasonable working life.

This comment was made by an Irish manager but applied equally to small British undertakings.

The inefficiency of many old appliances had been specifically noted by an official enquiry in 1923.

> We are not satisfied that gas appliances now in use, many of which have been in service for twenty years and upwards, are in all cases as satisfactory as can be desired for the economical consumption of gas. It appears to us desirable that gas undertakings should be required to test all fittings supplied by them with a view to the rejection of those that are inefficient.

Despite this official critical comment, some smaller undertakings were only just beginning, by the 1930s, to provide lagged instead of uninsulated cookers. The makers obviously wanted to sell modern appliances but some undertakings even actively discouraged their efforts. In 1934 Benham, a maker of commercial catering equipment, contrasted the attitude in one town where he received every assistance with another where 'the gas company was as difficult as possible and did its utmost to disparage our fittings'. Elsewhere 'we get nothing but opposition from the gas company, who say we are taking away the orders from them'.

There were some attempts to promote major replacement programmes. The *Gas World* proclaimed,

> There are millions of old fashioned cookers which should be replaced by the better modern type, either by direct sale or

through a hire-purchase arrangement... This would bind [customers] more firmly to gas cooking.

Nevertheless, the old black cookers survived beyond 1939 in huge numbers. The claims by the makers that the cookers supplied for prepayment customers were almost indestructible were borne out in practice; many of them were still in use when the industry was nationalised in 1949 (one estimate suggests one cooker in two was an old black one) and some even survived until natural gas conversion between 1967 and 1977. The newly nationalised Area Boards were acutely aware of the poor image conveyed by these relics from the distant past; they did all they could to replace them with something more modern. All but one of the twelve Area Boards refer to this problem in their first two reports, 1949-50 and 1950-51. Some do not make the distinction between appliances issued to prepayment supplement customers and those on 'free' hire; numbers of hired appliances may include either or both black and enamelled cookers and other appliances, eg. gas fires.

The gas industry did not only have to consider competition in terms of the price and performance of its appliances or the desirability of continuing its policy of subsidised hire. There was a more insidious challenge. Politicians were beginning to look to electricity, with its perceived potential to improve life for ordinary voters, as the fuel of the future. In the years after the 1914-18 war, despite its negligible penetration of the domestic market at that time, its convenience and modernity made it a useful symbol of a hopeful bright post-war world. According to David Milne-Watson in 1918, 'apparently the Government and the Labour Party had taken electricity as a plank in their platform'. He led a deputation to the President of the Board of Trade, Sir Auckland Geddes, to protest at the eulogistic references to electricity in the government's post-war reconstruction programme, which suggested that the adoption of electricity in the home was to the national advantage; all he achieved was a promise from Geddes that the gas industry would not be 'pushed to the wall'.

Herbert Morrison, Leader of the London County Council, was another early supporter of electricity, leaning over backwards to give tenants the opportunity to choose electricity for cooking as well as lighting in LCC flats. His advocacy of electricity had its roots in the battle of the LCC to bring some order into London's electricity supply. This battle was complicated by political rivalries, the conflict of municipal traders with the apostles of market forces and free enterprise (although of course there was demonstrably little scope for competition and the operation of the 'invisible hand' of the market where monopoly powers had been granted). When he was appointed Minister of Transport (with responsibility for the electricity industry) in 1929 he continued to proclaim his support for electricity and campaign actively for its adoption for lighting and heating.

> It is my duty, as one politically responsible for the electrical industry, to further its interests in every possible way if it is for the national good that I should do so. I do not agree that harm is being done to the gas industry.

A couple of years later he was reported as wishing to see electricity in every home for lighting and heating. Ellen Wilkinson, trade unionist and MP, was apocalyptic in her support; 'Women have now got votes and electricity... When I was working to get that vote I was sure these were the twin keys to women's Earthly Paradise'.

Apart from the political bandwagon, the gas industry was also under threat from another quarter. Some local authorities who controlled their own municipal electricity undertakings but not the gas supply were prepared to use openly discriminatory tactics to keep gas out of council property. The Ilford municipal electricity undertaking attempted to introduce a tariff offering lower rates to premises lighted throughout by electricity. In fact the council was forced to withdraw it as it was deemed to be showing undue preference and therefore *ultra vires* under the Electric Lighting Acts. This tariff may well have been introduced to counter earlier aggressive tactics by the Ilford Gas Company, which refused to install a prepayment meter and cooker in homes with electric lighting, unless the customer also requested the installation of several gas lights. The Woolwich Corporation included a condition in the tenancy agreement for a newly developed estate (Well Hall, Eltham) that tenants should not use gas for any domestic purpose. As owners of the estate, the Corporation even refused at first to dedicate the roads as public highways, thus depriving the SMGC of its statutory right to lay mains in the streets. Sheffield, Liverpool and Barnsley insisted that their tenants should use (municipal) electricity rather than gas from a private company. In Cardiff, Fulham and Tilbury, tenants were threatened with eviction if they did not use electric lighting. If municipal gas undertakings used the same tactics, they were not reported in the gas press.

Lobbying by the gas industry was occasionally successful. When the Newport (Mon.) Corporation sponsored a Bill in parliament, representations by the gas company were successful in ensuring that the

Corporation was not permitted to impose any condition on the form of light or heating used by its tenants. A similar threat in Kettering was also warded off.

The threat of unfair competition was becoming so widespread in the late 1920s that the National Gas Council with trade union support lobbied the Ministry of Health. The deputation was rebuffed; it was 'the practice of the Ministry in the past not to interfere in questions of this character but to leave municipal authorities a free hand'. The NGC pressed for a clause in the Housing Bill under consideration in 1930 to prevent discrimination in any scheme enjoying aid from public money; about 80,000 of the 1.5 million houses built since the war were affected. The clause was opposed by the Minister of Health, Arthur Greenwood, and defeated. 'Nobody' he said 'wished to have gas for lighting where electricity was available, and it is the customary thing to permit gas for heating and cooking'. Gradually the threat of exclusion by municipal diktat receded, as politicians came to realise that electricity was not cheap; nor was it producing the benefits that its more enthusiastic advocates had claimed. Early in 1931 the LCC abandoned its policy, dating back some 8 years, of forbidding the use of gas in some of its estates. Henceforward tenants would have complete freedom of choice. Finally the Board of Trade inserted a similar clause in the Gas Undertakings Bill of 1934 to cover the whole country. This policy survived the war. In 1946 the Ministry of Health issued a circular to all housing authorities asking that estates should be serviced by both gas and electricity, with full freedom of choice for tenants.

These references confirm the view that the gas industry was less well served by the Board of Trade (BoT) than electricity was by its sponsoring departments. 'The organisation of the BoT for dealing with the problems of the gas industry... was notably small'. The BoT had no powers to (or interest in) treating the industry 'as a coherent whole rather than an aggregation of scattered and unconnected undertakings'. As the *Gas Journal* remarked in 1920,

> In past years it has been very difficult... to effect statutory changes. Parliament has hitherto been very conservative in its treatment of the industry; there has been a cold insensitivity and obdurateness on its part to scientific progress and change in the requirements of the community and strong reluctance to make departures from precedent.

These attitudes persisted throughout the inter-war period; a 1937 report commented thus:

Even well-informed public opinion was to a great extent influenced by the impression that the gas industry was dying and would soon be superseded by electricity. The Gas Regulation Act of 1920 did not represent any breach with the traditional policy and the BoT limited itself to the enforcement of the legislation relating to the industry.

The lack of dynamism in the Board of Trade had implications for the appliance market in one particular respect, the lack of promotional (eg. two-part) tariffs. The report cited above went on to say that there was no generally accepted system of price-fixing throughout the industry, other than supply on a flat rate. In 1945 the Ministry of Fuel & Power reported that three quarters of the 800 undertakings were still on flat rate. Promotional tariffs might have substantially enlarged the market for gas fires and water heaters. Because of the way the market for appliances grew, small customers tended to benefit at the expense of large customers.

By an examination of the records by one Undertaking [probably the GLCC] it has been found that 90% of the whole of consumers are not paying their full share of charges, which, of course, means that the balance of 10% representing large and mostly industrial consumers are carrying unfair burdens. The gas undertakings in many cases are therefore severely handicapped in competing for industrial business which economically should be theirs. The Industry feels that it should be given greater freedom in its methods of charge...

Some of the problems of the gas industry were linked with the BoT's attitudes to regulation; others were firmly in the court of the supply industry itself. In the words of the *Gas World* in 1934 there was a tendency to treat the [electrical] challenge with contempt.

[The gas industry] has worked out the cost figures and finds them so much to its liking that it is once again inclined to sit tight and let the other fellow do his worst. Gas cannot afford to commit another blunder of that kind if the progress of gas in the past fifty years is to be repeated in the fifty years which lie ahead.

If attitudes among gas engineers were wrongheaded, was there anything the makers could do? This will now be examined.

Between the wars;
the appliance makers

It is clear from the last chapter that, between the wars, the supply industry wished to play the dominant role in the appliance business, controlling both the types of appliances to be supplied and the terms of trade. This was a major turnaround from the attitude of the majority of undertakings before 1914, when they were happy to leave most aspects of marketing to the makers. Between the wars paternalistic attitudes of undertakings towards their customers were widespread, taking no account of what customers might actually want. In Portsmouth in 1927, for example, the company had been pushing the hiring of appliances rather than the sale of them because they felt they had greater control under the hire system. It was admitted that a company had not got the same authority over sold appliances as they had over those sent out on hire... there was a tendency for appliances to be neglected and that did not bring the undertaking new business.

In Stalybridge in 1930 the gas undertaking actually arranged demonstrations featuring renovated cookers, to persuade customers that they did not need new ones!

Before 1914 it was the makers who had generally taken the lead in managing showrooms and exhibitions, employing salesmen and fitters, and advertising their products. Between the wars showrooms operated by makers were few and far between as the supply undertakings opened their own. R & A Main opened a Dublin showroom in 1930 in premises leased from the undertaking; this was still operating in 1946. Main's Bristol showroom was closed in 1920. When Main proposed to open a new showroom there in 1930 there was such opposition from the local undertaking that the idea was dropped. Radiation had a showroom in Nottingham which was taken over by the Corporation in 1936, shortly after the discovery of corruption in the Nottingham Gas Department. Relations between the company and the corporation were strained.

As the management of gas and appliance marketing at large exhibitions such as the British Industries Fair, Ideal Home Exhibition, Building Trades Exhibition and Smoke Abatement Exhibition was largely centralised under the British Commercial Gas Association, and undertakings were employing their own sales staff and sometimes appointing ironmongers as local sales agents, there was less need for makers to employ a large sales staff themselves. They did however provide support where they could for specific sales functions. For example, R & A Main appointed their first demonstrator in 1927 and a second in 1930. A first travelling showroom was bought in 1930 and a second in 1933. No doubt this would have been manned by a team of canvassing representatives. Main certainly employed canvassers. Main also provided technical support where necessary, including lectures to gas audiences, who often had no other ready source of up-to-date and authoritative technical information. No doubt the other makers used similar sales support methods, although documentary evidence is missing. As far as is known, no makers were engaged in fitting work between the wars. Larger undertakings at least were by then building up and training their own labour force; they were also repairing and in some cases making some of their own meters; most smaller undertakings were still largely reliant on private gasfitters.

In general the makers' trade association, the Society of British Gas Industries discouraged member firms from providing excessive support to individual undertakings. It refused to co-operate with any professional exhibition organisers. Where undertakings wished to arrange an exhibition, the SBGI's recommendations to its members were: to lend goods for exhibition, supply ordinary literature and arrange for attendants and demonstrator only. All other expenses were to be paid by the promoter. As regards canvassing, 'while it was not practical to entirely dispense with canvassing, a strong desire was expressed that it should be discouraged as far as possible'. Where undertakings invited makers to bear part of the costs of local advertising, the recommendation was that makers should never bear more than 60% of the cost.

Individual makers made substantial investments in advertising between the wars. Main budgeted to spend around £8,000 each year from 1928-32, rising to an average of £20,000 from 1933-38. This expenditure was a major increase on the £1,000 campaign planned with the help of Benson's agency in 1911. Main's expenditure was surpassed by the promotional activities of H James Yates, chairman of John Wright & Co and later Radiation. Wright spent over £10,000 in 1913 and the Radiation group spent £52,000 in the second six months of 1935.

The pioneering work of Radiation with its New World cookers mentioned earlier was soon copied by other makers, with their own designs. This, followed by the adoption of pressed steel technology, made British appliances more like German or American cookers. Where necessary, British makers imported new technologies, for example Parkinson & Cowan bought rights to an American wet enamelling process and American thermostats for gas and electric cookers. Perhaps surprisingly, the changing market for appliances in the UK did not attract any serious interest from continental or American appliance makers. There was certainly a market for some German products, Kromschröder Perfecta thermostats, self-priming pumps, baths, anthracite stoves but not apparently for appliances. There was one major exception, the phenomenal success of Junkers water heaters, later sold in Britain as Ascot water heaters. The history of Ascot water heaters cannot be separated from the career of Dr Bernard Friedman. Friedman was a vigorous entrepreneurial character with a strong technical background and an international perspective. As his obituary in the *Gas World* remarked,

> There is no doubt that the difficult introduction of new and almost revolutionary types of appliances to an industry always conservative in the best interests of its customers, proved a stern test of the tenacity and perseverance of this remarkable man in the first few years.

By the end of the 19th century Junkers (the firm later made aircraft) had established a reputation in Britain for high quality instruments, calorimeters etc. The firm also made appliances but had been unsuccessful in their attempts to interest British undertakings in their water heaters, radiators and cookers. They lost their UK market in 1914 but by 1920 were keen to re-establish themselves in the largest European market for gas apparatus. At first they relied on an agent in Coventry; this arrangement proved unsatisfactory and in 1927 the agency was transferred to someone with whom the firm had previously done business.

Dr Bernard Friedman came from Latvia, where his father was governor of the State Bank in Riga. After a visit to England to learn the language, he went to Moscow, where he designed new types of gas burners for cookers and water heaters and set up a flourishing business; he held the Russian agency for Junkers appliances. In the revolution he lost everything and decided in 1926 to move to London to re-establish himself. Friedman requested and was given the Junkers agency for Britain and the Empire; Junkers considered there might also be a market for gas cookers and introduced Friedman to the firm of Senking, a large German maker. Crucial to the success of Friedman's import agency, Cookers and Geysers Ltd, was the support he received from German firms, especially

Junkers but also Senking and Kromschröder.

There can be no doubt of the scale of the problems faced by Friedman when he first attempted to sell Junkers appliances. He was a Latvian/ Russian with a strong accent, which remained with him to the end of his life. He was selling technically advanced German appliances less than ten years after the end of the war at a time when anti-German feelings were running strongly. Some advertisements of the time inviting tenders for gasworks equipment specifically stated that British makers would be favoured. Added to this was the innate conservatism of many senior managers in the UK gas industry, accustomed to dealing with well-known makers. These included Ewart, an old-established firm which supplied traditional copper geysers, and Radiation who supplied storage water heaters.

At first Friedman found it almost impossible to sell German appliances. Senking gave up their attempt to sell cookers but Friedman proposed to Junkers that their heaters should be assembled in the UK to avoid import tariffs. Junkers & Co (Great Britain) Ltd was incorporated in May 1929 as a wholly owned subsidiary under Friedman's management. In the following year it began assembly of water heaters from Junkers components in a small factory in south London, previously used by Kromschröder. In an attempt to overcome anti-German prejudice, Friedman's girlfriend suggested that the name of the business should be changed. The tiny factory was renamed the Ascot Geyser Works. From then on, Junkers appliances appeared under a quintessentially British upper-class cachet. Despite this, orders were very slow in coming. When the SMGC came to visit the firm to inspect its methods of production, Friedman took on another half dozen men for the day to make the place look busy. The outcome was the firm's first significant order, for 500 sink water heaters. Shortly afterwards, the GLCC placed an order. Once Ascot appliances had been accepted as satisfactory by these two companies, no further credentials or recommendations were necessary; Ascot appliances were acceptable to any undertaking in the UK.

Friedman had to tread a delicate balance with his gas industry customers. If he was to keep in good standing with the largest companies he had to give the appearance of dealing primarily with gas undertakings, while leaving himself leeway to sell direct to builders' merchants, architects etc. Smaller undertakings made no problems as he gave them commission on all the orders he booked. One early problem was the German origin of his appliances. The Ascot name did not deceive British gas industry customers. Friedman reported to his board in 1932 that 'he had given his promise to some of the principal concerns in the gas industry that the manufacture of the goods supplied should ultimately be entirely within this country'. Junkers responded by building a brand new model factory designed for mass production and equipped with the most up-to-date plant and machinery. The new Ascot facory was opened in 1934; within a year it was producing 4,000 heaters a month, more, in fact, than Junkers in Germany.

Ascot water heaters were designed with both appearance and performance in mind. They were a far cry from their geyser predecessors such as Ewart were making. A telling anecdote of what these were like comes from Stirling Everard, historian of the GLCC. On a visit to London before he had anything to do with the GLCC he stayed at a boarding house which boasted the first bathroom geyser he had ever seen. On it were two notices. One proclaimed it was the property of the GLCC; the other merely said DANGER without specifying its nature or how it might be avoided. Everard's geyser was probably the typical copper cylinder with spout, knobs and taps, often unsightly with verdigris, whose design had changed little since Maughan made his original geyser in 1868. At first Friedman advertised his Ascots as geysers, until a gas manager pointed out the negative image conveyed by the word. Friedman adopted his suggestion that Ascots should thenceforth be described as water heaters.

By contrast with knobbly geysers, all the operating parts of the Ascot were concealed under a gleaming white enamel case. The differences between the Ascot and the geyser were not only skin-deep. When the case was removed, the Ascot was designed for easy servicing; it could be dismantled easily by the fitter either in part or completely. This was illustrated in a *Gas World* article and photo juxtaposed with another article referring to the problems of fitters attempting to service other geysers, with the tart comment

> Most of the trouble in connection with the maintenance of geysers is due to the impossibility of getting at the essential places, such as burner and condensation gutter, for cleaning purposes.

The GLCC suggested that Ewart should provide enamelled cases for their geysers but the firm was not prepared to make the necessary investment.

As the technology of Ascots was so much more advanced than that of geysers, Friedman realised that gas industry personnel would have to be educated to install and maintain Ascots correctly if they were to work efficiently. He and his son Leopold lectured extensively and wrote many technical and practical papers for gas industry groups. Factory visits were welcomed and courses were run for gas fitters (and their supervisors). This emphasis on education echoes the Dessau tradition. Dessau had been the German gas industry's centre for training fitting and supervisory staff since around 1900. The firm of Junkers, based in Dessau, would know this well. Even during the 1939-45 war Ascot continued to provide instruction, not only on technical matters but also on sales organisation, commercial management and general publicity.

What distinguished the selling of Ascots from other brands of water heater was that Friedman went out of his way to find new outlets to sell his heaters; possibly he was disappointed at the discouraging response of gas undertakings when he first approached them. Apart from resistance on purely chauvinistic grounds, Friedman had to overcome other problems. His instantaneous water heaters needed large gas and water inlet pipes to produce their high output of hot water; the Ascot typically used twice as much gas per minute as a Ewart geyser (and four or five times as much as a gas fire or a gas cooker). Both gas and water undertakings feared that such appliances might expose the inadequacies of their distribution networks. Some water authorities introduced bye-laws specifically intended to prevent the connection of appliances such as Ascots. The Radiation group, while innovative in cookers and fires, concentrated on making low-rated storage water heaters and did not encounter the same objections from undertakings.

Builders or architects wanted a cheap and efficient method of water heating for the huge numbers of houses being built for the speculative market in the 1930s. The Ascot met the need and was sold direct to builders themselves and to architects who could specify Ascot in new houses. Friedman had the idea of writing a book, *Gas, The National Fuel; Its Uses for Domestic Water Heating* specifically aimed at architects and builders; it was lavishly illustrated and appeared in 1935; no less than 15,000 copies were produced. It included a chapter by a consulting engineer on the relative costs of gas, coal, oil and electricity in the home and another by Friedman on the virtues of instantaneous water heating. The rest of the book provided plans and photos of developments where Ascots had been specified. These range from flats for the Shoreditch Housing Association to Chelsea mews houses and the Junior Carlton Club in Pall Mall. The emphasis is clearly on demonstrating that Ascots are sufficiently versatile to be used anywhere. The photographs have the (perhaps unintended) effect of showing a sharp contrast between the smooth white case of the Ascot and the traditional cookers and wash boilers (and even gas lighting) supplied on hire by the gas undertaking.

By doing their own aggressive selling, Ascot were only returning to the situation of the 1890s when all active promotion was undertaken by the makers for passive undertakings. By the mid 1930s Ascot was very profitable and other makers began to look at the opportunities in this long-established market which had been revitalised by Ascot. Ewart, for so long the market leader in the old copper geysers, made no major changes; it considered importing a Belgian water heater but did not

The modern exterior of these flats (left) in Peckham, south London, contrasts with the old-fashioned look of the kitchen (below right) with its gas lighting, cookers, wash copper and smart Ascot water heater. The SMGC had its headquarters in Peckham.

(below left) This kitchen in a 1934 council-built flat in London has a large Ascot to serve bath and sink, a gas-heated wash copper and a GLCC rented cooker.

proceed with this. It had missed the boat. After making substantial profits for most of the inter-war period Ewart buckled under the pressure of Ascot competition and was taken over by Ascot in the mid 1950s. R & A Main bought a small water heater firm, Omnia Water Heaters of Croydon, and put much research effort into developing their own water heaters. Radiation forged a link with another German firm, Askania, and supplied their instantaneous water heaters under the Radiation name. Radiation's main interest remained in storage heaters, even after 1945.

Although Ascot's British credentials were fully established by the mid 1930s, the firm was still wholly foreign-owned; more seriously, it still relied on Junkers for its advanced technology. A hardcore of senior technical staff were German and imported components represented a substantial portion of output, gradually declining from 35% in 1935 to 13% in 1938. At first this did not matter overmuch but after the Munich crisis the board was forced to take action to emphasise the Britishness of the firm. The five remaining Germans were given notice and plans were made to make in the UK those few components still imported from Dessau. Application was made to the Board of Trade for permission to label Ascot products 'British Made'. Early in 1939 and to emphasise the firm's patriotism, its modern factory was offered to the government for the production of munitions. Until his death in 1941, Ascot was Bernard Friedman's creation. In the words of a *Gas World* obituary,

> He brought new ideas to bear, employing new business methods and obtaining orders which, though so badly needed by the industry, had been allowed to lay(sic) dormant for so long. He had a vision of greater things to come.

When the first amalgamations to form the Radiation group took place in 1919 and 1920, Yates the chairman was well aware that the supply industry had long been deeply concerned at the risk of the establishment of an appliance cartel. When the merger was announced, assurances were given that the individual factories would remain under their old names and would continue to give service to individual undertakings as before. 'Each of the companies had its own specialities... the valuable characteristics and qualities of each firm would be conserved'. Working parts and burners would be standardised, but undertakings could continue to negotiate variations to suit their own needs if they wished. The giving of this assurance was later greatly regretted, as far more advantage was taken of it was taken than had been hoped. The board attempted to limit the number of local variations to their standard production models; any variation required board approval and also approval by Radiation central laboratories. Nevertheless there are dozens of references to minor changes every year in the minutes. This problem was not unique to Radiation. As late as 1939 the chairman of Parkinson & Cowan made a plea at the company's annual general meeting;

> Our friends in the gas industry can largely assist in keeping down manufacturing and maintenance costs by adhering to the standard article produced and not asking for variations which may appear small individually but which collectively involve a very heavy addition to the cost of manufacture. We shall very much appreciate their help in this direction.

Identical 'New World' appliances were made at the five main Radiation factories but they appeared under different makers' badges and with different names. The Wright 'Eureka' was also the Wilsons & Mathiesons 'Carlton' and so on. Gradually Radiation sought to gain acceptance of the idea that undertakings in different parts of the UK should look to their 'local' Radiation factory for their needs, Davis for London; Richmond for the south-west and Wright for Yorkshire but old habits die hard, and this was a slow process.

The firm central control and strategic direction given by Yates and the Radiation board contrasted sharply with some earlier amalgamations. In 1897 the first attempt to create a meter cartel, Meters Ltd, was a financial success only for the promoters. No attempt was made by the promoters (or the former proprietors who had been bought out) to instal central management to rationalise the business. Meters Ltd continued to operate as it had done before, a group of independent firms under the same managements. After bitter complaints by shareholders, the promoters agreed that no dividend should be paid on a block of 50,000 shares owned by them until the ordinary shareholders received a 7% dividend; this was not achieved until 1914.

Similarly, the agreed amalgamation of the old-established Parkinson and Cowan family firms led in practice to serious operating difficulties. Both firms were of similar size and had equal representation on the board. For the best part of ten years after the merger, board minutes contain a series of references to splits on the board along family lines. Some disagreements were about technical matters, some about strategy. In 1917 Parkinson & Cowan (P&C) was in discussion with Glover & Main (G&M) about a possible amalgamation. Matters were sufficiently advanced for Price, Waterhouse to be engaged to prepare a scheme.

G&M saw agreement on certain consequences of the amalgamation as an essential pre-condition. These were;
   i)   centralisation of control,
   ii) reorganisation of works with a view to centralising manufacture,
   iii) closing of superfluous branches.
   It seems probable that P&C, having been unable to implement such changes since their own amalgamation in 1900, were unable to accept such conditions. There are no further references to the proposal. It seems probable that when Yates began to make soundings about amalgamations in the appliance industry, P&C and G&M were unwilling to come under his control and began discuss closer working between themselves as a means of self-protection. When they realised that they could continue as independent makers despite the establishment of the Radiation group, they decided to carry on as before.
   Disputes within the P&C board became fewer with the passage of time, but the problems of succession became acute after the death of Sir Henry Cowan in 1932. None of the other family directors wished to, or was capable of taking the chair. The financial institutions attempted to resolve the crisis by imposing a chairman of their choice but the board persuaded H W Woodall, Corbet Woodall's son, to accept. He was a third-generation gas engineer, co-founder of the Woodall-Duckham contracting firm and latterly chairman of the large gas Bournemouth undertaking. He had the independence and authority to impose schemes of rationalisation, both in manufacture and administration. His appointment reassured the financial institutions, particularly after a director of Barclays Bank joined the board.

So far the discussion of the appliance business has centred on the market in Britain and British makers. What scope existed for foreign maufacturers to sell in Britain or for British makers to export? There was an attempt to import foreign Haas meters before 1914 but this was seen off by the combined British meter makers. Between the wars Ascot succeeded so well that they made their name synonymous with instantaneous water heating and even water heating by gas, and, like Hoover, grew larger in their adopted home than in their home markets.
   What about British exports? It might have been expected that British makers would be major exporters of appliances. They had the advantages of a large secure home market and some economies of scale. With the exception of Australia, where the industry developed along lines very

similar to the UK, they failed to exploit their advantages. They were unable to make inroads in foreign markets, although they knew that other countries, France, Germany, America, were already active exporters.

Various possible explanations for this poor export performance might be considered. The first must be entrepreneurial failure, allied to the persistence of family control. This was still a feature of many appliance firms until the inter-war period, delaying the introduction of professional management. The breakdown of family control caused major problems for Parkinson & Cowan and Cannon among others. Against this must be set the success within the UK of the Radiation group under H J Yates; he brought together a group of family firms and through strong centralised management welded them into a highly profitable concern. All the makers managed to meet the needs of the home market but failed in competitive export markets.

Another possible explanation for the poor export performance of the makers is that they were supplying what was something of a technical backwater in world markets, despite its size. The British appliance market was second only to that of the USA, whose makers provided appliances for natural gas and electricity as well as gas, larger than any other European country, and could not be ignored. However in foreign markets, newer styles of cookers became popular decades before they appeared in Britain. Here clearly the British makers were handicapped by the preferences of their institutional customers who were still preoccupied with prepayment customers. There were occasional pleas from the makers that undertakings should accept the slight cost penalty of more efficient appliances, which would bring benefits to customers and ultimately to the industry as a whole; these pleas generally seem to have fallen on deaf ears.

The supply industry's preoccupation with low first-cost appliances was compounded by the failure of the makers to establish an effective cartel to protect profit margins. For the whole of the period studied, there was considerable competition between the various appliance makers. Despite a general tendency in British industry towards combination both before and after the 1914-18 war, extended efforts to establish an effective makers' cartel never came to anything. Evidence of the negotiations, particularly for the period 1890-1914 was found in the archives of various makers. This provides new insights into the motivations of those involved, and how they planned to set limits on unfettered competition and protect profit margins. The unwillingness of makers to submerge their individualities within a combine was reinforced by supply industry opinion. Leading gas engineers were determined to prevent the establishment of any cartel which might be in a position to dictate to them. Larger undertakings set up workshops to make and repair meters and to repair appliances. The largest undertakings also contracted direct with particular makers for the supply of their most popular lines, for example R & A Main supplied appliances to the GLCC, Flavel to the SMGC. An awareness of the power of the supply industry as a monopoly buyer and potential competitor must have strengthened the resolve of those unwilling to join a combine.

This failure to secure comfortable profit margins in the home market must to some extent have constrained the ability of the makers to embark on extended efforts to win export markets. The makers knew that many of their standard appliances were unsuitable for export. There are instances in board minutes of discussions about the requirements of foreign buyers, and how these might be met. These never reached the point of a decision to allocate adequate resources to mount a serious export drive. Independent foreign agencies operating with little supervision could not achieve the desired breakthrough. Even in Australia, both Main and Parkinson & Cowan, who each had a substantial market share before 1914, based on their meter business, failed to retain their places, Main abandoning its Australian operation in the early 1920s; P&C slowly lost contact during the 1930s.

The success of Ascot gives one indication of how markets for improved appliances might have developed if the supply industry had been a little more receptive. Another example is the success of pressed steel cookers in Britain when they finally came on to the market.

In the early 1930s Main were involved with the GLCC in designing and making a replacement for the venerable Horseferry cooker, as described in chapter 10. These light-weight cookers would be in sharp contrast with the black cast-iron cookers traditionally favoured by the British gas industry. Their introduction released an enormous pent-up demand for a modern cooker. The GLCC at first asked for 2,000 of the new cookers per week from Main; these were not enough to meet demand and Main boosted production to 2,500 by dint of double-shift working. This was nowhere near sufficient so the GLCC also placed orders for 100,000 each from Radiation and P&C. Once GLCC needs were met, the makers were licenced to supply to other undertakings. Main broke decisively from tradition by insisting that, apart from any stencilled name, it was not prepared to make any variations to the standard production model.

Such bulk orders were very important for the makers, allowing them to move from batch to production line technology. These orders also allowed them the opportunity to develop their own expertise with pressed steel technology. The first moving conveyor belt for cooker assembly had been introduced by Radiation by 1930; Main followed suit shortly after. Flavel's experience was different. When the SMGC asked Flavel to make steel appliances, this placed Flavel in considerable difficulty as the firm had just invested heavily in a new foundry. The ill-timed investment in obsolete technology and a drying up of SMGC orders in 1938 caused the failure of the firm and its takeover.

Another example of major change in an old-established business is seen at Cannon. This was set up in 1826 to make cast iron pots and pans and began making cast iron gas appliances in 1894/5. The company's gas business grew rapidly, but the firm was held back by its hollowware business, 'a diminishing business with no prospect of revival', according to a board comment of 1926. Two of the directors, both in their late seventies were not willing to entertain any scheme 'which would probably snuff them out as [hollowware] producers'. By 1934 the general casting business was 'bad without any redeeming feature'; the decision was taken to bring in outside investors in the hope that this would revitalise the business, even though the previous chairman still held 50% of the shares.

The company was turned round, but not by financial restructuring. A F Oatley, sales manager of the United Kingdom Gas Co approached the company in 1939 offering his services and making a presentation of how he proposed to increase sales. He was appointed sales manager in July 1939 and immediately began to make his mark. Despite wartime problems he worked on the development of new appliances and held presentations for major gas industry customers to establish the acceptability of his ideas. He explored the possibility of Cannon producing refrigerators and water heaters, proposed gas fires delivering convected as well as radiant heat and suggested a cooker with an eye-level grill which created a sensation when it first appeared in the 1950s.

Oatley did not always manage to carry his board with him. In 1944, unlike other makers, Oatley decided not to participate in the government programme to produce a standard cooker for prefabricated homes. He wanted to concentrate on producing a pre-war cooker, as a stopgap until new designs of cookers on which he was working were available; they were a great success on their introduction. He was however overruled by his board and forced to toe the industry line.

In view of the probable nationalisation of the industry after the war, Oatley attempted to develop an export business, using agents. His agents later started moving into the home market in an attempt to sidestep the deadening hand of normal supply industry 'marketing' by developing a direct selling organisation. Another maker, Main, was relaxed about Oatley's initiatives.

This would probably cause us some trouble in the future due to the fact that we do not deal direct with contractors or the public, but on the other hand it would also create difficulty between [Cannon] and the gas undertakings by their method of dealing direct with consumers.

It would have been interesting to see how this initiative might have developed, a quarter of a century before the supply industry began to relax its near monopoly of appliance selling. Instead, nationalisation created new opportunities, and direct selling by makers did not expand at that time.

13 Prospects for structural change; 1930s and 1940s

B y the later 1930s the gas industry had withstood the impact of competition fairly well. It was well established and reasonably profitable as a whole. Good-looking, efficient appliances were on the market though hired appliances made up the great majority. Gas was still cheaper than electricity for cooking and heating both in terms of first cost of appliances and in running costs. Even for lighting, gas was not much more expensive than electricity. Despite the undoubted convenience of electric light, some people still preferred the mellow light of gas, even though it tended to make the decorations dirty much more quickly. It must not be forgotten that as late as 1939 one third of all houses had no electricity supply. Some were away from main centres of population and had no connection to the grid; others were old rented properties in town centres where landlords did not or could not afford to have the houses wired up. These were the properties where the prepayment supplement had made such an impact half a century earlier.

Gas however lacked the appeal of electricity as a modern and versatile fuel. Because gas had enjoyed its greatest expansion before the first world war, it seemed to belong to a bygone era, of hansom cabs rather than the motor car. Electricity was in the public mind the fuel of the future. Apart from lighting it was associated with labour-saving in the home. Electric irons and vacuum cleaners were enormously popular (and affordable). By 1939 there were about 9 million radios in use, 6 or 7 million irons and well over a million vacuum cleaners. There were also something like $1^1/_2$ million electric cookers in use, against five or six times as many gas cookers. The better-off could buy electric cookers and fires and heat their water by electricity but for most people the cost would be prohibitive, four times as much as coal and twice as much as gas. For the great majority of 1930s British housewives the all-electric house remained an unattainable dream. Ironically this was in part due to the success of gas over the previous half century.

In Britain between the wars it was very apparent that reorganisation of the electricity supply industry and in particular the construction of the national grid had dramatically improved the prospects of the industry and provided the chance for it to fulfil its potential. Could something similar be done for gas? Certainly the statutory framework within which the industry operated was outdated and needed fresh consideration. This whole question was tackled by Political and Economic Planning (PEP), a non-political body set up in 1931 which produced a number of careful reports on different aspects of British political economy to stimulate wider debate. PEP was interested in the possibility of developing a national fuel policy; its report on the gas industry, published in 1939, was intended as a part of this wider study, seeking to optimise the role of gas for the national good. It represents an independent attempt to answer the questions posed earlier but based on the perspective and attitudes of the late 1930s. Other PEP reports include its report on electricity supply, fuel and power and household appliances.

The first point recognised by PEP was that, whatever the theoretical situation, gas was in practical terms operating in a competitive market, seeking market share against coal, oil and electricity. Unlike electricity, gas had no effective monopoly in any area of heat service provision (with the possible exception of instantaneous water heating exploited by Ascot). If it was to compete on level terms it was therefore important that it should be in a position to set realistic tariffs which reflected the costs of supply. These were of two kinds, the fixed costs of making a supply available, including street mains, gas metering etc, and the variable costs directly proportional to the amount of gas used, ie. cost of coal and manufacture. Electrical tariffs reflected this split between fixed and variable costs. There was a standard quarterly charge which took account of fixed costs and corresponded roughly to a charge for electric light; thereafter electricity for all other purposes was charged at a low commodity rate. This allowed the electricity supply industry to promote its low running charges heavily for loads such as cooking, heating and hot water (which could also be provided by gas) while conveniently overlooking the fixed element, wrapped up with charges for lighting where electricity had the advantage over gas. In practice the electrical marketing men were so keen to develop new markets that the commodity charge was set so low that it did not cover costs; this only became apparent after the war when better costing systems were developed.

By contrast, the gas industry was much more circumscribed in the way it could draw up its tariffs. The great bulk of gas customers were charged at a flat rate per therm, with no variation according to the size of consumption (except in a few cases for large industrial users). This meant that customers who used only a little gas were not meeting their fair share of fixed costs, while there was no incentive for customers who might wish to use more gas to increase their consumption. PEP estimated that 35% of all gas customers were not bearing their full share of fixed costs.

It was a common fallacy to equate small users with poor users. Prepayment customers with a 'free' cooker (who might be considered poor users) used an average of over 70 therms per annum, which would be sufficient to cover all the costs of supply. The problem arose with those who had only lighting or particularly electric customers who used a gas ring in conjunction with their electric cooker or kept gas as a standby for emergencies. The gas industry had a statutory obligation to supply, without any reference to customers paying their fair share of costs; small customers did not pay their way but they could not be shed. By contrast small electrical customers either paid a high flat rate or a minimum charge under a two-part tariff.

PEP described in its report the endorsement of two-part tariffs for electricity in a number of enquiries and the political objection to allowing similar freedom to the gas industry. In 1927 the Board of Trade (responsible for regulation of the industry) summed up its attitude in comments on the Commercial Gas Bill as follows:–

> The Board assume that the primary object in regulating prices and dividends of the statutory gas companies is to secure the protection of the ordinary (small) consumer, and the continuance of legislation for the attainment of this end is desirable.

In 1933 the Board of Trade Gas Legislation Committee recommended that the industry should be entitled to impose a minimum charge on small consumers but the suggestion was shelved for political reasons.

The particular problem for the gas industry was that there was a long history of statutorily linking prices to dividends, dating back to 1867 and reinforced by the introduction of the sliding scale in 1875, legislation that was in force right up to nationalisation. All the efforts of companies were devoted to reducing the maximum price at which gas was sold in order to justify the payment of dividends rather than developing a more realistic pricing policy. This imperative ran counter to the need to charge small customers an economic (high) rate if costs of supply were to be recovered. When in 1934 special legislation permitted the introduction of two-part tariffs, this was not a general power but a permission to exclude two-part tariff charges in the calculation of regulated dividends under the Basic Price system. By no means all companies who could have benefited from this liberalisation did so. PEP calculated that of 407 company undertakings for whom it might have been a help, only 30 had adopted it, although these included most of the important companies. Municipal undertakings were even slower to use this new freedom to set promotional tariffs.

In 1937 a Joint Committee of the Lords and Commons on Gas Prices recommended that the refusal to allow the gas industry to impose minimum charges should be reconsidered; nothing had been done to implement this and

PEP recommended that it should be put into effect.

Regulation of maximum prices has provided no incentive to reduce costs or to increase the use of gas and Parliament has tried various ways of overcoming the difficulty without allowing the industry sufficient freedom over price policy to adopt a modern promotional tariff... Besides failing to stimulate development, existing price regulation is unreliable. There is now an effective safeguard for the consumer in the shape of strong competition in every department of gas sales, and this makes the system of control created when gas was a monopoly still more inappropriate...

Whilst PEP had some sympathy with the gas industry's problems with its regulatory framework, there were other areas associated with charging where it was very critical. It considered that the industry should have taken steps to explain its problems to its customers. Such an educational initiative would have explained the desirability of a minimum charge if all customers were to be charged fairly, and large customers could get the benefits of reduced unit charges to match the reduced costs of supply. It was a great pity that Carpenter's SMGC did not consider such an educational programme before it imposed new tariffs as soon as the new legislation allowed. These were rationally designed but the method of their introduction aroused such a public storm of protest that the company was forced to abandon them (and Carpenter resigned soon after). Apart from the larger customers who would benefit from promotional tariffs, PEP was also concerned with the two-thirds of customers who took their supply through a prepayment meter; they should not be excluded from the benefits of promotional tariffs if their consumption justified it. More significantly, PEP attributed the slow rate of progress towards a more effective tariff policy to 'an apathetic attitude in some sections of the industry, and an insufficient realisation of the importance of tariff policy as against technical efficiency'.

PEP noted that the various undertakings purchased their appliances in an unco-ordinated fashion, and their individual tastes were responsible for a 'multiplicity of small variations in their design and operation'. In consequence, makers were producing a wide range of models which varied in insignificant degree, and lost any possibility of gaining economies of scale.

While it is essential that the consumer should have a good range of choice and that his preferences should be observed and catered for, there is beyond question a wasteful multiplicity of types in use today. The consumer is paying for a meaningless wealth of choice... even a low degree of standardisation should have an immediate beneficial effect on costs. This is an evil for which both undertakings and makers must bear some responsibility.

PEP recommended that undertakings and makers should recognise the need for research and testing and that with co-operation on both sides a joint programme could be put in hand. As far as possible duplication of testing by individual undertakings should be eliminated. The undesirability of concentrating all research and testing in one centre was recognised; this would have given that centre undue influence over the makers and possibly restricted desirable innovation if this ran counter to the preferred ways of the centre. It was suggested earlier that Watson House may have been in this position.

It was recognised that research and testing, like customer service and advertising, would be a cost to the industry. However the benefits of better appliances would accrue to the industry as a whole. Undertakings would have less complaints to deal with and customers would be readier to buy new appliances if they could be assured of their quality. Undertakings were counselled not to attempt to screw unduly low prices from the makers at the risk of reduced quality; 'the supply industry would only have to shoulder expenses now met by them'.

On the customer service front PEP noted that the gas industry was very much more involved in installation and maintenance than the electricity industry, while the water industry did not get involved at all. PEP attributed this to the importance of the lighting business to the gas industry; the renewal of mantles was a necessary and important function. PEP might also have noted, but did not, that the enormous number of 'free' appliances supplied to prepayment supplement customers and other hired appliances represented a huge workload for the industry. Practice varied in different parts of the country. Some undertakings did all installation, repairs and maintenance with their own staff, while others subcontracted to a lesser or greater degree.

This comment led on to another recommendation, that common standards of performance should be applied and that both in-house staff and outside contractors should be trained to the same standards and work to the same codes of practice. This would be difficult and costly for small undertakings to apply by themselves but could be arranged on a regional basis without impairing local responsibility for customer service.

The small size of the average gas undertaking, allied to a traditional engineering bias, made it difficult for the industry to develop a strong and unified marketing effort. In PEP's words

> There is little or no co-ordination of commercial policy in the industry; no unified approach to the customer; no central source of information on questions of economic policy... The small undertaking may not have either the financial margin to embark on a bold commercial programme or the sales and publicity staff to put it into effect. There is an obvious

need here for co-operation in marketing and, at least in some respects, for a national approach to the public.

To deal with all the problems of the industry and not only those with marketing importance emphasised here, PEP proposed a national gas authority whose main functions would be:–

* to promote the grouping of undertakings
* to promote the rationalisation of production and distribution
* to supervise the marketing of coke and other by-products
* to guide the commercial policy of the industry as a whole
* to be responsible for public relations
* to be responsible for training
* to advise on economic problems affecting the industry

It is always easier for outsiders to draw up an action plan if they are unaware of the day-to-day problems and constraints which handicap the individual manager in his efforts to innovate and improve, and do not have to deal with them. Nevertheless the conclusions reached by PEP must be regarded as a criticism of the state of the industry at the time and of the framework within which it was forced to operate. Some matters could properly be laid at the door of regulatory authority, but far too many were clearly within the range of what the industry and makers could have done for themselves given sufficient impetus. There was no obvious failure to justify government intervention; merely a widespread impression that in other circumstances things could be managed much better. Some drastic action was necessary.

This was certainly the conclusion of the Heyworth Committee on the gas industry published early in 1945 (while the war was still on). The committee was charged with reviewing the structure and organisation of the industry and was to make recommendations on changes necessary to develop and cheapen gas for all types of consumers. There was no remit to consider the commercial operation of the industry; that would be left to those in charge.

The Heyworth recommendations were that the industry should be nationalised and a number of area boards set up, responsible to the Minister of Fuel and Power. The boards should be responsible for the efficient operation of the industry. They should be given freedom to carry out this task, and be judged by results. The industry must be given freedom to compete effectively and without restriction with other fuel industries. The plan should be put into effect as a whole and not piecemeal. The outcome was the Gas Act 1948 and the nationalisation of the industry in 1949.

14

Nationalisation
and after

Nationalisation became inevitable following Labour's victory in the 1945 election. Whilst in their public statements some leaders of the gas industry expressed their opposition, privately it was almost universally welcomed. The industry was fragmented; gasmaking technology had hardly changed over half a century. Its public image was that of a dying industry and all its markets were threatened by a popular and energetic competitor. Without some radical changes its future would be bleak. It might have retained some niche markets but its mass appeal in the domestic market would be gone.

The changes which followed nationalisation were of various kinds, managerial, engineering, commercial. These must all be touched on as each had a bearing on the growth of markets for gas. We shall also examine the competitive state of the electricity industry, nationalised before the gas industry; whilst it performed well, the gas industry for various reasons performed better and these reasons are what will now be examined.

In terms of the management of the gas industry, over 1000 pre-existing undertakings were combined into twelve area boards. The Gas Light & Coke Co being by far the largest of the former undertakings most nearly matched the new organisation, being only slightly enlarged when it became the North Thames Gas Board. NTGB retained most of the GLCC senior officers, and was able to hit the ground running on vesting day, May 1st, 1949. No other undertakings came anywhere near the size of the GLCC, which was three times the size of the next largest undertakings, the South Metropolitan Gas Co and Birmingham's municipal gas department, and six times larger than Glasgow and Sheffield. Apart from individual undertakings, some holding companies established in the late 1930s were swept up into the new area gas boards. Apart from North Thames, the other boards had to build their new organisations on the basis of the larger undertakings and holding companies in their areas. They had both to take control of dozens of previously proud and independent undertakings and maintain supplies to customers while working to create new organisational structures and management appropriate to the tasks they faced.

In view of often ill-informed comments on the management of the industry at the time, it is interesting to note the outcome of nationalisation. In an apparently unfavourable economic and political climate the leaders of the industry, many of whom had held senior positions before 1939, carried through a major technical and commercial restructuring of the industry with notable vigour and effectiveness. The resurgence of the industry due to the popularity of gas fires and central heating was well under way years before natural gas became available, and it must not be forgotten that the leaders of the industry were deeply involved in the search for and subsequent exploitation of North Sea gas. The impression is gained that, at a corporate if not always at an individual level, nationalisation was a liberating experience. Opportunities not available before 1949 were seized enthusiastically.

In engineering and especially marketing terms a major rationalisation of gas supply was long overdue, as the industry well knew. The gas supplied by all the various undertakings came in no less than 26 different calorific values, for which the makers had to produce suitable appliances. There were hundreds of different tariffs charged throughout the country. Rationalising tariffs within each board was relatively simple. Providing gas of standard quality was a more complex business. Gas manufacture was as quickly as practicable concentrated at the most efficient works, and small local works whose costs were high and gas quality sometimes idiosyncratic were closed down at the earliest opportunity. As gas quality was standardised within boards, it was necessary to ensure that appliances were correctly adjusted. On a small scale and piecemeal, this exercise foreshadowed the work necessary when natural gas was introduced throughout Britain twenty years later.

Modernising the stock of appliances inherited from the previous undertakings was a major task which was only finally completed when all appliances had to be converted to accept natural gas whose calorific value was twice of manufactured gas. In 1949 something like half of all customers, perhaps six million, still had the old black cookers supplied with prepayment meters; in addition many of the cookers hired out by undertakings were old and inefficient. Occasionally some effort had been made to improve cookers, for instance by partial enamelling, but most were unimproved. Most undertakings had been unable to afford to modernise their stocks of appliances before the war; the task now fell to the new nationalised boards. This was their top marketing priority. Because of all these old appliances, customers by and large associated gas with dirt and obsolescence and were open to persuasion that modern appliances had to be electric. It has to be said that some employees of the boards in the immediate aftermath of nationalisation, with all the disruption that entailed, were less than confident of the industry's future. The author recalls participating in a sales staff debate on the topic that gas was a dying industry; the audience was deeply split.

Apart from the costs of modernising the appliance population, there were other physical problems to be overcome. There were shortages of raw materials for manufacturing industry; government policy directed production towards export markets rather than the home market. This meant that new appliances were in short supply as makers struggled to obtain raw materials and attempted to meet the urgent demands by the boards for spare parts for existing old appliances, whose servicing had been a low priority during the war.

Other difficulties were caused by post-war government policy. New appliances attracted purchase tax, imposed not only to raise revenue but also to influence patterns of consumer spending, luxury goods being charged at higher rates than essentials. Purchase tax regulations changed quite frequently. The highest rate in the mid 1950s was 90%; the highest rate between 1968 and 1971 was 55% although between1963 and 1967 it had been 45% or less. Similarly government controls on hire purchase terms were varied frequently as a means of fine-tuning consumer demand in the economy. Controls affected both the amount of deposit and the period over which the purchase could be spread. Obviously this seriously disrupted the market for appliances. There were a couple of periods, 1954 and 1958-9 when consumer demand was to be stimulated and all controls were lifted, only to be re-imposed shortly after. These controls on hire purchase were finally abandoned towards the end of the 1960s and purchase tax was replaced by VAT in 1973. Needless to say this regime of fluctuating controls caused major headaches for the appliance manufacturers who had to speed up production schedules or cut back without warning at the Chancellor's behest.

Given these problems, it would seem that gas was extremely vulnerable to electric competition. This however was less severe than might have been expected. Electricity had its own problems. Despite the development of the national grid between the wars, the supply industry was almost as fragmented as gas at the time of its nationalisation, 500 undertakings being taken into public ownership. The lack of standardisation was if anything worse for the electricity boards than for gas; for example the London Electricity Board inherited no less than 17 different DC and 20 different AC voltages within its area. Average domestic consumption had almost doubled between 1938 and 1948, leading to a severe shortage of generating capacity to meet the demands on the supply network.

Shortage of capacity was aggravated by the popularity of electric fires. These were cheap to buy though expensive to run, and provided an instant source of heat when needed. In 1948 three quarters of all domestic electric customers had an electric fire. Unfortunately for the supply industry, these tended to be switched on in very cold weather when the system was already stretched to the utmost, leading to voltage reductions and load-shedding. Unlike gas, electricity cannot be stored, and power stations had to be built to meet peak demand. In the short run either the industry had to invest heavily for an occasional peak load or it had to condone load-shedding. Longer term solutions, such as building up off-peak tariff loads and persuading customers to use night-storage heaters, could not be implemented quickly.

Large additions to peak loads were highly unwelcome but there was little the electricity supply industry could do about it. Unlike the gas boards which controlled virtually all appliance sales through their own showrooms and outlets, the electricity boards only handled about a quarter of appliance sales. Whilst its own showrooms did not feature fires prominently, they were readily available at other electrical retailers and sold like hot cakes, further embarrassing the supply industry.

The only appliances where electric showrooms handled the majority of sales were cookers; the industry was extremely keen to promote these to counter the influence of gas in the kitchen. Electric cookers were heavy users of power but unlike fires tended to be used off-peak. In consequence boards were prepared to slash their normal profit margins to gain the business. Unable to match the prices offered by electricity boards, the business of selling cookers was unattractive to other retailers who needed their full mark-up. Despite this aggressive pricing, in the 1950s electric cookers cost more to buy and to run than gas. The industry contemplated the development of a cheap standard cooker, just as the gas industry had done in the 1920s. Unlike the gas industry, the electricity boards decided not to proceed along that road. The industry was however making steady inroads into what had been a gas domain; by the later 1950s a quarter of all electric customers had electric cookers.

Throughout the 1950s the electricity industry was concentrating on standardising its supplies, connecting new customers (9 out of 10 households were connected by 1958) and investing heavily to ensure that generating capacity kept pace with demand. One area where it had no problems was with its public image of modernity. Gas had nothing to

THE MODERN TWIST

Lighting might lead to electric cooking and ultimately the all-electric house.

offer which could compete with the labour-saving image and the reality of the electric iron, the vacuum cleaner, washing machines, televisions, power tools and so on. Gas scored where heat was required, for cooking, water heating and space heating, increasingly including central heating. Elsewhere there was no comparison in customers' minds; electricity scored every time. However if prices of electricity continued to fall relative to gas, as they had done steadily over the whole life of the industry, gas would not only lose those few eccentric souls who had retained their gas lighting but all their other customers as well.

The gas industry's campaign to retain its markets had two main thrusts. First it sought to cheapen the cost of gas manufacture; secondly it set about improving its image.

Whilst the cost of electricity was falling steadily in real terms, that of gas was rising, not least because of its dependence on particular grades of coal for carbonisation. The nationalised coal board seeing a captive market raised the prices of gas coal rather faster than prices for other grades, including power staton coal, threatening the competitiveness of the gas industry, which after all was battling with coal for the domestic heating market at the time.

The dangers of being totally dependent on particular processes of gasmaking had been apparent to gas engineers for some time. There was considerable interest in alternatives to carbonisation. From 1935, Dr F J Dent, sponsored by the University of Leeds and the Institution of Gas Engineers, had been investigating the German Lurgi process for gasification of lignite under high pressure. Nationalisation transformed Dent's prospects; he was put in charge of a national research centre responsible for high pressure gasification with resources to match. Two Lurgi plants were built in the UK in 1960 and 1969 but while these operated successfully, alternative methods of gasmaking proved more economic. Even more exotic methods of gasmaking were explored, including the underground gasification of coal. This promised the enormous advantage of gasifying coal in situ, without the necessity for mining it and bringing it to the surface. Despite much effort over many years particularly in Europe, the process never proved practicable.

In the meantime British research efforts turned to the possibility of producing gas direct from oil, rather than simply using oil as an enricher for low calorific value coal gas. From the 1950s oil supplies were plentiful and as the refining process did not produce the exact mix of products, petrol, fuel oil etc required by the market, certain oil products were available in quantity at very low prices, particularly naphtha. Dent's team developed several processes which could use naphtha and whatever other oil fractions were currently a glut on the market to produce cheap gas which was interchangeable with coal gas. These processes had the added advantage that they operated at high pressure, unlike carbonisation. This opened up the possibility of distributing gas at high pressure, which had previously been uneconomic.

Another option considered was the possibility of finding natural gas (methane) in Britain. Apart from its low cost, natural gas had twice the calorific value of coal gas and could therefore be used for enrichment instead of oil. British engineers had been impressed by the advantages for the American gas industry of huge quantities of cheap natural gas distributed at high pressure across the country which was rapidly displacing coal gas. It was first used In the United States as early as 1821 in Fredonia, NY. In the late nineteenth and early twentieth centuries natural gas was widely used as a feedstock or enricher in gas making. In the US, sales of manufactured gas grew until 1948 but then collapsed as soon as long-distance pipeline technology could transport natural gas to the north eastern states, which were then converted to direct natural gas supply. In volumetric terms American sales of natural gas have exceeded those of manufactured gas for as long as reliable records were kept, and it was always vastly cheaper. There had been a few insignificant discoveries of natural gas onshore in the UK but although in 1953 the industry commissioned BP to undertake further onshore seismic surveys, nothing significant was found.

The attraction of natural gas in quantity was so great that the industry decided to explore the possibility of importing natural gas, but in liquid form. Natural gas liquified at -162°C or less was reduced in volume to $^1/_{600}$th of its volume at atmospheric pressure. In 1959 arrangements were made to import liquified natural gas from America; a few trial voyages using a specially converted vessel, the *Methane Pioneer*, proved the practicality of the scheme. Permission was given by the government for the construction of two full size insulated tankers which entered service in 1963, bringing liquified natural gas not this time from the USA but from Algeria, where abundant supplies had been found and a long-term contract was negotiated on favourable terms. These two vessels brought in quantities equivalent to 10% of British gas demand at the time. The liquified natural gas was landed at Canvey Island in Essex from where it was transmitted by high pressure pipeline, initially to eight of the twelve area boards, either for enriching gas made by other processes or to be reformed into a coal gas equivalent.

While processes for making gas from oil were being introduced and liquid natural gas imported by sea, huge quantities of natural gas were discovered nearer at hand. After some years of exploration, gas was found in the north of the Netherlands in 1959. As an indication of the size of this discovery, it would have provided the whole needs of the UK for a century at the rates of consumption then prevailing. As well as developing the field for their own use, the Dutch were able to export gas in huge quantities. The British gas industry entered into talks about taking a supply but in the meantime began to investigate whether the geological strata which contained gas in the Netherlands might extend into the British sector of the North Sea. They entered into partnership with Amoco, the international oil company and were one of several consortia allocated licences to hunt for gas and oil offshore in the first round of applications in 1964.

The first discovery was by BP in the following year, and within a few months other consortia, including British Gas, had discovered three major gas fields. At this stage British Gas was more concerned about gaining knowledge and experience of the exploration process to strengthen its hand in the negotiations to buy the gas than in becoming a major world player in the search for and exploitation of natural gas. British Gas had the statutory right to buy all gas found in the British sector of the North Sea if it wished, and intended to exercise it. Within a couple of years enough reserves had been confirmed to convince British Gas that it should plan a future based entirely on natural gas. This needed virtually no treatment other than the addition of the highly characteristic coal gas smell; this was for safety reasons, so that any leaks would be noticed immediately.

Coal gas manufacture would cease, and despite their promise, the new methods of making oil gas would be superfluous and could be phased out. (Some research was undertaken into the production of a substitute natural gas to be available if supplies proved insufficient in the long term.)

Even in the 1960s a few gas lamps survived, mainly because they were not charged at an economic rate.

The development of oil gas processes and then the discovery of natural gas transformed the economics of the industry. In round terms oil gas cut the price of gasmaking by half; natural gas halved the price once more. Coal and oil could still compete for some bulk business but in domestic markets, wherever gas was available, it was cheaper than any alternative fuel for heating purposes. Obviously electricity was used widely for ancillary appliances, kettles, toasters and so on, but for space and water heating, natural gas became the fuel of choice. The main programme for converting 13 million homes and 440,000 commercial and industrial premises to use natural gas began in 1967 and lasted ten years. In domestic premises alone, no less than 8,000 different types of appliances were identified, most of which it proved possible to convert, although many customers took advantage of the conversion process, and the attractive special bargain offers which went with it, to upgrade to a modern appliance.

The industry benefited from an oil company campaign in the 1960s to popularise central heating; the "Mrs 1970s" targeted by the advertisements bought gas central heating rather than oil. It was also able to take full advantage of the concept of small-bore central heating with clock and thermostatic controls pioneered by the coal industry.

The first modern central heating boilers introduced by Potterton in both gas and oil models appeared around 1960. In their sleek white enamelled cases, so different from the coke boilers they would soon replace, they exemplified a higher standard of living, a new labour-saving way of life. Within a few years the cleanliness, convenience and economy of gas was winning the competitive battle for the domestic heating market. By the 1990s gas heating and hot water has come to be almost as essential in the home as the TV.

As conversion was completed over twenty years ago it is sometimes hard to remember that the resurgence of the industry was already well under way, based on the new oil gas processes and the domestic heating market, long before natural gas was available in bulk. Sales had increased by a third between 1960 and 1965. In 1960 coal gas accounted for 85% of production and oil gas the balance. By 1965 the share of coal gas had fallen to 50%, oil gas increased to 42% and sea-borne natural gas 8%.

Once natural gas was available in bulk the effect on sales was dramatic. In 1972 when the conversion programme was half-completed, sales had more than doubled from 1965 levels, coal gas had almost disappeared, oil gas accounted for 10% and all the balance was natural gas, either supplied direct where conversion was complete or reformed using one of the oil gas processes to produce a coal-gas equivalent. Ten years after the conversion programme began sales had increased almost fourfold and the price per therm in cash terms, taking no account of price inflation, had fallen by 16%. Thereafter sales have continued to increase to the point that in the UK gas is the fuel of choice for new electric power stations, rather than coal, oil or nuclear power.

In 1960 this was all in the future. In that year sales of gas had been falling for ten years. The number of customers had risen slightly, which meant that each customer on average was burning considerably less gas. A market survey of attitudes to gas concluded that

> As a fuel gas had a weak image, and when it was not weak it was negative. Though the image of oil was also negative, it managed to be a commercial success. The image of coal, by contrast, was positive – it was homely and comfortable. The image of electricity was both positive and strong – it was clean modern and convenient.

Whilst attitudes to gas as a fuel were discouraging, gas appliances such as cookers and water heaters had a more favourable image. In fact since the easing of HP restrictions on gas appliances in 1957/8 sales of gas fires had shown a most encouraging rise, almost doubling over three years, and contributing to a rise in gas sales too. Sales of heating apparatus were encouraged by the move towards gas two-part tariffs similar to those electricity had been promoting from between the wars.

The first step towards countering the adverse image of gas was to strengthen the national publicity effort. Till then the individual area gas boards had been responsible for the main thrust of advertising. While there was some co-operation between boards, the federal structure of the industry did not allow for a strong national campaign to improve the image of gas. This had to change and the steady progress is described by its architect, Sir Kenneth Hutchison, deputy chairman of the Gas Council, in his autobiography, *High Speed Gas* (1987).

The advertising agency appointed to mastermind the campaign undertook its own research. Whilst criticisms of gas were severe, it was dirty, smelly, dangerous, old-fashioned, customers could recognise its advantages. As one housewife said, 'turn it on – and its on'; another commented 'with gas I'm in charge – the flame does what I tell it'. These provided the basis for a new look for gas. The innocuous figure of Mr Therm had been around too long and some new image was required. Thus

(above) The first
efforts of the newly
nationalised boards
at marketing were
not very sophis-
ticated. In the 1950s
wash boilers were
offered with wringers
and (hand) agitators
in competition with
electric washing
machines.

(right) New
gasmaking processes
made gas economic
for fires and central
heating; the Flavel
Debonair combined
high efficiency and
an innovatory wood surround.
Over 700,000 were sold.

were born the slogans *High Speed Gas* and *Heat That Obeys You*, associated with the stylised flame symbol. The emphasis was on speed and flexibility, attributes where gas was sure it held the advantage.

Of course image is not enough. The campaign came just when those in the industry had begun to suspect that their fortunes had taken a turn for the better. Gas was being made more cheaply. Popular two-part tariffs were available. Customers were finding that the new gas fires were not only far cleaner and more convenient than coal, but their efficiency made them cheaper too.

The traditionalists of the British gas industry were in for further shocks. Just as central heating boilers with their pumps and controls had forced them to begin to learn basic electrical technology, the new appliances used electricity as a matter of course, for timers and spark ignition. Hotplates with both gas and electric burners found favour with customers, as did electric ovens combined with gas hotplates. It is understandable that when the industry appeared to be fighting for its existence, it should provide no loopholes for infiltration by the opposition. However this opposition was carried on a little too long, perpetuated in the technical standards demanded by Watson House, the industry's appliance test centre. Burner ignition by spark was cheaper and easier to manufacture than the pilot light ignition favoured by the industry's technical watchdogs. Electric clocks to control central heating or cooking were easier to fit than clockwork mechanisms. Central heating systems had shown the benefits of electrical controls for convenience and flexibility. The reluctance of the industry to welcome electrical controls is reminiscent of its flirtation with a gas-powered radio; some things were possible but made no commercial sense.

Conversion brought a different kind of shock to gas fitters trained through a traditional apprenticeship. First they had to accept that central heating installations were put in by plumbers who had not had a specific gas apprenticeship training, but that these men who could fit radiators and piping and do the electrical wiring had no trouble at all connecting and adjusting the gas. When the physical conversion programme got under way, the industry needed large numbers of additional men to instal and convert appliances; they were given six weeks' basic training before starting work. This destroyed the mystique of the gasfitting trade for ever. Those who could satisfy the industry's watchdog CORGI (the confederation of registered gas installers) of certain basic competences were authorised to work with gas. Gasfitting and maintenance which had formed a considerable part of the service offered by the industry to its customers was no longer its prerogative; anyone with CORGI registration could do it. Similarly appliances which had largely been retailed through gas showrooms could now be obtained anywhere. The commercial development of the gas industry now mirrored that of electricity.

For the first half century of its life the gas industry had no competition because no-one else could provide a service to compare with gas lighting. With the onset of competition gas had to learn new skills. It had to discover new markets for its products and ensure that suitable appliances were available. It had to learn to supply, fit and service such appliances or make arrangements for others to act on its behalf. It had to set standards of safety and performance to ensure that poor and inefficient appliances did not damage the reputation of gas itself. It set up its own research centres both for gas and appliances. It had to learn the skills of marketing and especially of satisfying customers.

Competition forced the industry to learn all these new tricks. Now the wheel has turned full circle. Once again the industry has become a supplier of fuel for which there is no direct competition; natural gas is so plentiful and cheap at present and appliances so effective that British Gas can separate out its customer service and selling activities; these are no longer a core function for an organisation which is once again operating in a near-monopoly situation. British Gas, Transco and Centrica are now separate identities.

The conversion of the industry to natural gas brought even greater challenges to the appliance makers. No longer was the UK a closed market. Customers could choose appliances from Europe or elsewhere designed to operate on natural gas. British makers had to be able to compete in a pan-European market if they were to be sure of survival. What made the situation worse was that during the decade of conversion, the makers were obliged to meet demands for conversion kits rather than concentrating all their efforts on developing new appliances for a European market. With huge international appliance makers such as Electrolux and Whirlpool actively promoting their products, there was no possibility of protecting an isolated national market.

Regulation and the opening up of the gas market to competition may possibly once again necessitate the learning of marketing skills which were so painfully acquired over a century ago. Perhaps customers are now sufficiently affluent to change their appliances long before they require servicing. Perhaps they would prefer to make their own arrangements to locate a gasfitter through 'yellow pages'. Perhaps the current cheapness of gas compensates for other minor inconveniences. This favourable situation which has existed for the last quarter century may not persist for long. Certainly it would be unwise to take it for granted. A hundred years ago gas engineers were reluctantly having to learn the new skills of marketing. Will their counterparts beyond the millenium have to learn the same lessons anew?

This history has shown how in adverse conditions, various factors may affect the survival or demise of a business. New technology in the shape of electric lighting caused the first major crisis in the industry's history. The danger for gas was averted partly by the adventitious invention of the incandescent mantle, but far more important in the long run was the move towards a marketing rather than an engineering solution to the challenge.

Similarly half a century later the industry was in danger of becoming paralysed by inappropriate regulation, outdated attitudes and an organisation that frustrated the efforts of those attempting to modernise and reform the industry. Only those outside the traditional gas establishment could easily introduce new ideas and operate in novel and entrepreneurial ways; the eruption of Ascot into the appliance business springs to mind.

Nationalisation, while introducing its own dogmas, provided the opportunity to recreate the industry without its traditional baggage of attitudes and regulation. It made possible the introduction of major technological and marketing breakthroughs; its new organisation enabled it to take the revolution of natural gas into its stride without a hiccup. Now privatised, new challenges await.

One thing is certain. The history of the industry has demonstrated the impact of various factors in its successful adaptation to crises and challenges. It has embraced new technology. It has adopted new marketing strategies. Its leaders have on occasion shown entrepreneurship of a high order. No single cause can account for such a history of survival and achievement.

This surely is the most important lesson to be learned from an industry study such as this. In real life there are conflicts and lost causes as well as examples of success. The best managers are those who, rather than turning to the latest nostrum peddled by theoreticians, are not too proud to consider the lessons of history and their implications for the pressing problems of today and the challenges of tomorrow.

Further Reading

CHAPTER 1

Braunholtz, W T K; *The Institution of Gas Engineers; the first hundred years*, (IGE 1963)
Cowan, R S; *More work for mother*, (Basic Books, New York 1983)
Encyclopedia Britannica, 11th edition
Griffiths, J; *The third man, the life and times of William Murdoch, 1754-1839; inventor of gaslight* (Andre Deutsch 1992)
Hill, N K; *History of the Imperial Continental Gas Association* (unpublished London PhD 1951)
Körting, J; *Geschichte der Deutschen Gasindustrie*, (Vulkan-Verlag, Essen 1963)
Newbigging, T & Fewtrell, W T eds; *King's Treatise* (3 vols. King 1882)
Pearson, R; *Fire insurance and the British textile industries during the industrial revolution*, (Bus Hist, vol 34, 4 1992); *Taking risks and containing competition, fire insurance in N England in early 19th century*, (Econ Hist Rev, XLVI, 1, 1993)
PP 1867/8, XXX, pt. II.
PP 1878/9, XI, Select Committee on Lighting by Electricity
Ravetz, A; *Victorian coal kitchen and its reformers*, (Victorian Studies, xi, 4, Indiana)
Rowlinson, P J; *Regulation of the gas industry in the early 19th century*, (unpublished Oxford DPhil 1983)
Société Technique, *L'Industrie du gaz en France 1824-1924*, (Paris 1924)
Stewart, E G; *Samuel Clegg, 1781-1861, His life , work, inventions and family including a full account of his atmospheric railway*, (1962, unpublished manuscript in National Gas Archive)
Wright, L; *Home fires burning*, (Routledge & Kegan Paul 1964)

CHAPTER 2

Caron, F & Cardot, F; *L'Électricité en France*, vol 1, (Fayard, 1991)
Falkus, M; 'The development of municipal trading in the 19th century', Business History, XIX, 2; 1977
Gerretson, F C; *History of the Royal Dutch* (4 vols., Brill, Leyden 1958)
Hannah, L; *Electricity before nationalisation* (Macmillan, 1979)
Millward, R, Ward, R; 'From private to public ownership of gas undertakings in England and Wales 1851-1947, chronology, incidence and causes'. Paper presented to LSE quantitative economic history discussion group, Feb 14, 1991.

Moynet, M J; *L'envers du théâtre* (Paris 1873) translated as *French theatrical production in the 19th century* (Max Reinhardt 1976)
Passer, H C; *The electrical manufacturers 1875-1900*, (Harvard Univ. Press, 1953)
PP 1867/8, XXX, pt. II
PP 1868/9, LI; Report of the gas referees under the City of London Gas Act.
PP 1878/9, XI, Select Committee on Lighting by Electricity
PP 1900, LXXVIIII
PP 1905, LXXXIV, Board of Trade Statistics
Rees, T; *Theatre lighting in the age of gas* (Society for Theatre Research 1978)
Rostron, L W S; *The powers of charge of the metropolitan gas companies* (Benn 1927) cited in P Chantler, *British gas industry* (MUP 1938)
Yergin, D; *The prize; the epic quest for oil, money and power* (Simon & Schuster, 1991)

CHAPTER 3

Byatt, I C R; *The British Electrical Industry 1875-1914* (unpublished Oxford DPhil, 1962)
Byatt, I C R; *The British Electrical Industry 1914-1975* (Oxford, 1979)
Encyclopedia Britannica, 11 th edition (see fuel, gaseous; gas; gas engines)
Garrard, J; *The Great Salford Gas Scandal* (University of Salford 1987)
Hannah, L; *Electricity before Nationalisation* (Macmillan 1979)

CHAPTER 4

Ehrlich, C; *Social Emulation and Industrial Progress; The Victorian Piano* (Queen's University of Belfast 1975)
Jefferys, J B; *Retail Trading in Great Britain 1850-1950* (Cambridge U P 1954)

CHAPTER 5

Berlanstein, Lenard R; *Big Business and Industrial Conflict in Nineteenth-Century France; A Social History of the Parisian Gas Company*, (University of California Press, Berkeley 1991)
Chamon, *Note sur l'emploi des compteurs dits à payement préalable.* (Société Technique, 1894)
Körting, J; *Geschichte der Deutschen Gasindustrie*, (Vulkan-Verlag, Essen 1963)
Melon, *Les compteurs à prépaiement à Lille; douze mois d'exploitation.* (Société Technique, 1896)
PP 1899; *Metropolitan Gas Companies*

CHAPTER 6

BoT Returns of authorised gas undertakings, annual
BoT departmental committee on the electrical trades (PRO BT 55/21)
Bowden, S; Crawford & Sykes, *The public supply of gas in Leeds 1818-1949*,
    in *Leeds City business 1893-1993*, eds J Chartres & K Honeyman
Byatt, I C R; *The British Electrical Industry 1875-1914*
    (unpublished Oxford DPhil, 1962)
Byatt, I C R; *The British Electrical Industry 1914-1975* (Oxford, 1979)
Garcke's *Manual of electrical undertakings 1898-99*.
    annual
Hannah, L; *Electricity before Nationalisation* (Macmillan 1979)
Leicester Gas committee minutes; Leicestershire Record Office CM 18/1.
    I am indebted to Neil Wood for this reference.
Macrosty, H W; *The trust movement in British industry*
    (Longmans Green 1907)
Millward, R; *From private to public ownership of gas undertakings in
    England and Wales 1851-1947*, paper at LSE seminar Feb 1991.
P.P. 1900, VII, *Municipal Trading*
Passer, H C; *Electrical Manufacturers 1875-1900*, (Harvard U P 1953).

CHAPTER 7

Chandler, D; *Outline of the history of gas lighting*, (SMGC, 1936).
Société Technique de l'Industrie du Gaz;
    L' industrie du gaz en France 1824-1924
Sugg, P C; *Using gas, yesterday and tomorrow*;
    IGE Communication 1083, 1979.
Webber, W H G; *Town Gas and its Uses*; (Constable 1907)

CHAPTER 8

Macrosty, H W; *The trust movement in British industry*,
Mills, M; *'George Livesey and profit sharing'*, Business History, vol 33, 4, 1991.
PP 1899, X; Metropolitan Gas Companies
Rowlinson, *Regulation of the gas industry in the early 19th century*, 1800-1860,
    unpublished DPhil thesis, Oxford 1983

CHAPTER 9

Goodall, F; The problems with appliance and cost statistics are explored in
    more depth in the author's PhD thesis, London 1992
Coleman, D; *Uses and Abuses of Business History*, Business History, vol 29,
    no. 2 1987

Evetts, G; *Administration of gas undertakings*, (Benn, 1920)
Field, J W; *Accounts of Principal Gas Undertakings*, GLCC annual)
PP 1921, XVI; *Sale and hire of gas apparatus.*
Yearsley, I.; 'Light Rail - Who Pays?' in *Proceedings of the Chartered Institute of Transport*, vol. 5, no. 2, June 1996

CHAPTER 10

Körting, J; *Geschichte der Deutschen Gasindustrie*, (Vulkan-Verlag, Essen 1963)
Gilbert, A T; *Gas installations and appliances*, (Crosby Lockwood, 1931)

CHAPTER 11

Bowden, S M; *The market for domestic electric cookers in the 1930s; a regional analysis* (unpublished PhD London 1984)
Burnett, J; *A social history of housing*, (Methuen 1981)
CAB 102.334; Report; British gas industry before the war.
CAB 102.334; Memo. of National Gas Council in 2nd report of the National Fuel and Power Committee
CAB 102.337; Report by Joint Committee on Gas Prices, HC 110/1937
Corley, T A B; *Domestic electrical appliances*, (Cape 1966)
Hannah, L; *Electricity before nationalisation*, (Macmillan 1979)
PEP; *The Market for household appliances*, (1945)
PP, 1923, XI; Charging for gas on a thermal basis.
Ridley, T P; *Public control of gas undertakings*, (paper at 2nd World Power Conference, Berlin 1930)

CHAPTER 12/13/14

Elliott, C; *The History of Natural Gas Conversion in Great Britain* (Cambridge Info & Research Services 1980)
Foreman-Peck, J & Millward, R; *Public and private ownership of British industry 1820-1990* (Oxford 1994)
Hannah, L; *Engineers, Managers and Politicians* (Macmillan 1982)
Harvie, Christopher; *Fool's Gold; The story of North Sea Oil* (Penguin 1995)
Millward, R & Singleton, J; *The political economy of nationalisation in Britain 1920-1950* (Cambridge 1995)
PEP; *Report on the Gas Industry in Great Britain* (1939)
PEP; *The Market for Household Appliances* (1945)
PEP; *The British Fuel and Power Industries* (1947)
PP, 1947-8m VIII; *The Gas Industry* (Heyworth report, Cmd 6699, 1945)

Index

A

Advertising; 78, 204, 217, 245
Algeria, natural gas from; 242
Amalgamations; 156, 195, 223
American Gas Association laboratories; 181
American Gas Institute; 171
American Meter Company; 40
Appliance efficiency, see Efficiency
Appliance exports; 147
Appliance makers; 58, 69, 81, 85, 156, 218ff, 223, 248
Appliance testing; 84, 170
Appliances, gas; 13, 159, 233
Appliances, life of; 167
Argand lamps; 19, 47, 124
Ascot water heaters; 218ff
Auer, Carl, von Welsbach (1858-1929), see Welsbach

B

Barker, A H, appliance tests; 179
Barlow brothers; 23
Barralet, J H; 39
Beck, Simon Adams (1803-1883); 61, 198
Beckton; 45, 61, 199
Beeton, Mrs; 31
Birmingham; 118, 121, 179, 210
Black cookers; 210
Board of Trade; 48, 55, 146, 158, 192, 195, 200, 212, 232
Bodmin Gas Co.; 10, 69
Boulton & Watt; 19
Bray, George; 84, 141
Bribery, corruption; 73, 85, 115, 144
British Commercial Gas Association (BCGA); 199, 205, 217
Brownhill's prepayment meter; 100
BSS (British Standard Specifications); 181
Bunsen, Robert; 36
Bunte, Hans (1848-1925); Karl (1878-1944); 174
Burner jets; 47, 124

C

Calorific value, charging by; 195
Candlepower, measuring; 48, 173
Candles; see Lighting
Cannel coal; 47
Cannon; 228
Canvassing; 86, 143
Canvey Island, natural gas terminal; 242
Carbon Monoxide (CO); 25
Carbonisation; 47, 65
Carburetted Water Gas (CWG); 66, 117
Carpenter, Dr Charles; 170, 178, 187ff, 200, 205, 233
Cartels; 150, 223, 227
Chadwick, Edwin; 27, 36
City & Guilds of London Institute (C & G); 76
Claire-Deville, Henri Sainte; 174
Clegg, Samuel (1781-1861); 21ff, 28, 39
Clerkenwell meter makers; 39
Co-partnership; 145
Cockburn, Malcolm, ironmaster of Falkirk; 150
Coke; 64
Colman, Dr Harold G; 173
Colson, Alfred (1849-1910); 93
Commercial Gas Co; 61
Commission; 71ff, 140, 153
Comparative costs; 89, 128, 203, 230, 239, 243
Competition, onset of electrical; 11, 57, 168
Competition; 226, 231, 238
Consultants; 62, 71, 85, 168
Contractors, early; 23
Conversion; 243, 247
Cooker sales; 107, 208
Cookers, development of; 35, 40, 147
Cookery tuition; 88, 142
Cooking by gas, early efforts at; 28
Core functions; 10, 58, 75, 83, 90, 139, 248
CORGI; 247
Cost of gas installation; 89, 149, 202
Cost of gas, see gas prices

Cowan, W & B; 111
Crosley, S & J; 39
Crossley Bros.; 76, 175
Croydon Gas Co; 53, 114
Crystal Palace Gas Co; 92
Customers, definition; 16

D

Davis, H & C; 149
Demonstrations; 86, 143
Dent, Dr F J (1905-73); 241
Deposits as security; 101
Depreciation; 93, 162
Dessau; 175, 223
Differential prices; 67, 111
Direct selling, see marketing
Distribution, high pressure; 241
Dividends, regulation of; 53
Dowson, J E, low cv gas plants; 77
Dual-fuel appliances proposed; 192

E

Economies of scale; 63, 117, 195, 224, 236
Edison, Thomas A (1847-1931); 16, 45
Efficiency, appliance; 57, 75, 156, 170, 175, 181, 185, 192, 211
Electric competition; 68, 194, 202, 213, 230, 238
Electric controls for gas appliances, opposition to; 193
Electric lighting, see Lighting, electric
Electrical Association for Women (EAW); 208
Electrical retail outlets; 239
Enamelled appliances; 193, 216, 220
Entrepreneurial failure; 169, 226
Environmental pollution; 45
Evetts, G; 161, 167
Ewarts; 219
Exhibitions, Crystal Palace 1882/3; 84
Exhibitions, Great 1851; 32
Exhibitions, Paris 1867; 27, 34, 36, 39, 42
Exhibitions, Paris 1878; 40, 43